ADVAN[CE PRAISE FOR]
LIVING WELL W[ITH MULTIPLE SCLEROSIS]

"Delightful, funny, insightful, poignant, and compelling. *Living well with Multiple Sclerosis* should be mandatory reading for every patient dealing with any chronic health condition and for the doctors treating them."

DR MICHELLE TOSHIMA, PhD - The Multiple Sclerosis Center
at Swedish Neuroscience Institute

"Trevis is bold, insightful, and sensitive as he explores the taboo and often neglected subjects that impact the survival of people living with MS."

BARBARA (BOBBIE) SEVERSON - Cpt, USAF, Ret. MSN, ARNP-C, MSCN

"An open, honest, and real account of life with MS. It's confronting, uplifting, challenging, emotional and all things in between. A great read."

TRISHNA BHARADIA - MS patient advocate MS Society UK

"Humorous, self-deprecating, pragmatic, and enlightened, Trevis provides a must-read account of playing the hand that MS has dealt him the best he can."

AVA BATTLES - Chief Executive Officer, Multiple Sclerosis Society of Ireland

"Trevis paints a picture that gives readers an inside look at what it's like to live and thrive with MS."

DR. PAMELA VALENTINE - President & Chief Executive Officer,
MS Society of Canada

"It's like spending time with your new warm, wise, and funny best friend. You'll feel as though you are hanging out while learning what it means to live and love with multiple sclerosis."

SARA LOUD - Chief Executive Officer, Accelerated Cure Project

"A vivid diary of a personal journey through multiple sclerosis. While every journey is different, Trevis has managed to bring us into the shared experience of people with chronic illness."

DR PAOLA ZARATAN P.HD -Director of Scientific Research. Italian Multiple Sclerosis Society

"You don't have to have MS to appreciate Trevis Gleason's writings. While he's never less than honest about the hard parts, he also manages to keep it light and find the humor in what he's going through."

INGRID STRAUCH - Editor, Everyday Health

"Trevis touches on the core themes that are at the heart of communities of people living with chronic conditions: solidarity, agency, knowledge and education, discrimination and stigma."

NICOLA BEDLINGTON - Former Secretary General, European Patients' Forum

"The description of an individual life path that can give people living with chronic illness both courage and hope."

HERBERT TEMMES – President, European Multiple Sclerosis Platform

"This book gives context and life to the words, to the questions and to the fears that so many of us living with a chronic illness are too afraid to speak of or too embarrassed to ask."

CIARA O'MEARA - MHSc, M.A.T., BNS, RNT, RGN

"This is the book that newly-diagnosed as well as long-haul multiple sclerosis patients and their families should have on their bookshelves."

MEREDITH O'BRIEN – Author, Uncomfortably Numb: A Memoir

LIVING
WELL
WITH
MULTIPLE
SCLEROSIS

Trevis L. Gleason
with Emma Rogan

Foreword by
Dr Timothy Coetzee, PhD
Chief Advocacy, Services, and Science Officer, National MS Society

coffeetownpress

Kenmore, WA

A Coffeetown Press book published by Epicenter Press

Epicenter Press
6524 NE 181st St.
Suite 2
Kenmore, WA 98028

For more information go to:
www.Camelpress.com
www.Coffeetownpress.com
www.Epicenterpress.com
www.TrevisGleason.com

Cover design by Scott Book
Design by Melissa Vail Coffman

Living Well with Multiple Sclerosis

Library of Congress Control Number: 2023945699

ISBN: 978-1-68492-139-3 (Trade Paper)
ISBN: 978-1-68492-140-9 (eBook)

For Caryn, Thalia & Kai
Because "DINGLE ROCKS!"

Contents

Foreword

IF YOU'VE PICKED UP THIS BOOK in the bookstore (or if you're like me, reading a sample on your electronic reader), chances are you've got a connection to a chronic illness. Perhaps like the author of this book, you have multiple sclerosis—a disease of the central nervous system that can cause disabling symptoms like fatigue, numbness and tingling, loss of balance, weakness, vision problems and cognitive changes. While there are medications to treat the disease, there is currently no cure.

Nearly 3 million people live with MS worldwide and every single person has their own unique journey with this disease. No two cases are exactly alike. But some effects of this disease are fairly universal. MS is disruptive and unpredictable. People with MS live with the uncertainty of how the disease will behave—today, tomorrow, 10 years from now. They wonder what it will take away, and when. They worry about how they'll cope, how it will affect the people they love, their careers and the ability to do the things they love. Often, that disruption and fear manifests in a deep sense of resilience, adaptability, and hope. As the Chief Advocacy, Services and Science Officer for the National Multiple Sclerosis Society in the United States, I've seen this firsthand. And there is perhaps no better example than the author of this book, Trevis Gleason.

In my work with the Society, I'm dedicated to finding a cure for every single person with MS, and to changing the journey for those living with the disease today. I have the joy of working with remarkable leaders in the global MS movement. I first met Trevis at a National MS Society fundraising dinner in San Francisco. He was serving as the emcee for one of the many galas we host to raise awareness about MS and importantly—raise funds to support the National MS Society's work. We formed a quick bond over our mutual interest in solving MS along with our shared fondness for fine beers (a tradition that has continued to this day along with a healthy debate about who owes who a pint).

Not long after we met, I began to follow Trevis and his Life with MS blog. The blog now, in its latest incarnation on the Everyday Health digital platform, has been a constant source for me of information and insight for how MS affects individuals and the people around them. Through the years Trevis has blogged about virtually every subject in the MS journey with his trademark wit and first-person insight about living with the disease. Now he has woven those decades of writing into the book you hold.

In this compendium, Trevis has something for everyone affected by this chronic disease—the person who has lived with MS for 3 days or 30 years; the person who has a loved one, significant other, or friend that lives with MS; and the person who is just curious about how a chronic brain disease can affect a person over time. He guides us through the early years of navigating the disease and his reactions to hearing this diagnosis, becoming versed in the disease; and grappling with the aspects of life that MS robs. He carefully explores the contours—both personal and medical—of living with MS; all with the gentle and knowing care that each person who hears the words 'you have MS' will respond in their own unique way. With humor and easy-to-digest language, Trevis vividly reminds us that we are all on a journey and that when you live with MS, the journey is punctuated by highs, lows, twists, turns, detours and the more than occasional unpleasant surprise. He reminds us that while MS affects people in so many ways—both visible and invisible—there is power in recognizing these moments for what they are, the inevitable challenge of living with MS.

This book is essential reading for anyone who wants to fully understand the journey of MS, or any chronic illness, from the perspective of the person living with the disease. If you live with MS—whether for a brief time or a long time—you will find a welcoming traveling companion whose insights and experiences will inspire, comfort and prepare you for the road ahead. If someone you care about lives with MS, this book will equip you to be a supportive partner. And if you don't have any connections, don't worry, this book is also for you. We need you to read it and be inspired to see how one individual has navigated the challenges of this disease and served as a beacon to countless others to make their own life with MS. Perhaps through reading these personal accounts you may be motivated to join our movement in some way—whether as a donor, supporter, inventor, researcher or whatever works for you. We need you!

While you may be tempted to see life with MS as nothing but challenges, Trevis tells a different story. I often hear people with MS say—'I have MS, MS doesn't have me.' This expression of resolve courses through this anthology. Trevis heard the words—'you have MS' in 2001 but as you will see with clarity, the disease has not had him for the last 23 years, nor will it have him in the years to come. It is my hope that by reading this book, you too will see that if you have MS, you are more powerful than this disease will ever be. Above all else, Trevis shows us that we each have agency and can chart a journey that is uniquely ours. It has been my honor to travel alongside Trevis all these years. Together we are stronger than MS.

Tim Coetzee, PhD
Albany, New York

CHAPTER 1

It Doesn't Smell Like Roses

I AM A FORMER UNITED STATES COAST Guard navigator. I am a chef by training, a food scientist by education. I am an advocate for people with disabilities . . . out of necessity, really.

I'm a writer because of a passion.

My love of words—in their hearing, in the reading of them, and in their writing—had a 20-odd year hiatus because I believed the callous words of a frustrated instructor while I was at school. Oddly, it was my experiences in the disability advocacy world, specifically multiple sclerosis, that oiled the hinges of the door I had allowed that teacher to shut.

My first writings on the topic of multiple sclerosis were in the form of scripts for MS webcasts I'd begun hosting on the Seattle-based website, HealthTalk.com, founded by Andrew Schorr. I stumbled into the hosting seat after being interviewed by the show's producer about the disease modifying drug treatment that I was on at the time.

The scheduled 15-minute recorded interview with Carolynn Delany turned into a (harmlessly) flirtatious hour and a half conversation. She and I still laugh at the fact that it was her husband, Dennis, who was the camera operator for the shoot.

While wrapping up our interview, Carolynn asked if I might

consider sitting in for the vacationing host of an upcoming phone-in/webcast program on a specific MS topic that I can't rightly remember after all these years. She had wanted to try having a person living with the health condition being covered act as moderator, and she thought I might be a good fit for the experiment. This was the spring of 2005. I was 39 and it was, ironically, nearly 4 years to the day that I was diagnosed with a disease, the symptoms of which I'd been ignoring, explaining away, or having misdiagnosed for at least 18 years before that.

It had been since the late 1980s that I'd sat behind a professional microphone. I moonlighted as a classical music radio broadcaster during my final Coast Guard assignment in Boston. The old skills were rusty but Carolynn was forgiving and considered the experiment a success. I found the monthly interaction with our medical guests, patient advocates, and the nation-wide MS audience stimulating. I followed the pre-written scripts but couldn't help myself in asking follow-up questions that I wanted (and I rightly assumed the patients listening wanted) answered.

Within a few months, producers ditched the sponsored patient advocates and asked me to write the script outlines for our programs. The audiences grew and we were soon adding bigger and bigger trunklines to accommodate the call-in side of the programs.

Upon my return from a winter in Ireland—the winter during which my memoire, *Chef Interrupted; Discovering Life's Second Course in Ireland with Multiple Sclerosis*, is set—Carolynn introduced me to Rose Pike, her boss at HealthTalk. Rose (now rather infamously) asked if I might be interested in writing a blog about my experiences living with MS. My answer, now equally infamous, "Sure! What's a blog?"

In April of 2006, I submitted my first attempt at this new (at least new to me) form of communication. I entitled the piece *It's All About You; Really*! And it was. As a recovering egotist (my self-diagnosis), it was imperative to me that I not be the center of attention in this new endeavor. I tried to focus on MS-related topics that I wanted to know more about the same way I did as I wrote questions for the researchers and doctors and followed-up as the interested patient/host I was.

Rose named the feature *Trevis L Gleason's Life with Multiple Sclerosis*.

Our webcast audience began reading and readers who found the new blog started participating in our webcasts. Readers started commenting on the blogs and, to our great surprise and delight, they began responding to one another. Our blog readers—a growing audience of people living with MS from around the world—began to respond and reply to one another's comments.

They stopped being merely blog readers. We evolved into the *Life With MS Blog* Community.

The most repeated (and rewarding) comments were in the vein of, "I thought I was the only one," "It's like you're reading my mind," "It's so good to know that I'm *normal*," and "I'm going to use that to explain what I'm feeling to my . . ."

We began to cut and paste descriptions of our symptoms and experiences from the pages of Life With MS into our own stories of living our experiences with the disease. We incorporated others' words into our conversations. We became a chorus not singing in unison but, rather, in a multi-part harmony, the likes of which we'd never heard before.

While I knew our reach was international, it wasn't until a chance encounter in Dublin, Ireland that I came to understand what a global community we had become.

While at dinner before the 2013 International MS Patients' Summit and enjoying the company (and wine) at our table, I was tapped on the shoulder by a young woman at the next table.

"Excuse me," she said in a lovely accent I couldn't place, "But you are The Trevis, no?"

Her name was Luisa, she lives with MS, and she was from Portugal. I was (though I'd not yet learned the phrase) gob-smacked to learn that, while she never commented on the blog, that she followed the writings and would often translate them for members of SPEM, the Portuguese MS Society in Lisbon, where she is also the communications director. She extoled her appreciation for the community to the point that I would have been a little embarrassed if I hadn't been so stunned.

When I introduced my wife, Caryn, who had also been enjoying the company (and the wine) on the night, Luisa began to gush to the point where I *was* embarrassed.

Trying to put her at ease with a bit of folksy 'just Jenny from the block' type anecdote, Caryn said, "He's just like anyone else with MS. I mean, everybody poops, and it doesn't smell like roses."

It took Luisa a few confused moments to translate the words in her head and decipher the intended meaning of the colloquialism but she got there on her own and we all had a good laugh about it. It must be said, however, that Caryn and I now have a two-glass-limit policy at events such as these . . .

As with many tech startups (and while it was a patient-focused, web-based, information company, HealthTalk.com was indeed a tech startup), the company was bought and sold a number of times. Along the way it became EverydayHealth.Com and, although even that organization has lived under and within several larger firms, Trevis L Gleason's Life With MS Blog is one of the longest running, consistent forums of its kind on the internet.

I lost track of the number of proofreaders, copy editors, interns, Directors, and Content VPs that have come and gone while I've been banging out blog posts. Each one of them left a mark on both the writings and the writer.

The platform isn't really a blog anymore, per se. It has become something of an opinion column as the comments function (with its years' worth invaluable comments and interactions) has been disabled. We have shifted the conversation part of Life With MS onto social media and it's good, but I'll admit that it's not quite the same as those early days of monikers and pseudonyms.

I developed deep respect for the courage and candor of readers like 'Rusty', 'Lisa *Wales*', 'MangaManga', 'WI Dawn', 'SPAZ', and so many others. We were (and are) there for our community and our community is there for us. Even in (and maybe particularly during) the difficult times in our lives with MS, we *got* one another like no one else in our lives could understand us.

In recent years, I have found it more and more difficult to locate some of our older postings as I research for new ones.

Search Engine Optimization (SEO) experts decided that over 2,000 blog posts (with hundreds, and sometimes thousands, of comments) took up too much space on servers. They say that, on the internet, nothing dies. That might be true for the drunken selfies and overzealous restaurant reviews, but not so in this case.

As I have always done, I kept in mind what I might want to know more about and by extension, what others with MS (or any chronic illness, really) might want to read as we combed through over a decade-and-a-half of writings. It's an ethos which has worked for so long that it seemed silly to approach this book in any other way. I found pieces I'd been looking to reference in more recent posts and stumbled over a few that I'd forgotten about entirely.

We expect that you'll recognize the experiences and sentiment of many entries we've culled from the archives. In doing so we updated where appropriate, incorporated responses from our community when we could, and hope to shed new light on the individuality of our shared experiences. I am humbled to know that these writings have helped my MS sisters and brothers describe their experiences and that they have informed conversations with doctors, nurses, and families. We see this collection as something of a reference for you to keep on your shelf and revisit as required.

I recall the advice of a mentor before I headed into a packed room to give a presentation on some new and very advanced cooking technology during my former professional life. I had only recently been trained on the equipment myself and was feeling more than a few trepidations about my lack of full understanding.

"Just remember," he said to me, "You know more about this thing than anyone else in the room."

It's the same thing as living with this, or any, chronic illness. We know what we know, and it's more than anyone else knows about our experience. We all have our own stories to tell about getting over, getting through, getting stuck under, and getting on with our lives. We all have our own stories, but the words we use are the same and they are stronger and louder and more beautiful because they are collectively ours . . . even if it doesn't smell like roses.

CHAPTER 2

The Early Years

MY EARLIEST DAYS, MONTHS, AND YEARS *after diagnosis, first with relapsing remitting multiple sclerosis (RRMS) and soon after, with secondary progressive (SPMS), were spent grasping for answers, flailing about in my personal life, and losing my grip on my chosen, much-loved profession. It wasn't a pretty time for me, nor for those around me. I'm not proud of how I handled myself during the early years. To be brutally honest it took me a good few years to get my head around the idea of multiple sclerosis, the disease, and what it was doing both to my body and mind. There is more to that statement, but it fits better later. I promise.*

Of all the things I am asked about living life well with MS, those having to do with those early struggles are the ones that are a challenge to answer. We each must find our own way and, like the disease itself, it is a very personal experience. What worked, and how I gathered myself after finding something which did not work, were all part of how I learned to make the best decisions for me as I continued my trek down life's path with a big backpack of MS on my back.

The early years, both as I lived them and as I looked back at them for Life With MS, were about asking questions, finding answers, and adapting my new life within the very hard borders which MS had erected (and continues to build) around my desired life.

At the end of the day, life with MS isn't about the crap cards the disease deals us. It's about playing our hand as best we can.

A History Lesson Part I:
The Vikings, The Saint, and The Bastard
03/11/2013 – New York, USA

Most of the 'awareness' of MS Awareness Week is aimed at getting the word about multiple sclerosis out to the world. It got me wondering how much we know about this disease. We know symptoms and our own experience with MS, but do we know the history?

I found many interesting tidbits that I'd not known, only heard snippets of, and had forgotten I dug up interesting research reports, unusual literary references, and scholarly tomes. I hope you enjoy the product of my MS Archeology and feel more 'aware' at some point during the series.

THE VIKINGS

It is the conundrum of the historical sciences; to look at ourselves we must look to our past. To understand the past, we must look to our present. So it is when trying to nail down where MS came from, we see latitudinal diversions in MS epidemiology and we see many clues as to susceptibility to MS owing to genetic factors.

I found allusions to an interesting report on MS in Kuwait which has been sighted as evidence of a genealogical trace back to the Norseland people. In the study it was observed that Arabs of Palestinian descent, living in Kuwait, were 2.5 times more likely to develop MS than Arabs of Kuwaiti origin. Along with significant differences in eye color, blood type and other factors, it was determined that susceptibility to MS was related to origination to the Eastern Mediterranean Basin.

One of the authors of the study, neuroepidemiologist Dr Charles Poser, proposed that a traceable genetic susceptibility may be at work and followed that with historical, anecdotal and genetic clues to the Vikings of Scandinavia.

While Poser does not say that the Vikings *had* multiple sclerosis or 'spread' MS, he simply states that, through a series of genetic mutations for susceptibility to the disease, the Vikings "may have contributed to the dissemination of MS" to parts of the world they conquered and to the rest of the world via their progeny. It can be argued that wherever the Vikings are known to have landed and established themselves, MS rates appear to be higher than places they did not (if you're wondering about the Palestinian Arabs in Kuwait, that is postulated to go back to the days of the Crusades when Normans—of Viking lineage—spent a great deal of time in that area).

With all we know about the human genome, we have yet to nail down any one gene responsible for MS (which actually may support this theory as it may take a blending of genetic material to create susceptibility). It's an interesting theory and, like much of history, may never be fully proven or disproven.

If you are interested in this way of looking at MS, I highly recommend Richard M Swiderski's book *Multiple Sclerosis Through History And Human Life*.

It is fortunate that we live in *this* time and place in history with multiple sclerosis, not only because of the state of treatment and research but also because, quite frankly, we are not thought to be witches!

Looking back through the Dark Ages and into the late Middle Ages to the first recorded (likely) case of MS and fast forward a couple of more centuries to a knight's writing, the tales will be surprisingly, all too familiar to us.

THE SAINT

First the tale of a young Dutch girl who fell while ice skating on a cold February day in 1395 and never fully recovered. It was fortunate for young Lidwina that she had declared to her family her intention to remain a pious virgin three years earlier. Had she not, the waxing of symptoms for the next 39 years until her death would surely have been attributed to demonic possession; her 'ability' to overcome them for periods considered evidence of witchcraft.

She was canonized in 1895 (she is the patron saint of ice skaters), her bones were treated as holy relics and even protected against protestant ransacking of such things in her native land. When they were rediscovered and examined at the end of World War II, in fact, her bones were helpful to researchers hypothesizing (corroborating with several written texts) that Lidwina most likely lived with multiple sclerosis. Because of the extensive (for the time) religious writings about her, she became accepted as the first 'documented' case of MS.

THE BASTARD

You'll often hear a senior Non-Com (non-commissioned officer) in the military bristle at being called "Sir" with the retort, "Don't call me 'sir'. My parents were married!" This harkens back to the day when the boys born outside of marriage and with titled male parents were sent off to be officers in the royal armed forces. Such was the case with Sir Augustus D'est, the illegitimate grandson of England's King George III.

Keeping with the Victorian fashion of diary keeping, we are able to follow the young Calvary officer through much of his life. In December of 1822, however, we begin to see entries which could have been written by many of us.

Sir Augustus writes of his progression of symptoms from minor vision nuisances and heat intolerance to restless leg syndrome and hyper-sensitivity.

I was *fascinated* reading such a detailed account of his symptoms and I felt an odd kinship with the young officer. I almost cheered when I read that he avoided the hot spa treatment offered to him at one point in his journey. I know what a hot tub does to me, into bed for days . . . once I've been fished out!

So, we're not possessed, we're not witches but I can sometimes feel as lost as Sir Augustus in finding answers

A History Lesson Part II:
"Sclerose en Plaques." And So It Was Named
03/13/2013 – New York, USA

The name Josephine Paget may mean nothing to you now, but the 40-year-old French woman is likely the first case of multiple sclerosis to be confirmed by medical science of the day. The problem for the Mlle. Paget is that the confirmation was done in 1841 Paris, postmortem.

The convergence of art and science in those early days of the 19th century became important to multiple sclerosis 'research' as postmortem examination (and illustration of) became more and more associated with pathology of symptoms.

The brilliant Scottish artist cum medical doctor, Robert Carswell, drew some of the first white-matter lesions of spinal tissue in his 1838 atlas of pathology (still regarded as one of the greatest and most beautiful of all medical books). Only a couple of hundred of Carswell's atlas were ever printed so, due to the intricacy of the lithographs, if you have a chance to see the prints online, I'd encourage it for the art as well as the science.

When he drew the spine with what we now expect to be MS disease scars, he didn't know anything about the patient other than he had been paralyzed in life.

Around the same time, a French medical illustrator, Jean Cruveilhier published his version of nearly identical gray-white spinal lesions. Cruveilhier was later given more credit by his countryman and the Father of Neurology, Jean Martin Charcot, in his landmark *Scleroses en Plaques* of 1868. It was Cruveilhier who examined Josephine Paget in the months leading up to her death—diagnosing her with an illness of the spinal tissue—and he was particularly interested in autopsy of his patient.

I found it intriguing that Charcot defined MS with several cognitive symptoms of "marked enfeeblement of the memory" and "conceptions that formed slowly." It was only in the past decade or so that such dysfunction was accepted as a symptom by modern MS clinicians.

I take a moment today and remember Josephine Paget of 19th century France. She slowly deteriorated in her neurologic condition in hospital bed number 16 of St. Joseph's ward of La Charité hospital in Paris. She wasn't hospitalized for MS, but rather a lung infection which would eventually be her end. She happened to come under the care of a doctor who could (literally) illustrate what had been going on in her body and in the use of her body to science, she helped establish the field of Multiple Sclerosis research.

The Honeymoon Period
08/08/2011 – Seattle, USA

Diagnostic tools are better. Primary care doctors are more aware. Patients are seeking knowledge. The general population of people newly diagnosed with MS seems to be getting a bit younger. Truth be told, it's likely that they are being diagnosed earlier in the course of Multiple Sclerosis and that's a good thing.

Meds appear to be more effective earlier in the course of MS. That's not just to say they seem to work better at keeping attacks down. The meds seem to slow the progression to the point where we may have some extra 'good years' before (if) our MS decides to get progressive.

Herein lay my thoughts for today—The MS Honeymoon.

Many, if not most, of us, can think back to some physical oddities we experienced prior to diagnosis. It wasn't until a few months ago that I began to equate some things in high school to possibly being MS. I know for fact that I had symptoms going back into my early 20s. Yet, I wasn't hit with a big (and diagnosing) attack until I was 35.

Now if I had been diagnosed in my 20s, I would likely have equated some minor stuff here and there as MS. It was all minor enough that I never sought any medical advice for any of it. If I'd heard "You have MS" when I was 23 and had begun a regimen of healthy eating, vitamin D, Yoga, positive thinking, you name it, would I have given credit to my new health regime?

Is there a natural time for many (depending on the course of your disease) from onset to major symptoms? Are we sometimes lulled into thinking that our MS might be that 2% kind that the medicos call benign MS? Could this *MS Honeymoon* be what people are talking about when I hear them say they "cured" their MS or they "control" their disease with *fill-in-the-blank*? Is it the honeymoon phase that they are really experiencing?

Might that same factor be involved in the efficacy numbers we see with newer MS drugs on the market? Hell, if I'd started meds at 23, I would have had 12 years practically symptom-free!

I know that for some this discussion will be moot as your MS never went into hiding, not even for a moment. I'm sorry and I respect your course of disease and the way you handle it.

We've much to learn about Multiple Sclerosis—far more than has already been learned. And I know that my little chats with others are far from scientific but I believe there is much to be learned from our conversations.

A Prime of Life Disease
04/17/2006 – Seattle, USA

What does that mean, exactly? They are always calling MS a "Prime of Life Disease."

Yes, MS is typically diagnosed between the ages of 20 and 50, the prime years of many lives, but does that mean that those diagnosed on the shoulders of that age range are also in their prime? Does it mean that MS takes away our prime years? What does having a Prime of Life Disease mean to you?

For me, it's best explained as a story from my childhood.

I grew-up in the western part of Michigan, not too far from what we all called the "Big Lake"—Lake Michigan. When I was young, we would often go to the massive sand dunes (and I'm talking stories tall here!) that line the west coast of the state.

We would slog our way to the top of the burning sands for no other reason than to run back down. Run may be a stretch. We would assist gravity in a long and boisterous quest for preteen terminal velocity.

'Running' down the dune, faster and faster and faster, our strides grew from steps to leaps, leaps to bounds, and bounds to human touch-and-goes. In fact, and this is where the MS analogy comes in, we would truly feel as if we were about to break the very bounds of gravity. As a child racing down the side of a silica mountain, I really thought I was about to fly. Then it would happen, and it would *always* happen.

Face plant.

For me MS struck hard (although I probably showed some symptoms for 12-15 years before diagnosis) just as I felt my life was about to lift off. Career—check. Marriage—check. House, car, money—check! Ready for take-off!

Face Plant.

Within 6 months of the major attack that lead to my quick (not taking into account those 12 years) diagnosis, I had to leave my job, get rid of the Jag, I separated from my wife and was looking at short-term disability checks that were less per month than I made per week when I was a new culinary school graduate.

No pity party for Trevis; things have worked out as they most often do. My mantra has become reality—let the failure of my body be the doorway to my greatest work. I now feel that MS hasn't taken away my prime, just made me find a new one. I guess that's what prime of life meant to me. Just when my *life* was about to enter its *prime*, I got this *disease*.

Like the kids on the sand dunes all those years ago, we get up, brush ourselves off and finish our journey as best we can.

Morning Inventory
9/13/2006 – Seattle, USA

Back in my days as a chef, there was a monthly ritual that no-one looked forward to, but everyone knew had to be done, the monthly inventory. Most businesses have an inventory schedule and process. The idea is to see what materials you have on hand and compare it to what you purchased and what you sold. End of month inventories are a way of checking up on the past. Since being diagnosed with MS, I have begun my days with an inventory, which looks forward, rather than back.

Every morning, I have learned to take a survey or inventory of what I can move or not, what I can feel and not, what works and what does not. At this point in my disease progression, it's a pretty short and cursory scan to see if things are what they were the day before and I get on with my day. Other times, and I have a little trepidation right now about how things are sliding, this is the most important part of my day.

Once I figure out what I have 'in inventory', I can look to my day ahead and ask myself these questions:

"What *must* get done today?"

"What *should* get done today?"

"What would *be nice* to get done today?"

I am then able to match my abilities with my tasks. The difficulty, of course, lies when I do not have enough in inventory to complete even the tasks that *must* get done. I think we have all had that day more often than we care to admit, even to ourselves. For those of us living alone, these days can be an unwelcome slip into the bad places, places of fear and anger.

It is not always the most pleasant process; neither was taking inventory at hotels and restaurants. Just like in the old days, however, I do find a reward in it. It's not the monthly food cost bonus I could expect if my numbers worked. It is more a sense of acceptance of where I am on that singular day. It is a way for me to stay in the moment with my life and with my disease.

Often those *would be nice* to get done things, have to do with planning my future. Those are the really good days, the days I can step out of my disease and maybe not think about it again for most of that day. The reality is that I would much rather not have to engage in my morning ritual at all. I see it as a coping tool that helps me live with my Multiple Sclerosis.

My Drug Decision
04/07/2012 – Seattle, USA

After many long hours of deep thinking and discussion, Caryn and I—along with the guidance of my MS medical team, of course—have come to a decision as to what to do next as to disease modifying medication for my multiple sclerosis. This is not a decision that we made lightly nor is it the path for everyone. I wanted to take some time to discuss my choice; not to influence anyone's choice of medication but rather to illuminate the process we went through to come to the decisions we made.

Before I get into what we decided, let's have a recap of where I've been.

When I was diagnosed with MS in April of 2001 there were only three drugs on the market: Avonex, Betaseron & Copaxone—the famed 'ABC' drugs. My diagnosing neurologist recommended that I see a leading specialist in the field of MS treatment and do research to help me make up my mind as to which medication to start. I'm pretty sure that I didn't make an effort to look into the therapies before that next appointment (some 3 months later) as I wasn't aware of how intricate the decision was to be . . . ..

I had, however, done a lot (a LOT-a lot) of research into the disease. When I met with this new doc (and an MS Fellow who was training under him) I asked loads of questions and spoke with language obtained in years of study and practice of science (albeit *food* science; the lingo isn't really different). Acknowledging my understanding of biology and the body, we discussed the way in which each of the drugs was *thought* to work. I was sent away with a massively thick binder of information to digest and make my decision.

About two weeks later, I got in touch and told him of my decision; Betaseron. Arrangements were made for a nurse to come by and teach me how to mix my shots (yes, these were the days before pre-mixed medication, pre-filled syringes and even before the auto-injection aids now available), how to inject myself and how to care for both site and whole body after the every-other-evening ritual.

I spent a little longer titrating my dose up, as I had read the stories of side-effects and wanted to give my body as much time to adapt as I could. I think it was just over a month before I was using a full dose. In the ensuing 18 months, I experienced six relapses and was put on six different 3-day courses of steroids. I was 100% compliant with my shot schedule—never in that year and a half missing a single dose.

Still, my disease progressed.

My doc and I decided that, since my MS was getting aggressive, that it was time for us to get aggressive. Though there had been the addition of Rebif to the list of FDA approved MS meds, the only 'big gun' available to us was Novantrone, a chemotherapy agent approved for use in the US for "breakthrough" disease. In my case, this meant my MS wasn't responding to the (now) ABCR drugs.

We made the call to begin a 60-day wash-out from Betaseron in order to prep for my new regiment of medication. Within a week of stopping treatment with the interferon med, I felt better than I had in nearly two years. I hadn't realized the cloud of flu-like symptoms under which I had lived for so long. It wasn't just me; my live-in girlfriend even noted that I seemed more "alive" once I stopped taking my shots.

Thus ended the first phase of MS medications for me.

I want to make it clear again that these decisions are very personal and not to be taken lightly. I do not share my experience with the intention to change anyone's mind about their therapy nor to entice you into my decision. I do believe that medications are part of the answer to living better lives with MS. I feel like there is medical evidence that they do work, just at different levels for different people's disease.

Now . . . where were we?

I was about to begin treatment with Novantrone, a chemotherapy agent which had some pretty nasty side-effects and potential hazards (at the time the chances of contracting leukemia were listed as 1:500, they are now around 1:300. Also, the drug can do permanent heart damage, so a maximum lifetime dose is usually met in apx 2.5-3 years). These hazards weighed heavily on me and my girlfriend at the time. The fact was, however, that I felt like the risk was worth the potential benefit for the place my MS was heading.

Though I tried and tried to fight it, I was very near acquiescing to the need for motorized transport. I couldn't walk more than a block or so—even with the assistance of a walker—and even that was at a pace which had our locally famous Seattle slugs lapping me when I went out to the grocery or some such.

The way I explain Novantrone's method is that the drug kills the fast-reproducing cells of the body—the immune system being its main target—and stays toxic in the blood for about 2 weeks thus killing the new replacement cells as they migrate from the bone marrow. By the time the drug is out of your system, the immune cells don't 'remember' that they like to munch on myelin.

The concoction of chemicals in Novantrone is a bright, deep royal blue and the protective garb the chemo nurses don before even touching the pouch woke the dark humor side of me. Special gloves, thick apron & smock, goggles, face shield for them; bare veins for me. I seemed under-prepared . . . Sometimes we laugh so we don't cry.

I would get my infusions (every 3 months) in the evenings; I schedule them that way so I could just go home and sleep after the treatment.

I was probably overly cautious in the beginning, sequestering myself for two weeks, sanitizing the house before a treatment and avoiding contact for fear of contracting EVERYTHING. I even (and this wasn't overreacting) skipped my dose twice because of some nasty contagions making their way around (one year the flu season was particularly bad). As my dosing progressed, however, I lightened up to the point where I would even go to the market during the quiet hours if I needed something.

This drug therapy worked wonders for me. In fact, were I able to take more, I'd decline as I'm in a much better place than I was then.

With my doc's approval, I kept about two and a half doses in my hip pocket to use in case it 'got bad' again—steroids being an unwelcomed interloper in my life. Over the course of more like five and a half years—rather than 2.5—I expended my allotment of Novantrone.

The good part is that this drug was shown to be efficacious, in studies, for at least 2 years after dosing. As I had spread those last doses over a few years, I have been 'coasting' for quite a while . . . but the time has come.

My MS has begun to progress a little bit faster and a little bit more oppressively of late.

Caryn and I have been searching for what's out there, what is in the pipeline and the risk/ benefit ratio of all of our choices.

So, what's next? The choice of taking or not taking a disease modifying therapy and which of the options available to take, is one to be made with great care and thought. I will, however, say that like most parts of a life with MS, the decision can only be properly made by those who are well-informed. The simple fact that you are here makes a statement as to your commitment to say informed.

Caryn and I have decided *not* to start a new medication for my MS.

This was not something to which I/we came quickly. Only after doing much research and far more soul searching (and consultations with my docs) did we decide. There were many factors which contributed to this course (and I'll explain; it *is* a course) of treatment.

Very high on our list of considerations was the out-of-pocket price I would be paying for any medication. Even with the best insurance I can buy in my state, our portion was anywhere from $6500 to well above $9000. Due to my prescription insurance's rules, I am not eligible for any of the drug companies' assistance programs. That said, one pharma company did offer to give me the drug free of charge (because of my "involvement in the MS community.") I read that as "you can influence people" and that is well beyond acceptable to me—as I know it is to you. Please do not read that as backhand-to-forehead and "'Tis a far, far better thing I do . . ." I just cannot be a part of such dealings.

Price was not the only consideration—but those numbers get your attention pretty quickly.

Our imminent shift to my ancestral homeland also put a twist into the process. Getting my prescription medications from here to there in timely fashion wouldn't be an insurmountable hurdle—in fact, I'll still have to obtain my symptom management meds—but it was <u>an</u> obstacle.

I want to speak to camera here and make sure everyone understands this: I believe that MS medications do work. I believe that the right med for the right course of MS and the right personal biology makes a difference in the rates of relapse, in the acuity of progression and the long-term course of this disease. I understand and believe that no matter the *other* things I do (and I'll go into detail), my multiple sclerosis will progress.

I hope it does not; but I expect that it will.

So, to that course of action . . . I have decided to actively—very actively—pursue complementary and alternative methods of healthcare to strengthen my overall health and wellness. Through diet, exercise, information and research, I intend to make my mind, body and spirit as strong as I can—not in spite of MS but rather <u>with</u> Multiple Sclerosis.

I'm not going to say that my attitude will beat MS. I don't anticipate some physical or spiritual epiphany nor do I anticipate 'curing' my disease with some fad diet or medical procedure. I simply intend to live with my MS . . . whatever that brings.

We intend to spend some of the money we would have shelled-out for meds on education, on help and on the things I will need to live with this new decision. Physical therapy, occupational therapy, gym membership, more organic produce, 'living well' programs, etc. are all going to cost money. We intend this period to be as active a course of treatment as meds would have been. I don't expect them to be 'disease modifying' . . . this is important for me to get across—particularly to those new to my writing.

The other point I'd like to stress is that this is not intended to be a lifetime decision for me. New (and better) meds are sure to be on the way. We will reevaluate this decision every step of the way and keep my docs up to speed as we go along. I have a new baseline MRI scheduled for the end of summer and we'll switch to annual (from bi-annual) updates of that process. MRIs are expensive, but that's where some of the savings will go as well.

Some people will think I'm crazy for taking this step some will think I'm crazy for not having taken it before. The truth of the matter is I probably am a bit crazy . . . but that has nothing to do with multiple sclerosis!

Dear Newly Diagnosed Me
06/14/2013 – Dublin, Ireland

At the recent international MS Patient Summit, I heard of an idea that I really liked. It's one of those things that can not only help the person completing the exercise, but also for those who are just now hearing that they have multiple sclerosis.

The idea is writing a letter to the newly diagnosed *you*.

I'm going to expand on that thought because you can be a resource to so many who have come (and unfortunately will continue to be diagnosed) after us. Today, I'd like you to jot a quick paragraph to the newly diagnosed <u>you</u>.

I've seen a few television adverts to this effect. I've even (and I'm sorry, I can't remember where . . . cog fog day) seen a version of it on one of the MS sites.

The sheer mass of knowledge that our cohort in the MS community possesses could be crushing. I'd like to crush difficulties of our newly diagnosed friends. You now know what you wished you had heard; what you now know that would have been *so* helpful to you when you were first told you had MS.

Maybe you quit your job too soon, maybe you stayed working longer than you should have. Perhaps something about parenting with MS would have been nice to know or what about when you told your boss, boyfriend, family? Did you handle something particularly well or rather poorly and you'd like to offer your knowledge to someone who might just today have heard the words "You have multiple sclerosis"?

Well, here is your chance.

One paragraph. What have you learned that you wish someone had said to you or wish you had read when you were first diagnosed?? What would someone newly diagnosed like to know?

Dear Newly Diagnosed Me,

It going to suck today . . . and it's going to suck tomorrow. For the next weeks and months, it's going to suck. But one day, not that far down the road, you're going to wake up and realize that living with MS sucks just a little bit less than it did the day before. You have the power to bring on that day much quicker if you simply realize that things are no longer the same. Don't try to do them the same, don't try to think of them the same and accept that some of the things you did are just not worth the effort any longer. There are so many things that you can do. Focus there and you'll be surprised at what a difference it will make.

Oh, and the stuff you thought was important . . . 9 times out of 10 wasn't anywhere as important as you believed.

Now your turn.

Dear Newly Diagnosed me . . .

Helping One Another Out of the Hole
9/30/2013 – Kerry, Ireland

Recently, I ended the panel discussion I led at the national meeting of the MS Society of Ireland with a story about a man with multiple sclerosis who fell down a hole. It's not an original story. I first heard a version on the American television program, *The West Wing*—a show in which the President of the USA has MS.

MS didn't play in the original version and I've, well . . . let's just say that all good stories get embellished along the way.

I received many comments about the story so I thought I'd share it with you.

A man leaves a pub and begins to walk home in the dark evening when he falls into a hole. This hole is very deep and very dark, and he can see no way out.

Just as panic was about to set in, our man sees his priest walking by and he shouts up to him,

"Hey, Father! It's me . . . I'm down here in this hole. Can you help me?"

The priest writes out a prayer on a piece of paper and tosses it to the man in the hole and walks away.

Not long after, a family member is walking by, and the lad shouts up,

"Hey, Cousin! It's me . . . I'm down here in this hole. Can you help me?

The family member writes out a greeting card and tosses it down in the hole and walks away.

In succession, his old professor and his doctor walk by and down into the hole come a homework assignment and a prescription . . . and he is alone.

Finally, when our hero is about to give up hope, his friend walks by the opening of the hole and he shouts up, in desperation,

"Hey, Pal! It's me . . . I'm down here in this hole. Can you help me?

And the man's friend jumps down into the hole.

"WHAT are you doing?," cries the man in the hole, "Now we're BOTH down here!"

"Yeah," says the friend, "but I've been down here before. And I know the way out."

I want you to know that I cannot tell you the number of times the Community has helped me out of that hole. I have seen you jump down into the hole with people from all over the world, people you've never met—and are likely to never get the chance to meet—and you have helped them out of one hole or another.

I encourage each and every one of you to call out when you are down in a dark place with your MS. I urge each of you to continue your practice of jumping in to help, to guide and to share your experiences in a way that will help one another out.

And remember, you're not only helping someone out of a dark place, but you're also creating a new guide for others.

Thank you for letting me share that story and I hope you understand just how helpful you have been to so many other people with MS over the years.

Becoming Students of Our Disease
06/21/2014 – New York, USA

You know those times that you feel like the weakest link in a chain? The smallest oar in the boat? Like you read the wrong test prep? That was me yesterday. There were enough letters after peoples' names in my meeting that you could write a small phone directory with them.

Phew! I'm glad that's over . . . but I learned a lot and, while my oar may have been small, I got my sweeps in like everyone else.

And I heard an analogy that made me think of living with MS.

Someone very important referred to the medical system as not unlike the educational system, particularly in reference to all of the responsibility for teaching and learning being put on the teacher.

We can't expect teachers to turn out ace pupils if the other parts of their students' lives are fraught with challenges. Teachers can't change home environments, nutrition outside of their walls, or ensure that parents help with assignments. School systems can't make up for unsupportive family systems or the lack of support systems for those families.

Sometimes I think that some of us feel that our doctors and medical teams should be able to 'fix' our MS and everything around it and all *we* have to do is show up for our annual appointments. Other times it's like we're simply sitting in the wrong classroom.

If our docs tell us we should see a supporting medical player that either isn't in our area or in our insurance network, isn't that the same as sending a kid home to write a paper and not knowing if she even has access to paper at home? If our physical therapist gives us exercises to perform in-between appointments and we only do them in-session, isn't that like not studying for a test and expecting to pass?

If the rest of the class is in the library studying literature and we're flipping through comic books, are we getting the same knowledge and information?

It is time that we all learn how to be good students of our disease (I'm pointing the finger at myself as well). The doctors don't know it all but they do have something to give. If you don't believe that, then it's time to find another class.

We will sometimes know more about our subject than our docs. There are some practices where we may be one of only a handful of people with MS. If Dr Joe Soap has 200 stroke patients and 2 people with MS, should we really expect him to know everything we need him to? If an illustrious professor of MS can only see us every 18 months, should we only 'study' and 'learn' when are in her exam room?

Should we seek out tutors, nurses, coaches, peers, delve deeply into scientific research journals and also take a well-deserved recess from our studies now and again? You bet we should.

And let us all remember that The Googeler doesn't have a filter for correct and incorrect information. Popular is what you get there, and the popular kids weren't always right.

So, here's to being good students of life with multiple sclerosis. We all look forward to an eventual graduation day.

On Being a Man with Multiple Sclerosis
01/29/2018 – Kerry, Ireland

In late 2017, the estimated number of people living with multiple sclerosis in the United States was revised upwards from 400,000 to 1 million. The old figure had been suspect to people who had been decades living with the disease. While still an estimate (as MS is still not a disease doctors are required to report to the US

Centers for Disease Control), it's likely much closer to the actual number of people with MS than the previous figure.

If we don't know the exact number then, as you might imagine, it's also difficult to tease out specifics as to who gets multiple sclerosis.

The epidemiology of MS in the United States shows that all ethnic groups in America—Caucasian, African American, Asian, Hispanic/Latino, American Indian, Alaska Native, and Native Hawaiian/Pacific Islander—are affected by multiple sclerosis with white American of northern European decent having the greatest risk of the disease. This data is confirmation that MS affects citizens and people of nearly every country in the world.

Sociological studies also illuminate that MS occurs in all sexual orientations.

One thing that has been ascertained without doubt, however, is women are diagnosed with MS at a rate three times higher than men. This wasn't always the case. As little as a century ago men were diagnosed with the disease at nearly the same rate over woman as women are now diagnosed over men.

While there is no scientific reasoning as to why men were once diagnosed three times more than women and now the trend is reversed, anecdotal evidence suggests that women presenting with what we now know as relapsing-remitting symptoms of MS were often discounted, dismissed, and told it was all in their head (this appalling invalidation of women's experiences continues).

The irony isn't lost on anyone that it really is 'all in our head' . . . and spinal cord.

Each of us has many facets to our lives, and our disease is only one of them. The light which enters and is then reflected back though our diverse facets makes each of our sparkles different, even if the angle of the MS cut is deep.

I have had the great good fortune of getting to know thousands of people from all over the world who live with MS and have learned much from them. I am, however, just one straight, white, middle-class, American male living with this disease. I am not qualified to speak or write from any other perspective than that. So then, what is it like for me to be a man living with a disease that affects three-times more women than men?

Different today than it was when I was diagnosed.

At the time of my diagnosis in 2001, I'll admit to some trepidation as to that very topic of being a minority. As that average white man living in America, it was my first time being in anything even close to a minority category. I didn't know what to expect from the disease in general, let alone what to expect from such a gender difference. So, I suppose I may have felt apprehensive about that part of it, and now I'm a little bit embarrassed by that. At the time, I don't remember thinking that much about it.

You might say I had other issues about MS on my mind . . .

In the years that followed, however, I'd have to say that, while there may be societal issues to do with being a man and not being the main earner/provider, I haven't found the experience of the disease itself much different than that described by my women friends living with MS.

It took about 15 years of symptoms being misdiagnosed by doctors (and sometimes ignored or excused by me), so my diagnosis process wasn't unlike that of many women. I've found the services (and even male representation in literature) from patient advocacy organizations like the National MS Society and MS Ireland to be even-handed, color neutral, and non-gender bias, but we could all work harder on inclusion issues.

I have found that many organizations are particularly reaching out to men in order to meet any specific needs men with MS might have. I would like to see stepped-up efforts focusing on the underserved members of our community.

So, how does it feel to be a man living with MS? With very few exceptions I guess you could ask a woman as well as you could ask me.

Multiple sclerosis is an incurable, degenerative, immune-mediated neurological disease that interferes with the transmission of nerve signals between the brain, spinal cord and other parts of the body. MS is all of that for men, women, black, white, brown, straight, gay, bi, trans . . . It is the same disease, but it affects each person differently, Full Stop.

I may process and cope differently than other cohorts with the disease, but at the end of the day, there really isn't much of a difference in the disease that I can see from this side of diagnosis. How our individual communities—those beyond the MS community— treat us and how we now fit into those communities; that is an uneven playing field which should concern us all.

How Can It Be Just One Disease?
03/28/2019 – Kerry, Ireland

I've oft spoken and written about our desire to be normal taking into consideration the abnormalities of multiple sclerosis. Particularly newly diagnosed people want to know if what they are experiencing is common, to be expected, and/or typical for someone with MS.

In fact, it's one of the things I have found most difficult to cope with beyond the intellectual understanding of the disease. In the 13 years since I started writing for someone other than myself, the similarity of symptoms coupled with the incontinuity of experiences with them has been ever-present in my conversations with other people with MS.

The list of MS symptoms is long, and most of us only experience a fraction of them at any one time. It is said that about 80% of us will experience profound fatigue—when it significantly interferes with the ability to function at home and work—as part of living with MS. Even that near universal failing of energy manifests itself in each of us differently.

It's part of the frustration of living with MS and part of the frustration of explaining the disease to others. It's likely the reason that multiple sclerosis is so misunderstood by those who don't live with a diagnosis—even those closest to us.

How is it that someone diagnosed years (or decades) before me appears to be less affected than me? Why are some friends' MS symptoms so much more advanced than mine when they've only been a member of our club for a few years?

We're a compassionate, empathetic, and commiserative lot. But still we find it difficult to understand, let alone explain, why we're all so different.

From survivor guilt to wondering if we're doing something wrong, the broad spectrum of MS has many of us wondering how we can be experiencing the same disease. The come-and-go nature of our own early symptoms clouds our apprehension. That we seem on an individual track can be frustrating, to say the least.

Considering our frustration from the inside, it's not a stretch to see why those trying to understand MS from the outside can have a difficult time. That we often don't have (or can't find) the words is an additional challenge to the situation.

Both from the inside and the outside—from patient, relations, and researchers alike—it's another aspect of multiple sclerosis that remains beyond comprehension.

10 Things I'd Tell Someone Diagnosed in Their 20s
06/20/2019 – Kerry, Ireland

If I am ever asked to talk to someone who is newly diagnosed with our shared disease, I never hesitate. Now that I'm nearing two decades of diagnosis (and well over three decades with the disease), I've plenty to offer . . . but there are some special things I'd have to say to someone just diagnosed while still in their 20s.

#1 FIGHT

Your youth is on your side. Take the time now to get healthy and keep yourself healthy. This thing isn't a sprint, it's a marathon. You're likely to recover pretty well from these first few episodes. That's because your body is young and you're healthy. It'll serve you in good stead to keep that mortal vehicle of yours in the best shape possible.

#2 MEDICATE

This one is going to draw some ire from some of the older crowd (see #3). The best medical evidence out there is that actively—even aggressively—treating multiple sclerosis in the early days will significantly prevent the onset of disability. Don't take a wait-and-see attitude. Trust your medical team (See #4) but push them as well. This is your life, your future we're talking about.

#3 DON'T TALK TO 'THE OLD ONES'

Here I am, in my 50s and giving advice to NOT listen to people my age. Well, as I said in the introduction, being diagnosed today is different than it was then. Getting diagnosed at 23 is different than getting diagnosed at 33, 45, or 53. Our experience is valuable to those who have similar histories but not nearly as valuable to you as that of your own cohort. Seek out the growing cadre of young people getting on with their lives with MS (The Shift.ms platform is a great place for this if you're still listening to this Old One.).

#4 FIND THE RIGHT MEDICAL TEAM

This isn't just a "what neurologist is in my insurance portfolio?" choice (see #7). Find a specialist who fits your expectations. Talk to others your age to see who they find helpful and supportive. If you have to travel a good distance, it's just what it is for now. You likely won't have to visit them much more than once a year for a good while. This is a 'Perfect Jeans' kind of thing. Quality and fit trumps price and convenience every time.

#5 DIET

If you take the time to search out changing your diet as part of how you cope, expect to find outrageous claims of success, all (at this writing) without strong science behind them (yet). That being said, I know that in my 20s I wasn't too concerned with my long-term wellbeing. At some point, MS may slow you down and make maintaining a healthy weight more difficult. Maintaining is much (much!) easier than regaining. Besides, there is a growing body of evidence that gut health may be a factor in many aspects of auto-immune diseases. No harm in modifying one's diet . . . just do it as complimentary to your healthcare regime, not alternatively to one.

#6 BALANCE

Your young adulthood is for the fun of it. Don't deny yourself the experiences you crave. Do consider long-term consequences. My father, a working-class Sage in my opinion, likened life to how you treat the engine of a car. When you abuse a car, you don't notice the effects at the time, or even soon after. It's towards the end of the engine's life that you'll notice the damage. Work hard, play hard, but recover well. Now is a good time to explore methods of mental/spiritual restoration like yoga, meditation, mindfulness or some other practice usually sought after by the closer to middle-aged set.

#7 INSURE

This one is specifically for young readers who don't live in countries where universal healthcare is part of the plan. Get health insurance and never, NEVER let it lapse. Far too many plans have pre-existing conditions clauses which can limit or even exempt you from coverage if you let your coverage slip—even for just a day.

Health insurance can be expensive. This is just going to be a life-long line item in your budget. Sorry, no getting around it.

#8 MS FRIENDS (OR AT LEAST MS ACQUAINTANCES)

Find a group (or a few) of like-minded people of your similar age and stage in life. You needn't have regular, formal or self-help type meetings. Just have some contacts who will understand if you're having a skiddy patch and can either a) offer suggestions, b) commiserate, or c) simply listen. There's something to be said for just being heard.

This also harkens back to #3. Don't sit in on support groups with people who have been living with MS for decades. Our needs are different than yours and some of us are pretty jaded about how the young ones are coping with their MS. It's your life, not ours. Live it your way.

#9 YOU STILL HAVE MS

Many of us who were diagnosed in our 30s and 40s can tell you when we had our first symptoms in our late teens or early 20s. I can identify several episodes which were either misdiagnosed by doctors or explained away, ignored, and otherwise dismissed by me.

There were long periods of 'normal' in between niggling symptoms which I now know to be MS. With medication onboard, you may experience extended space between MS 'things'. That's GREAT! Don't stop living the life you want to live, but don't stop treating your disease either. It's still there.

#10 TAKE ADVANTAGE

I am one who fervently argues with people who say things like, "MS gave me . . ." *or* "I'm a better person because of MS" and other such self-talk nonsense. MS is a thief. It takes, not gives. If one is a better person after MS, it's because of the person one already was not thanks to the disease.

What MS *will* do is afford you opportunities you may not have had before. It could be the opportunity to examine priorities in your life, or additional time when it sidelines you from everyday activity now and again.

Take those opportunities and do something useful with them. Life with MS is still an amazing thing. Use it for the good of yourself, those around you and other people around the world.

Building a Filter
08/20/2020 – Cork, Ireland

One of the common questions I'm asked about living with multiple sclerosis is what I would tell my newly diagnosed self. Like everything in my thinking about living with this disease, my responses have evolved over the years. In an era of social media echo-chambers, paid influencers, and the many who believe their unqualified opinions are facts, my response has yet again changed.

A person who has recently heard the words, "You have multiple sclerosis" would be well served to quickly and skillfully build an effective MS filter.

Early on, the filter will be vital. It will only allow information from reputable sources to pass through. In those early years when one goes in search of answers, facts and science will be most important in filling one's MS toolbox. While uncomfortable at times, it is salient to understand as many as possible aspects and outcomes of MS as one can stand to absorb. The good and the bad.

Once a tight grid of facts is established, the filter will help us to sort the kernels of useful information from the chaff of *opinion* and *bad science*. We can discern what is true and what others want us to believe is true. Much heartache can be avoided if your MS filter is equipped with a BS detector. There will be more people than you can imagine presenting plenty of BS pseudoscience vehemently as unequivocal fact.

After a while, you'll learn to temper your responses to unsolicited comments and 'helpful' information. A simple nod of the head and "Thank you, I'll look into that" may be all that is needed for a well-intentioned friend or relative. For others, a full-throated rebuke may be in order for someone spouting cures and conspiracy theories. In time, you'll learn to pick your battles and work out what's best for you.

Creating an MS-filter will also help you identify supportive people and places where you not only garner information but also camaraderie and support. As we progress through our lives with multiple sclerosis, it will be those people who will be the greatest life-affirming sources for us; those who, without judgement or agenda, offer us genuine support, understanding and the occasional nudge.

But it is through building, maintaining, and upgrading my MS filter that I have learned how to sort and stack the useless. All the while I am curating and nurturing those people and organizations that have helped me attain and maintain a quality life with multiple sclerosis.

I've Been Robbed
04/26/2021 – Kerry, Ireland

About 30 meters from the end of our lane is an old stone bridge which crosses a small river as it enters the harbor. The tidal estuary upstream from the bridge is a great refuge when only a short walk is allowed by my neuro-degenerative nemesis, multiple sclerosis.

All manner of birdlife can be observed from the solitary bench in the postage stamp-sized park on the north bank. This time of the year we can even see the wakes from the mullet as they follow the tide upstream to feed. Along with waterfowl, Little Egrets, and Gray Heron feeding on edibles found under the water's surface, the occasional sheep will stray from a local farmer's field to nibble foliage from the salty marsh as well.

This time of year there is a particular plant that blooms with tiny white flowers on a low island in the middle of the river about 50 meters from that bench as well as on the opposite shore further upstream. It's not a plant with which I'm familiar and, as it's across the river I can't get close enough to get a good look at it to have a go at identifying it. It's a seasonal occurrence I look forward to as the bouquet from the flowers is a potent brew of peach pit, grape candy, wild honey, and the sea.

The flowers bloom only for a few days and their scent, carried to the bench by light breezes, is gone until the following late spring.

The flowers bloomed this past week and I made my way down to breathe in their heady aroma only to find that the prevailing wind during their short blossom whisked their briny fruit scent away from our side of the river so a grazing herd of dairy cattle could enjoy it instead.

This year a cold north wind of a West Kerry Scraveen carried away not only the faint warmth of the April sun, but also the aromatic harbinger of the Bealtaine—The Celtic celebration halfway between the spring equinox and summer solstice.

I had been robbed but it's not an unfamiliar experience for those of us with MS. Parties, outings, backyard barbeques when the temperatures rise; all get taken away from us by that thief.

Dances at daughters' weddings, trips to see new family members, anticipated reunions with old classmates can be snatched away from us as new symptoms take hold, old ones return, or familiar ones worsen. We look forward to things with the knowledge that a cold zephyr from our disease can blow them out of our reach.

We miss a dinner out, we have to cancel (yet again) after accepting an invitation, we let a membership lapse for the lack of use but not for the lack of desire.

I've stopped giving in to the thief. I've vowed to treasure the things left to me rather than lament those taken.

A wedding reception is about more than a dance. A hot day can be coped with (if not conquered) by pre-cooling, a shady spot and plenty of cold drinks (and even feet in a cool bath if it's a casual enough affair). Video links can't replace the form of in-person gatherings, but they can imitate the function when required.

The steady breezes which blew from the north for over a week and carried away my anticipated joy could not—did not—remove the beauty of the blossoms, the joy at watching the birds, and the respite from COVID and all the other stresses of the day-in/day-out world of living with MS.

Only had I allowed myself to not go out and see all that was there to behold would the thief have taken those from me. MS has stolen enough from us. There is no reason to surrender more than it willingly takes. It takes enough without me handing over more.

Standing Up for Ourselves
09/29/2021 – Kerry, Ireland

My name is Trevis. Not Travis, Trevor, Tracy, Trent, or Tervis (yes, I've been called that last one, too). It's an unusual name, but I like it. If for nothing else these days, I'm easy to google!

I've oft said that giving a child an unusual name could be beneficial as, at least in my case, it gave me permission to advocate for myself from an early age. How many times can a five- or six-year-old stand up to an adult and tell them that they are wrong (except when they mispronounce their name)?

It is empowerment that can stick with them for life. I found this to be the case when I was a Seaman Apprentice (SA, E-2, the second lowest rank of the enlisted military) in the Coast Guard.

During a Drum and Bugle Corps International (DCI) performance during the US Coast Guard Festival, I was asked to explain the competition to the Commandant of the Coast Guard (Admiral, O-10, the highest-ranking officer in the service). I had been the drum major of a nationally-ranked competitive marching band in high school and knew DCI rules pretty well.

Let's just say that not a lot of SAs had opportunity or cause to 'explain' things to an Admiral . . . I'd like to think that part of my confidence in doing so may have been seeded in my early defenses of my unique moniker.

Now that I live with multiple sclerosis, I see how important self-advocacy and being confident and comfortable standing up myself has become. It can be far too easy to simply do what we are told by doctors, nurses, other healthcare workers, family and even what I call the MS Know-It-Alls who populate the world.

Please don't misinterpret. We need to take the considered medical advice of professionals into account as we make our health decisions. At the end of the day, however, they are our decisions to make.

A good relationship with your medical team can help turn "my doctor put me on . . ." to "we decide the best treatment would be . . ." I'm a firm believer in collaborative problem solving, be it in the home, workplace, or doctors' office. We put together the team, we are part of the team, but we are also player-manager of the team.

As when I sat next to the Admiral in the stands and told him things that I knew and that he did not, a healthy dose of respect is part of conversations like these, but deference needn't be. These are our bodies, it is a disease with which we are living, and the final decisions,—though collaborative in their best origins—are ours to make.

It is all too easy to allow ourselves to feel diminished by our shared disease. Fatigue can leave us wanting for the energy to do just about anything. Cognitive Fog (Cog-Fog) can have us second-guessing whether or not we've even had a first guess at it. And physical limitations can take us so far out of the game that we wonder if we're even in the stadium.

MS can shake our confidence in just about every aspect of our lives. That is why it is of such importance to learn to advocate for ourselves. Simply because it would be so easy not to . . . and that's not who we are. No matter our name.

A Decade Living With My Diagnosis
04/25/2011 – Seattle, USA

There is a generation of Americans who can tell you *exactly* where they were when they heard of JFK's assassination. The next generation has space shuttle Challenger to hold as a common cultural experience. And 9/11 is etched into every living psyche the way December 7th, 1941, lives in the hearts of the Greatest Generation.

We all have personal dates which we cannot shake as well. Dates of births and deaths and, in the case of many of us with multiple sclerosis, there are dates of diagnosis.

Today is the 10-year anniversary of my diagnosis. When I look back, like many of us can, before I heard the words "You have MS," I know that I'd lived with this disease for many years. In fact, a reexamination of mysterious symptoms I experienced in high school lead me (along with my medical team) to believe that I likely lived with MS for about 18-19 years before my diagnosis.

So much happened in the field of MS in the decade before my diagnosis: the first MS drugs were released, stem cell research became a viable avenue, and the MRI revolutionized the diagnostic process.

In the decade since, there have been more research papers published on the topic than ever before, patients are diagnosed and treated earlier in the disease's progression and one Disease Modifying Drug treatment (DMT) option has become seven (*this was in 2011. As of publication, there are nearly two dozen approved DMT*)! And that's a number growing every year.

While I cannot help but look back for a little while today, I'd much rather look forward to the next decade and I'd rather look forward for the good than for the bad.

I was four months away from my 35th birthday when MS became a part of my lexicon. Looking to the day, a decade on from now, when I celebrate my 55th year my hope is for a healthscape for those living with multiple sclerosis much changed from what we see today. We have made tremendous advances but there is so far to go.

Advances in basic science on our horizon will change the way we see our disease in ways that we cannot even imagine today. Could micro-robots help deliver restorative treatments to our scarred myelin? Will geneticists be able to predict MS before it shows itself? Maybe there will be a vaccine to prevent the next generation from having to even know what the letters MS meant in their parents' generation?

Short answer to any of these questions? I don't know.

I will say, however, that if I look at the rate of advancement from the 10 years before my MS and I look at the past decade, I can only suspect that advancements will happen faster and faster in the next chunk of my mid-life.

I have witnessed far too many friends with this disease take very heavy hits over the years for me to tell you that I am not worried about my progress.

For today, I'll take a moment and think back before I turn around and refocus my sites on the good that will come in the next decade of MS research and treatment. I think we all owe that to the next generation.

CHAPTER 3

Love, Losses, and Family

I ONCE SIGHED THE PHRASE *"unicorn piss and butterfly farts" when one of the 'Attitude is Everything' police called me out for being too pragmatic for their taste. Pragmatism works for me. It's not glass half-full or half-empty; it's how I get done what I need to with half a glass.*

Part of the pragmatic approach I have learned works for me, not all of the time, but enough that it's my preferred option, is to understand, accept, and acknowledge that there are parts of my life which have been/are diminished because of multiple sclerosis. It's not a bad life. It's just that much is not the same, how I'd intended it to be, or how I'd have wanted it to be were it my choice.

I have struggled often, succeeded sometimes, and lost more often than I care to remember. I fall like it's my job but, to this point at least, I always get back up.

I Hate Multiple Sclerosis
07/30/2012 Seattle, USA

Have you ever needed to vent off steam? Have you ever wanted to say the things that you know you're not *supposed* to say even though they are true? Have you ever tried only to be met with an unknowing response from someone who just doesn't get it? Have you been looking for a place where you can safely scream at multiple sclerosis without someone admonishing you for whining?

Well, then, you're in luck. Today I'm going to let it all fly. Mother may have told us never to use the word "Hate." Sorry Mom: MS is something to hate.

I Hate Multiple Sclerosis.

I hate what is does to me, I hate what it does to my friends, I hate what it does to my family. I hate my symptoms, I hate my pal's symptoms, I hate your symptoms. I hate that I have to explain to others my disease even when I cannot understand it myself. I hate the questions, I hate the answers, and I hate when there are no answers.

I hate that MS makes me question myself and my abilities. I hate that this morning was different than yesterday, and that tomorrow will be different again.

I hate that *Anyone* thinks that they can understand my MS.

I hate being on meds, I hate being off meds, I hate what meds do to me, and I hate what meds don't do for me. I hate the decision process about medications, I hate the expense of the medications, I hate that there is no cure.

I hate when people lash out at those organizations who are trying to help us, I hate when organizations say they're trying to help but fight with other organizations about who helps better. I hate that some people would rather complain about the way things are rather than get involved and help change things for the better.

I hate that sometimes hyper-sensitivity has me feeling too much and that sometimes numbness has me not feeling at all. I hate that numbers can seem as foreign as the Cyrillic alphabet, that faces and names often orbit rather than attach. I hate what MS does to my Brain and I hate what it has done to my *Mind*.

I hate "It could be worse." I hate that the people who say they have "cured" their MS are wrong. I hate that I have not cured my own MS. I hate that no one else has cured my MS, our MS . . . ALL MS!

I hate that the best I can do isn't a fraction of what I was once able to do. I hate celebrating the effort the way I used to acknowledge success. I hate having the energy of a person twice my age and I hate all the reasons I'm tired.

I hate the hopeful promises and I hate the stark reality. I hate that best-case-scenario isn't good enough and I hate that worst-case is more than some of us can bear to think about.

I hate having the anger of a generation inside of me.

I hate that so many of us need to read my writings because it's one of the few places that we could even be having this kind of a conversation for fear that someone will think we are pitying ourselves. Who are they? They don't live in the shell of our former selves. You want to judge us? Walk a few paces in his leg brace, hobble around with her cane, try to get around with my forearm crutches. You think we're doing it all wrong? You try to load a scooter into the back of a car. You rely on someone for the most intimate parts of your day. YOU DON'T KNOW US.

Anger is not a productive emotion. Hate is not a good emotion to harbor. Bottling stuff like this up can lead to 650 words of vial sputum. I do feel better, however. I invite all of you to breathe deeply and expectorate your hate for MS.

You'll be surprised how much freer your next breath will feel.

By the way, I love our Life With MS Blog community. I want to make sure they all know that.

A Distasteful Disease
03/22/2006 Seattle, USA

For those of you who have not read my bio I was classically trained as a chef. I attended New England Culinary Institute in Vermont and did master's work in Food Science at Cornell

University. I've worked and taught in some of the best food places in America. MS took me away from the business of food. I didn't think it could take away from me my love for my old business.

Two weeks ago, I lost my sense of taste. Well, I thought I lost my sense of taste. After some investigating, I found that I'd lost my sense of the taste of salt. We taste four flavors and sense a fifth: Sweet, Salt, Sour and Bitter. The fifth sense is called Umami. I always refer to Umami as the third dimension of flavor. Anyway . . .

I was sitting having a bowl of Vietnamese noodle soup called Pho' when I noted something terribly wrong. This normally highly flavored dish was coming across flat. I lunch at this particular spot frequently and know the owner, so I knew that the dish had not changed. By the end of the day, I had forgotten about the soup for other MS reasons.

I had to nap four times that day and could hardly un-bed myself the next morn. The day progressed with profound fatigue and the 'loopieness' I experience around disease progression. I knew that something MS-y was happening. I didn't have the energy to eat, so I didn't think much about the prior day's lunch experience. Once that phase passed, however, I noted that something was seriously wrong in this chef's palate.

While we taste all over our tongue, cheeks and back of our throat, there are concentrations of certain tastes in areas of the mouth. I noted that things were heightened in some areas and absent in others. A big hole appeared in the center of my tongue, where salt receptors are concentrated. I wasn't tasting salt.

Some have said to me, "Well, that wouldn't be too bad. I don't like salt." It's not just the taste of salt. Flavors are balanced by one another. If a food doesn't have all a balance (that's not to say equal) of sweet, salt, sour and bitter, we ask the eternal question "Does this need something?" Think of bread or oatmeal when you forget to add that pinch of salt—YUCK! Toothpaste is shockingly sweet, pasta tastes like its namesake—paste, coffee is nothing but aftertaste. These are not just tastes for me but also tactile experiences. I have written and taught curricula on palate development and flavor manipulation. You can move flavors around the mouth with the addition or subtraction of tastes—ARGGGGGGG!!! Is there no end to what this disease will take?

My Nurse Practitioner told me she was unaware of losing one taste due to MS, though there was evidence of some people's taste being skewed. My guess is that theirs were not trained palates and that I was experiencing this same skew just describing it more accurately. I suppose a professional runner would describe my drop-foot better I do too.

In the last day, salt is starting to come back—ever so slowly. The way it came on, with the other MS symptoms, and that it is waning after two weeks tell me that it was MS related. My docs aren't so sure.

The Support Family
04/19/2006 Seattle, USA

Some of us have a strong support system to help us deal with our MS, some do not. Some feel that we are alone in our battle with a disease that robs us each day of something we hold dear, some do not. Some feel alone though those around us do want and try to help, some do not. Some with few in their lives feel totally ok with their MS, some do not.

It's said that MS is a different disease for every person. It is also true that the ways we cope with MS is different.

I live alone (well, with my Irish puppy, Sadie) in Seattle, Washington. I have been divorced for a few years and separated prior to that. My closest family lives in St Louis, then it's further east and south from there. I have no real family close to me geographically, but they are close in spirit and I'm lucky to have a support 'family' very close in body.

Friends, colleagues, former co-workers, volunteers, even the local greengrocer can be a support family, if you let them. I find that people who know us, even on casual basis, are willing and want to help if they can. It is not easy to give-in, if you will, to the charitable offers of those close to us. We have to remember that they may need to give help as much as we need the help.

I've noted during my community work, that there are indeed a variety of support families out there. An important part of good mental health with MS is to have *somebody* in your life to help. It doesn't have to be physically helping you, but someone you can talk to, someone you can call upon. Do you have that someone?

Those who are close to us may need to feel like they are part of the solution. Let them help. It's good for everybody in the 'family.'

Ode to the Service Dog
06/12/2006 Seattle, USA

I've written about Sadie only once but as the holidays near, I'd like to offer a reprint of an article published in *Killarney Magazine* in December 2005.

Happy Christmas to Me

It may be the consummate Christmas wish for every Irish lad (and lassie) to wake upon the holy morn and pad down the stairs to the front room, sleep still in little eyes, frost hard on the darkened pane, the scent of evergreen and bayberry blended with the memory of last eve's festivities to find a warm, fury, wet-nosed pal left behind by Father Christmas himself.

Approaching the halftime show of life, I am far from a boy. As my family left Ireland for America when there were fewer than 13 colonies, my 'Irishness' could be called into question as well. My desire for that Christmas puppy, however, cannot be denied and has yet to be filled by any chubby, red-suited elf.

In preparation for an extended, 3-month holiday to the west of Kerry, I decided that the time was ripe for this lad to get his Christmas wish. I would get that Christmas puppy and I would get her for myself. A happy Christmas gift to me! What better companion for a ramble than a furry, young canine?

My search for the 'perfect' breed for me had taken nearly 15 years. I will admit that it wasn't a full-time employ. Obviously, if I were to get my newest companion while in Ireland, she would have to be an Irish breed. That was easy. Which of the famed Irish breeds to choose, however? There are the ennobled Kerry Blue Terrier, the loyal and beautiful Irish Setter, its cousin the Red & White Setter, Water Spaniel, Glen of Imaal Terrier, and the very, very large Irish Wolf Hound. All have their draw, save the wolfhound, which I love, but would not make a cozy flat mate back in my home of Seattle.

It was, after all, a puppy for which I searched. I was looking for the dog that would forever live in Tir na nOg. I was in need of an Irish Soft Coated Wheaten Terrier.

Say what you will about the temporary society of today, but were it not for the Internet, my hunt for Herself would have taken months, not hours. As many things do, my hunt started with a venture to Google.com. After only a few moments, I was e-troduced to an auburn-haired petal called Helen Hubbok and the Newkadare kennel. Upon contacting her, I asked how long she had been involved with the breed and her answer was typically Irish.

"Oh, not that long really, maybe 14 or 15 years." Not long, 15 years?! I pondered aloud. "Well, my family has been breeding Wheatens for over 3 generations."

Come to find out, Helen's great-grandfather was breeding Wheatens prior to their acceptance into either the Irish or UK kennel clubs in the early part of the last century. Ah, the Internet . . .

Helen had a dam that would be having her pups in late July, making them ready for homing upon my arrival early in November. While she was to offer me the pick of the litter, I think we can all agree that mine was not the typical course of choosing a puppy. We started a weekly e-mail exchange of photos and personality updates of the three females of the litter of seven. So much for padding down the stairs on the 25th!

When the time came around, I was still up in the air as to which of the three would be my new partner. Once the week-8 photo came across the wires, however, it was as if the decision had been made for me. Her wee tail blocked out the letter *J* in a sporting headline, to appear to read "YOU LOSE." I was hers.

Now, I'm pleased to report, little Newkedare Sadie Peg O'My Heart and I are happily spending our winter in Dingle, together. Christmas will find us both in front of smoldering turf fire, a goose in the cooker and pudding steaming in the copper. "Living the dream", is what I tell friends back in America when they ask how I am getting on. Whenever I think of that, little Sadie's needle-like puppy teeth remind me that it is no dream but that a boy's Christmas dream can come true.

As you can tell from the photos, she has grown quite a bit since last Christmas. She has grown from a cute apparition on my computer screen to an integral part of my every day. She has yet to be formally trained as a Service Animal, but the joy and purpose of necessity she offers is the greatest service of all.

On the Market
09/20/2006 Seattle, USA

"Hello. My name is Trevis; I'm 40 years old and a Leo. I'm a classically trained chef and writer. I like good wine and great food, gardening, films, spending time with my friends and playing with my Soft Coated Irish Wheaten Terrier called Sadie. I also have a progressive, debilitating neurological disease that has kept me from working full-time for the past 5 years.

This condition leaves me physically weak, cognitively unstable and can have very personal symptoms such as bladder and bowel 'issues' and sexual dysfunction. It has an average adverse economic impact of over $50,000 per year in this country, may be passed on genetically (with evidence that men may pass it on more frequently than women) and has no known cause or cure . . . .

Would you maybe like to grab a coffee with me sometime?"

Not the intro I particularly like to use as I head back into the dating scene.

Many who read our postings are in long-term, committed relationships. Several of you have been coupled since before your diagnosis. There are a significant number, however, who are or have gone through what I am now attempting. How did you make it through?

I'm realizing that both women, with whom I have been involved since those fateful words were spoken to me, knew of my MS when we got together. Now, as I look to new potential dating partners, my symptoms are not as outwardly obvious. Now, after half a decade in this city, I realize that part of my new social horizon may not know I live with Multiple Sclerosis. When is the time to disclose? When do you mention, "Oh, and by the way . . ."

One woman I was flirting with pretty hard about a month ago made it clear in no uncertain terms that MS was not going to be something she could be a part of. I have to credit her maturity and tact in handling that conversation; it still stung to hear it.

I guess that I have looked down my path with MS in the picture for so long that it is now my norm. I must now imagine what that path must look like for others that may want to be close to me. It was pretty damned frightening for me the first couple of years, but I had no real choice but to look (and move) down said path. The women, with whom I now look to relate, do not have to choose that path.

Who would?

Thinking about Our Partners
02/13/2012 Seattle, USA

There are a lot of people who regularly read my blogs about life with multiple sclerosis but there are even more who stumble upon our pages via internet searches. Many people from these categories

do not have MS but they live with the disease; they are the partners of MS. They are our wives and husbands, our boyfriends, girl-
friends, our life partners. They look at multiple sclerosis from the
other side of the same mirror

No two of us have the same version of Multiple Sclerosis; symptoms are different, progression is different, the way we cope is different. None of us has the same 'relationship' with our disease. It
can also be noted that no two of us have the same relationship with
those closest to us when it comes to MS.

Some of us do not have (or no longer have) life partners beside
us in our daily MS grind. It breaks my heart when I read that some
have given up on the idea that you'll ever, or ever again, have a
close, romantic relationship due, in part, to this stupid disease.

MS partnerships can be divided into two and a half categories:
those that began after diagnosis, those that began before diagnosis and the half category of those that began after symptoms but
before diagnosis.

Every partnership—MS or not—has its strengths and each its
failings. Quite frankly I believe that age and experience have as
much to do with the relative success of a partnership as anything
else. Relationships do not fail or succeed of their own accord; peoples' actions and reactions to situations as they present are what
make our connections lasting or fleeting.

Some will run from us due to our disease and some may run
toward us (or stay with us) for the same reason. I prefer those who
would run to or from me for *me*, not because of my disease. Sure,
our lives are different with MS. But beyond the disease, at our core,
we are the same people we were before the day we were diagnosed.

I categorically reject that notion that we are better or worse, as
people and as partners, because of multiple sclerosis.

If you feel you are a 'better person' because of Multiple Sclerosis,
I argue that it is your truest self which has come to the fore. For
those who feel you have been diminished as a person because
of MS, I don't think you give yourself enough credit, or worse,

someone's trashy attitude or coercive talk into your life has left you so invalidated you believe it. This is a dangerous slope, and we would all be healthier people if we shed this attitude of ourselves right along with anyone spoon feeding us such toxic nonsense!

MS is a disease that takes so much from us. We mustn't offer even more of ourselves for it to feast on.

Multiple Sclerosis runs through every part of my day, but it is not like the air I breathe. MS is more like the dirt beneath my feet: some days it is firm but dusty, others it is ankle-deep mud that dirties me and everything that passes close to me. *I,* however, am the same or stronger for the slogging through the muddy mire of demyelization and its symptoms rather than wallowing in it.

There are as many successful MS relationships as those that are diminished, dwindle, and even completely broken.

Those who succeed have found a way to work through, and around, and under, or over the obstacles MS drops on our partnerships. This does not mean that those of us in relationships that fail are, ourselves, failures. What we must not accept is a sentence akin to rolling the stone of tormented Sisyphus because of the treatment meted out to us by an unkind partner.

We are the people we are for the experiences we have and the people we meet along the way. I congratulate those who have succeeded in their 3-way relationships with a partner and MS. I commiserate with those whose relationships have failed. I have been on both sides of the equation and, while success is a better feeling, we can also learn much from the failures once we understand that *we* are not failures as people simply because a relationship ends.

Lost Friends
06/03/2013 Kerry, Ireland

With all the really great people who have come into my life since my diagnosis with multiple sclerosis it's easy not to focus on those who have left it because of my disease . . . but I have lost friends and I'm sure you have as well.

Now, it would be easy to brush it off and say that they weren't friends to begin with. In the case of some, that could be true. We might chalk some abandonment up to the natural course that some friendships take. Some of us might still be in that place where we defend those who bail with, "I can't blame them . . . who'd want to be around this if they had a choice?"

All of those (and more) may be true at one time or another, but it still hurts.

To be fair, some of us are to blame for friendships that are no longer after MS. We can pull away for different reasons just as our former comrades might have. We should take responsibility to repair any damage we might have done. But this piece is about those who have turned tail on us.

Over the years I've read too many heartbreaking comments about best buds that stopped calling or faded away. You've written of childhood pals who treat you like you've a contagion and besties that now blame you for your disease so no longer want anything to do with you. Worst of all are the one-time chums who stuff us with negativity and feed on our pain.

Seriously, who needs them?

I'm a firm believer in "better bad breath than no breath" when it comes to living with MS. I cannot, however, say that we should be willing to suffer a bad friend just to have *someone* to call "friend."

There is only so much room in my Friend Ship. If someone doesn't want to come along for the ride, let them swim away. If another is causing toxic waste to fill up my boat—OVERBOARD! I would rather float around alone than to put up with those who don't want to be there or those who think that it's their gift to me that they are.

All the more room for the next bunch of really great people to jump in and help me row sometimes and enjoy the party others have abandoned. Who knows, if you push enough of the false fellow flotsam into the sea, you might just need a bigger ship for all your new friends.

So, good riddance to bad friends! I'm sorry you didn't find it worth your time to hang around and find out what this new turn of events was going to be about. MS is a mean, terrible and nasty thing . . . but we're still good people and good friends.

How about you? Old friends gone? Bad friends still around? New friends via MS?

Living With the Brakes On
2/06/2013 Kerry, Ireland

In a scene from one of my favorite Irish films, *The Commitments*—the story of a young soul band forming in 1980's Dublin—three of the band members are trying to come up with a name for their group.

"How about 'And, And, And'?" says one of the lads.

I mention that because it seems like something of a lifestyle choice here in Ireland. Everyone seems to be/do more than one thing. A grocer-and-member of the county council, a publican-and-lifeboat captain, the farmer-and-builder for example. Last week we took our bicycles to be reassembled by the local publican-and-bike repairman. As we don't yet have a car—and we know how walking can be with MS—the bikes make for easy transportation. and the flip-out pannier baskets on the back make carrying groceries (yes, from the grocer-and-MP) back home easier from the shops.

While I'll not pass judgment on the work of the bicycle man (he is after all, a publican and I do want to get a decent pint now and again!), let's just say that my bike will need a tune-up once the proper bike shop opens back up in the spring (I have neither the tools nor the mechanical inclination to figure out how to fix the issue).

While Caryn was riding further and further ahead of me on our first trip back from town, I noticed that my brakes needed major adjustment. The rear brakes weren't deployed completely, so I could still pedal and make my way along the road. Each crank, however, took more effort than it should have—even in the lowest gears—and, though I tried my hardest, I just couldn't keep up.

Something unseen to my eyes was dragging against my efforts. Somewhere in the workings of the machine that carried me, a small glitch was holding me back . . . making me tired . . . slowing me down.

I needn't, for those living with MS, put any finer point on the analogy. Living life with multiple sclerosis can sometimes be like riding along with the brakes on. Try as we might, it takes more for us to go just as far and sometimes it's just more than we can give to get only part of the way.

These brakes do not stop us, however. We pedal on, we work very hard to get our load to its final destination. We know this.

The important lesson for me this day was learned as I cranked and huffed and cursed the damned breaks past the last of the row of cottages at the end of the town. The sun broke from behind the stone buildings and the harbor glistened in the clear winter air. Birds picked into the muddy flats that the receding tide had laid bare for them to forage. The cold smell of the sea mingled with the warm scent of turf fire smoke and mixed with the fresh of the rain I hoped to beat to my door.

I came to realize that the living part of a life with MS goes on around us every day. While the brakes of this disease may slow us down, may make nearly everything more difficult and cause some parts of life to be just nearly impossible, it is important for me to look around and to live around it

We can choose to focus on the fact that the brakes slow us down or we can choose to see the journey—a little slower, a little more difficult, and perhaps not as fully as before—for the old saying that life is the journey not the destination is one of life's truest realizations . . . multiple sclerosis or not.

My 'Sick' Friends
12-05-2016 Kerry, Ireland

I have a lot of sick friends.

First let me say that I'm talking about their wonderfully off-center, mildly deranged, caustic sense of humor. I find a screw (or two) loose in the caprice macabre that many of my dearest friends share and I hope that they would say the same of me.

Many of those 'sick' friends are also ill.

I'm off this afternoon to have a cuppa with an acquaintance from our town who, since being diagnosed with MS this past winter, has become a friend. I've a good few friends in the MS world that I didn't have before, and mayn't have become friends with, had we not shared a diagnosis.

I was on a video conference call yesterday with a German woman with whom I will share a podium at an international MS patient summit in Prague later this month. She said, "I'm going to see your friend, Emma, in Oslo next week." And it got me thinking of the number of people I call friend now because of the way we all live with our diseases.

Last month, I was asked to present at an online health advocate/blogger conference in Chicago and got to meet people who I've known only online for the past several years. But we'd become friends in those years. I also met a whole cadre of like-minded people from other disease groups and now have fledgling friendships developing with them.

My experiences may be a bit exaggerated because of my real-life advocacy work and I've been blogging about life with MS for so long. But I'd have to guess that each of us have developed at least comraderies, if not true friendships, due to the similarities we might share with others who share our style of living.

Ours are not 'MS-all-the-time' friendships. Rather, we have a thing (our disease) in common as well as a shared set of coping skills which make us friend-worthy. We may not all have in-person MS friendships with people from dozens of countries and multiple continents, but we share our experiences with loads of people via social media friendships, blog relationships and those with whom we connect at fundraising events.

We all have sick friends . . . and some of them have our disease as well.

There will be representatives from 27 countries from five continents at the Prague meeting. I'll even get to share the stage with the Deputy Prime Minister of the Czech Republic, Mr. Pavel Bělobrádek, who also happens to have multiple sclerosis.

The theme of my workshop is a masterclass in online communications. I hope to share with patient advocacy organizations the importance—really the imperative—and the beneficial joys of engaging with our communities on-line. It is because of you that I get asked to speak at such events, because of our MS friendships and the way our Life With MS community has become a standard for how people with a disease can help one another get on with their lives.

We help one another feel better, live well and get on with the living part of a life with MS. Thanks for being my 'sick friends'.

Is the Question to Have Children or Not an MS Question?
05/07/2019 Vilnius, Lithuania

If not made under duress or by coercion, the decision as to whether or not to have children (and/or when to have them) is always the right one for you. If you decide to have kids, you are right. If you decide to forego having children, you too are right. Let's make that perfectly clear.

Let me also make clear that both my first and second marriage partners had come to the decision to not have children. Well, at least not the two-legged kind . . ..

I made the choice not to have kids very early on in my adulthood. There was only one time I thought about it with a partner, but that thought was nearly as fleeting as the relationship. That choice was made well before my diagnosis with multiple sclerosis. About 15 years before.

The question I began to ponder after another blog I wrote is whether multiple sclerosis should be part of the decision-making process for couple considering if/when to start (or continue) a family. Now that I have typed that I should also add single people considering having children.

Adoption of children would tick most of the same consideration boxes, save for the physical carrying and birthing for a woman. And to that, save for those two very significant aspects, a man's MS is as present in the conversation as is a woman's.

There are, of course, issues with MS specific to pregnancy, and to post-partum depression and MS. Before that, there may be issues dealing with conception as well. Many want to know the risks of passing the disease along to the next generation. Then there is parenting with MS.

Perhaps that last one is where the crux of this conversation eventually leads. Perhaps as well, I just answered my question about MS's place in family decision-making. At least that's how it has been.

Now people are being diagnosed earlier in life—thus earlier in the course of their disease. Treatments can, therefore, be started earlier with the aim of extending the time before significant disability sets in.

In the 1950s and into the 60s it was common medical advice to women with MS to not have children. Then research began to show what is sometimes called the "MS Holiday" for women during pregnancy. Now women (and men) are encouraged to start a family when they desire, as long as they can handle pregnancy in their current physical state.

So, have we reached a place where the decision of having kids has reached a post-MS place? Are the niggling fears every couple has when considering starting a family shaped by one partner having MS or is it just one of the many little things which made this a big decision?

This isn't a question of whether having children or not was the right decision for you. It was. The question I'm asking is if MS is (or should be) part of that decision? And if it still is, will it ever not be a part of that process?

F#@^*$ Dark in this G*$&*/)(# Town
12/17/2020 Kerry, Ireland

Save for a short stint assigned to a US Coast Guard base in Hawaii and a few years living in San Diego, California, I have lived my entire life near or above the 45th northern parallel. That means that I've come to know summer as a time of long, warm evenings that stretch well into the summer nights. It also means that this time of year can have me cursing the dark like I imagine our ancient cave-dwelling ancestors must have.

The mornings remain inky black until well after the morning radio news program has signed off. My days are quickly book-ended by the closing in of the velvet drapes of night well before the schools let out in the afternoon. The sun seems to barely raise itself a fist or two above the horizon before it begins to dip, again toward the sea.

I measure the length of the days by where the sun sets outside the large, westerly facing window. Well into the summer it finally dips behind the mountains far beyond the northern sill. These days it dives nearly as far out of sight beyond the southern frame of the glass.

It's difficult to find motivation to get out of bed with MS issues weighing heavier than the winter-weight duvet. Coupled with a morning that looks several hours younger than it is, even the dogs don't want to leave the warmth of their beds. I find myself wondering what's for dinner at around 3:30 because my eyes are telling me a different story from my stomach and the chronometer.

This lack of sunlight in our days and on our skin can also reduce the levels of Vitamin D—an important factor in immune modulation and bone health, which can be a concern for people with MS.

The more extremes of latitude (north and south) have long been considered to have a strong association with incidences of MS as well.

Until I started to dig into the more emotion-related effects of the shorter days and their relationship with MS, I had no idea that what I was experiencing every October thru February was something more than my own experience.

One old study I read reports that the prevalence of Seasonal Affective Disorder (SAD) (an illness for which latitude is a risk factor) appears to be related to the decrease in ambient light during the winter months/ It offers some relevant insights into the geographical distribution of risk for developing MS.

Now, it must be reiterated that this is an old study, but the researchers also hypothesized that "the risk of developing MS is related to impairment of the immune system caused by light deprivation prior to adulthood."

Sunlight = Vitamin D. Vitamin D helps regulate Immune system. Immune system/multiple sclerosis. You see where they were going . . ..

So, maybe my brain's subconscious is crying out to me that these long, dark nights with intermittent periods of slightly brighter grey of the winter months are bad for my health. Perhaps that's one of the reasons I mutter every morning, "It's F#@^*$ Dark in this G*$&*/)(# Town . . ." and then turn on a couple of extra lamps so that I don't trip over a sleeping dog as I stumble to the kitchen and reach for the cafetiere.

And we'll not talk about the increased caffeine intake here at Milltown Cottage between the autumnal and vernal equinoxes!

Notes From Rehab – Surrendering
10/26/2021, Tralee, Ireland

I was afforded the great opportunity to attend a residential rehabilitation program for multiple sclerosis recently. It was a week (five days, four nights) pilot attempt to create a template for recurring treatment in an area underserved to date. Physiotherapy, Occupational Therapy, Hydrotherapy, Dietary/Nutrition, Psychosocial, and Neurology disciplines all came together to create the program which was run for two consecutive series.

I took part in the second.

Though I was asked, as a 'patient expert', to attend partly to evaluate the program and offer suggestions, I also went in looking for as much benefit as I could take. That meant that I had to shed the expert modifier and simply surrender to becoming a patient.

It wasn't an easy molting at first, but one I found rewarding and a little bit telling if I'm to be completely honest. That I had to work at letting go informed me of how tightly I've been holding on to the things I can control in this life of mine with MS.

As I've written in the past, it is of great importance that we each learn to advocate for ourselves in medical (and life) situations. By 'surrender' I do not mean that I gave up. Rather, I allowed myself to expose the weakness I constantly fight or hide so that I am not seen as less-than by the world as a whole. By being a man with a debilitating disease and admitting to my current limitations, I allowed both the therapists and me to see where I really stand in my progression and to find interventions which could help.

I suppose that I've been hiding (covering up, avoiding, working-around) the aspects of my physical disability for so long that I believed my own lies. By actively letting go of the heavy cloak deception I was able to direct the significant energy I'd been expending on avoidance toward improvement.

The very act of clearing a week from my busy schedule and

making plans for 5 days in hospital was like an act of contrition for vainglory.

During those five days I listened to my body and gave it what it needed. If I was tired (and there were plenty of reasons to be tired, this was an intensive program), I rested. If something needed stretching, I stretched it. If doing something caused me pain, I avoided it rather than powering through. I listened, I learned, I was present, and gentle in my judgements of myself.

There will be plenty to share relating to the exercise programs, stretching regimes, routines to help with proprioception, and strength. Before I could get to any of the parts of the week that would help me to be stronger, I had to admit my weaknesses. Admit them to myself. The professionals around me could see them coming up the corridor no matter how I tried to hide them.

"The lady doth protest too much, methinks," said Queen Gertrude in Prince Hamlet's play within the play by Shakespeare. I was the insincere, overacting character in my own staging of a Life with MS. I was also the audience I was trying to convince that things were better than they really are.

Like a weary and wary boxer fighting our shared opponent, I found a stool in my corner where I could recuperate. There were helpful words and soothing salves to prepare me for the rounds ahead. I've ignored the bell allowing me to rest for far too long. I'll not fight those who are trying to help me again. The punches are better aimed at MS.

CHAPTER 4

Our Place in the World

THE BROADER WORLD IS PRETTY GOOD AT LABELING, *defining, and judging how we live our lives. I'll admit to falling into line like a good soldier and doing what was expected of me for more years than were good for me.*

Fighting my way out from under the collapsed shell of an MS-deflated ego gave me a new sense of not only what was important, but of what was and wasn't beneficial to my overall health.

I have changed my relationship with the labelers and judges. By "changed my relationship" I'm pretty much saying I've turned my back to them. "You don't get MS until you get MS," is the old saying and, while I'm not one for many of the old sayings, I find this one pretty accurate.

It doesn't suit us well to continue to struggle in conforming into a social mold which is more about aesthetics and construct than livability. I've more than enough difficulties to contend with without wondering what 'they' might think or say about how I live with my MS. We are our own image of modern success.

Proprioception: Finding our Place in the World
12/01/2016 Kerry, Ireland

We stood on a hillside near the edge of the sea, Sadie and I. She was tired from bounding around the thick tufts of grasses and heather that would one day would become peat turf. The sun was low in the sky and the only sound was of the breaking surf below us and the throaty croaking of a Northern Gannet.

I wanted to drink it all in, the smell of the sea, the warmth of the mid-winter sun and the joy of my puppy. I closed my eyes and inhaled deeply the sounds and smells . . . when I opened my eyes, I was laying in the soft grass with a 5-month-old wheaten puppy licking my face.

That was my first experience with the MS symptom of inter-rupted proprioception—the sense of my place in the physical world around me.

It is the through proprioceptor signals that our muscles and joints send back to the brain, we are able to perceive our physical self as it relates to the world around us. Are we standing? Sitting? Bending? Arms raised? Lying on our back, looking up at the sky receiving dog kisses?

It's why a neuro exam includes the bit where we put out our arms in front of us and close our eyes. (I always open them to find my left arm about a foot lower than my right).

Proprioception, or interruptions to it, can also be a major con-tributor to falls.

It's not just muscle weakness or drop-foot that can acquaint us with the ground. Sometimes confused with dizziness or vertigo, faulty proprioception signals may be the reason we use walls and furniture to get around the house. In fact, the jumble of signals *coming from* the body to the brain is just as likely to be the reason for the 'walk like a drunk' stagger as mucked-up signals *going to* the muscles.

MS, of course, isn't the only thing that can affect proprioception.

Alcohol and some drugs can dampen proprioception. It's the reason police use the Romberg's Test to see if people have been drinking and driving. Inner-ear problems can cause issues with balance as well.

It's 10 years on since that first fall into the grass on what we now call Sadie's Cliffs. I'm more aware of the problem now, but I still fall. And my no-longer-a-puppy is still there to make sure I'm alright and then shower me with kisses.

Home Modifications
05/05/2010 Seattle, USA

MS, by definition, is a degenerative disease of the central nervous system. That term "degenerative" has always bothered me but it's true. For most of us, it keeps getting a little worse—taking (at least) a little bit more from us—as we get older.

I mention the idea of modifications we may need to make to our homes after a fall and I have moved forward with plans to install a second handrail on the steps to our home office.

As we look to an eventual move back to Ireland, there are many considerations to keep in mind when buying a new home. Most of us won't go as far (unless it's mandatory) as moving out of our homes *because* of our MS. Many of us, however, have considered the need to make our current residences more accessible.

The thought of a wheelchair ramp in the front garden may be *far* beyond what some of us are willing to think about at this time; even little things like removing clutter can make living our lives with MS a good bit easier!

I have, for example, always found hardwood floors preferable to carpeting. When I go to a friend's home who has carpet, I now know, wall-to-wall carpet is a tripping hazard for me. I don't yet have to worry about things placed too high or too low in my kitchen (now), but it's something I've thought about.

There are many resources for assistance (planning and financial) in the endeavor of making our homes not only more convenient, but also safer. For good ideas, I've even attended a workshop for the elderly looking at making adjustments to their homes.

Most days it's just a cane for me, some days a walker. The difference between using those two devices in my home really brings to the fore how much modification I'd have to make were the latter to become the norm.

I don't bring up this topic for the purpose of stirring panic or bringing gloom. I've always thought that a bit of proactive thinking beats thoughtless, reactive actions any day!

So, have you made modifications to your home? Have you thought about it? Does it scare you? If you could change one thing today, what would it be?

Staring a (*Potential*) Future Square in the Eye
05/07/2010 Seattle, USA

Life With MS Blog is a place where several of us feel comfortable like nowhere else. For some this has taken a place of social importance. For others, it's a place for information and validation. For more than a few the blog I write is something of a support group.

Some, however, may need/desire a real, face-to-face group to attend while others avoid (sometimes at doctor's urging) such groups.

As many of you know, I co-lead such a group for men living with MS in the Seattle area. We call it "Poker Night" so that no one has to say they attend a support group. We even played poker . . . once!

The range of ability vs. disability is pretty broad in our group. We all know the 'invisible' symptoms; some of the guys are in really good shape while others are further progressed.

For those for whom MS has significantly progressed, the lack of other social outlets can make attending such meetings even more important. We once had a gentleman attend for a while who, while still very young, was living in an assisted living facility due to a combination of his symptoms and his family's inability to care for him properly (but was able to afford excellent care).

When this lad was no longer able to use local paratransit to attend, we missed him.

My memory of him came to the fore a couple of months ago when I heard of a large group of people living with MS in a long-term/rehabilitation home just a mile or so from my home. These folks are a full generation younger than the average residents of said facility and it *is* a rather large group (7) for such a home.

It had always bothered me that we were no longer to be a place for our guy to attend. What, I wondered, if we were able to bring a meeting to this community?

Yesterday, we had our first get together. I wouldn't call it a self-help group yet. It was more of an informational gathering to assess the need/desire of the group. I was a little nervous heading into the meeting. I've done a fair amount of work with kitchen staffs in this type of operation; they are not my favorite places . . .

Our group, as you might expect, was all confined to motorized wheelchair apparatus. I guess that the medical term for their conditions would be considered advanced. The age range for our group is 40's to 70's (while the average age of the residents in mid-80's). Difficulty with speech was a near universal symptom for our group as well, making communication a bit of a challenge.

We, together, decided that having a regularly meeting support group was a very good idea! This is an underserved community and, quite frankly, I felt the need to pay it forward.

None of us know what tomorrow will bring when it comes to MS, let alone looking down the road a decade or so. We hope. We work on what we can. We do our best to stave-off the scariest bits of a future with MS.

But still, none of us knows . . .

I <u>don't</u> write about this group looking for some kind of praise for the doing of it. I write to tell you about it to raise awareness for this group of people and others in like situations.

Far too many people in the prime years of their lives are relocated to nursing homes and rehab facilities where they are (by FAR) the youngest residents. It wouldn't be going very far to say that I fear such a life (as my MS has been very aggressive in the past). I think it's time to address this unacceptable situation.

Perspective From a Nursing Home
07/16/2010 Seattle, USA

We all cope with Multiple Sclerosis differently.

Some fight the good fight tooth and nail, kicking and screaming, never giving one inch without immense mental affray.

Others of us fake it until we make it by putting on a face for others all day long and collapse into heap at the end of nearly every day.

There are also those who, seemingly, get by on attitude alone.

I'd like to tell you about someone who lives the best life she can with her Multiple Sclerosis, and she has done it by gracefully understanding surrender. I've been working with a group of residents at a nursing home. We've had a few meetings and we're finding our way as to how best to serve their needs.

While waiting with one of our members for her 'ride' back to her room (she cannot control an electric chair/scooter, so she needs to be pushed about in a manual wheelchair) we continued to get to know one another.

Her speech is labored, and she has a bit of processing delay between when I say something and when she responds, but she *totally* gets it and is as sharp as a tack!

We have some places in our life in common (some pretty remote), so she was very excited that I knew some of the places about which she was reminiscing.

Then she hit me square between the eyes . . . "I like it here" she said. "I feel guilty for being happy in this place, but I really do like it."

The guilty was because she can spend the little bit of energy she has left each day—after help with daily essentials—on things she enjoys, not things the rest of us feel we *have to* do.

She gets to 'swim,' which is really assisted floating and stretching in a pool, and she says it makes her feel young and 'normal,' twice a week. She doesn't need to cook in order to feed herself nor (and this one got the biggest smile as she said it) does she have to dust!

She shares a room with someone nearly a generation older than she, but she has a window and a small space for a few of the things she holds most dear from a long and active (VERY ACTIVE) life.

She has found a peace in living her life by surrendering to much which cannot be fought anyway. Rather than struggling with every single aspect of daily life, not enjoying anything for the labor, she has accepted that she can enjoy a few things (and maybe enjoy them more because they are so few) by giving up the struggle.

Surrender is an evil word to many of us living with MS. I think, however, how much further I can walk with a cane than without. Is surrendering to the use of a cane bad as I can experience so much more of my life with it? If a person surrenders to the use of a scooter and they gain independence to go places they have been unable, is that evil?

I knew from the start that working with this group was going to be enriching for me and it is a joy to share thoughts and observations. It would be a shame to keep all their sage, hard-won wisdom to myself.

Do We Have a Research Obligation?
09/26/2011 Seattle, USA

At a research event this past week I heard the director of a major, multidisciplinary research center say something which got me thinking.

To paraphrase, *Once diagnosed, people with Multiple Sclerosis should understand their obligation to research.* I think responsibility and obligation can be interchangeable in this discussion, so I'll use both.

While no one would argue the point of personal choice in the decision to take part in a research study, I think it's an interesting point to ponder; our responsibility to research.

By obligation I did not take the doctor's comment to mean strictly one dimensional. The obvious association I made with his statement was signing up to a research study. There are many ways, beyond being a subject, which afford us the ability to be a part of research.

Research costs money—simple fact. We can directly donate our own money to specific research programs and/or institutions. We can help such institutions raise funds by partaking in various fundraising events with them. If finding a particular research institution proves difficult in your particular area of the world, there are MS service organizations that fund MS research whether that is grand international studies or more local, quality of life research that you could take part in.

Many of these service organizations allow for people dedicate their donations specifically to research.

So, there's money. But all of these organizations thrive on volunteer support for their day-to-day existence. If funding or fundraising is not your calling, consider helping answer the phones or manning a table at a health fair or stuffing envelopes.

If you're already involved with a university or MS center that conducts research, how about scheduling yourself to speak at an MS self-help group to talk about local opportunities around Multiple Sclerosis research?

Many of us think of MS research and automatically jump to MS *drug* research and are hesitant on taking part. However, the vast majority of research going on in Multiple Sclerosis does not involve disease modifying drugs. There are studies in lifestyle, exercise, nutrition, wellness, imaging, vitamin D, viral assays and that's just from looking on the website for one local MS center in my city!

Some—and you have to look kind of hard—studies even enroll people living in remote locations. This can be the perfect way to get involved for those living with MS outside the normal research zones. Some even have telephone survey studies.

I have taken part in well over a dozen research studies at a number of locations and only one of them used drugs at all—a study of MS and depression using an anti-depressant drug as part of the trial.

I agree with the research doc who said that I have an obligation to the research community and to my fellow MS patients. I have taken from the well of knowledge to find the best ways to live with Multiple Sclerosis. I must, therefore, avail myself to add back to the body of knowledge.

This is my personal view of MS research and my responsibility to be involved. Do you feel an obligation to be a part of research? Have you wanted to be a part of something but don't know where to start? Is research someone else's calling, not yours?

Einstein is credited with the quote "Nothing happens until something moves." His words go well beyond physics. In research, nothing happens until someone moves.

Is it our move?

Catching A Glimpse Of My Former Self
07/16/2012 Seattle, USA

The warmth and humidity of Seattle summer gave way to thundering storms and then on to a cold drizzle over the weekend. By Sunday evening, it was all I could do to not throw something over my legs for warmth as we snuggled in to watch a rented film. While Caryn was setting up the DVD player, I flitted between channels and was brought-up short by a vision on the screen.

One of our PBS stations was running an episode of *Monarchy; The Royal Family At Work*. The episode involved preparations for a state dinner was also intriguing to me as a former chef. When the shots of the palace kitchen flashed, it was fun and exciting to see the goings on before such a banquet. Then, they showed the chef.

Directing a brigade of culinary professionals was sprite looking chef Mark Flanagan, in crisp white jacket with a crown "E R" embroidered across the left breast (for Elizabeth Regina). With confidence, he spoke to the camera as the formal repast for heads of state was being prepared. As the lens widened and the shot changed to show the magnitude of the kitchen, I saw that the chef accessorized not only with the attire of my former career, but also with a forearm crutch of my current disorder.

I have seen interviews with Chef Flanagan before without a crutch, so I'm not sure what might have caused his need for support during this particular event.

There was part of me that admired the chef for carrying on his duties with the aid. Another part was deeply saddened that I can no longer answer such a call. It wasn't a 'feeling sorry for myself' kind of thing, please don't see it as that. Rather, it was yet another time that MS creeps up and surprises me with the opportunity to mourn a part of my former life. We all get those and we all know they pass.

It doesn't make them any easier.

Induced Frugality
02/11/2013 Kerry, Ireland

None of us will argue the fact that MS is a damned expensive disease. We are all affected financially by MS in one way or another.

One big one is how MS may have switched our career paths—as my friend Mike put it—from "thrive to survive." We may not be able to work any longer, may not be able to work as/hard/as much/

as long, we may not go for the promotion (or may simply be looked over for it) as we deal with the progression of multiple sclerosis in the workplace.

Even if we're still gainfully employed in our chosen field and advancing well, the thought of everything changing on a dime may cause us to save and invest and insure differently than others in our socioeconomic age group.

The increased cost of insurance associated medical expenses, and co-pays can put a dent in income, savings and beyond. Dual-income families may become single bread-winner households overnight and in some cases, marriages (and a level of financial status quo) fall victim to MS.

With all of our incomes stunted (or dwindling or disappearing), saving for the MS rainy day and added outlay for medical expenses how are we to make ends meet?

One way that would seem easy to some would be to eat lower on the food chain. Whole, unprocessed foods can be far cheaper (think bulk section vs boxed-prepared) to purchase but far more costly when it comes to time and energy to prepare. That bag of pre-washed greens is likely 3x more expensive than a regular old head of lettuce. Trimming washing, drying and mixing can be a price our MS bodies may not be able to pay at the end of a long day.

Utility bills can be a factor as we may be at home more than we might otherwise. At home means lights on, A/C going to keep us cool in the summer and so on. Charging power assistive devices can also run-up the power bill.

Larger cars may be needed to get into and out of and/or transport those freshly-charged devices. Rising fuel prices can hit a family living with MS in the pocketbook harder than a neighbor.

I guess that I'm not being very helpful here. It seems as all I'm doing is listing areas where it is or may be hard for us to save a few pennies.

I know finances can be a personal and touchy subject. But, let's face it, I've talked about just about everything else ... why not money?

That Look
09/04/2014 Kerry, Ireland

I think I was feeling better today than I have in weeks. I contracted a nasty bug on my flight home from New York, was exhausted from the travel and two five-hour time changes in four days is tough on anybody. Finally, I think I was back to near normal. I had some energy and even got up relatively early.

Maybe that's why it seemed so shocking to the new acquaintance I was talking with when I said that I have MS.

I got *THAT* look.

Part shock, part pity, half confusion, and a sprinkle of "Is it catching?" all crossed my companion's face in an instant. I could read every one of the thoughts like picking up the lines of a poem memorized from some long-ago literature class.

I'm kind of 'out there' as far as living with MS goes, so it's been quite some time since anyone new has learned of my MS face-to-face like that. It hurt a little bit. Okay, more than a little.

Not that this dear person was trying to hurt me; far from it. There were intelligent questions, empathetic listening, and an effort to understand MS. I couldn't have been happier about answering her questions. Still, that look—*THAT* LOOK—is one that I have to believe many of us have seen, have been stung by, and have even hated people for giving.

Some people who have given me that look disappeared from my life not long after. In the long run I think I'm happy for that. Others learned to live with my MS not unlike I have learned to. Some even rose to the occasion and helped me raise funds and awareness of the disease.

That look doesn't always mean that someone is also looking for the door (maybe not even most of the time). Maybe it's shocking because many of us have somehow grown used to MS, have grown somewhat accustomed to it, so aren't used to the new horror of it thrust upon us.

Risk Aversion
03/09/2015 Kerry, Ireland

There is a difference between falling over and falling off a cliff. So too is there a difference to be made between avoiding danger and avoiding risk. Danger is something to stay away from. Not putting ourselves in situations where risk is involved can also reduce significantly some of life's benefits.

The Oxford English Dictionary defines "risk" several ways. In the singular it is "the possibility that something unpleasant or unwelcome will happen." When taken as an adjective, however, risk is "a person or thing regarded as likely to turn out well or badly in a particular context or respect."

You see, risk can often turn out well. It's the old cost:benefit ratio. If we don't risk getting in a car and onto the highway, we don't have the benefit of getting where we're going quickly. If we don't risk the germs that fellow attendees are carrying, we won't enjoy the benefit of being at a ballgame. These are different than the dangers of driving drunk or walking into an infectious disease quarantine zone.

I see the difference between something 'dangerous' (or silly or irresponsible) and risk is the potential benefit to myself and my family if I/we do something after thinking through some of the possibilities.

As I wrote in *Chef Interrupted*, "*One cannot dwell on the 'what ifs' of life. I have found that two or three 'then I woulds' helps me to sit comfortably in the driver's seat of my new existence without either A) white-knuckling the passage or B) gazing so far ahead that I miss the beauty all around (or worse, end up in a ditch alongside my road).*" With a few of these 'then I woulds' answered I can feel more comfortable taking a bit of risk . . . and reaping the rewards.

People both in and out of my MS circle thought my wife, Caryn, and I certifiable when we decided to take a risk and move to Ireland from our home in Seattle. It was (and is) not without significant difficulty, but without taking the calculated risks we did, we would not have lived out this portion of our life's dream (okay, *my* dream . . . but Caryn and our Pack are pretty happy thus far, too).

If it all ended tomorrow and my MS or some other circumstances were to cause us to have to pack up and move back, the expense, the difficulty would all be worth the benefit.

When we visit sites like the Cliffs of Moher, many people go on the other (dangerous) side of the barriers to get a better view. That's dangerous. I may risk exertion getting up to the viewing area, I may risk stumbling over on the many steps along the path, but I'm not putting myself in any real danger. And the benefits, well, let's just say that the extra 3 feet doesn't give one any better vista . . ..

Life isn't for existing; life is for living. I may live in a zone of 'MS Détente' but that doesn't mean that I'm going to sit the rest of my life in a bomb shelter of safety and miss out on living. This is always how I've lived my life, before MS and now. Perhaps that's why it's so important to me . . . it makes me feel like I did before.

The benefits and the potential success rate in achieving said benefits may have to be a bit higher in my new ratio analysis, but I'm going to keep on taking risks while keeping an eye out for potential dangers.

How about you?

The Knowing Nod
06/05/2015 Montreal, Canada

Yesterday I had the opportunity to speak with two groups of people about my former career as a chef, about my book, and about living with multiple sclerosis.

In both chats there were people who knew MS very well (and some who did not really know about our disease). Some have MS, some were family members and others were friends or co-workers. When I started to speak about the symptoms or my reactions to the disease I looked up and saw those who know give what I now recognize as the 'knowing MS nod.'

Like with others in the MS community and across social media, some people just get it. Some people have been there themselves or seen it in those they love. Whether embarrassing bladder or bowel references, talk about the mind-numbing disease, or getting stuck in the middle of a sentence and forgetting where we are in a conversation, a gentle nodding of the head and kind softening of the eyes let me know that I am not alone.

Sometimes those who have been there will frown or grimace at one particular aspect of MS or another as they have had (or seen) how difficult that one can be. Other times there is a wry smile that lets me know that someone else has stumbled with this or that about which I might quip. And there is one other knowing MS nod that I find particularly noteworthy.

When we speak of something in a way that finally gives words and definition to something we've been experiencing but been unable to explain to someone else the eyes brighten, grow large, and a person has their eureka moment as they turn to someone dear and give a giant slow MS nod as if to say, "See, *that's* what I've been trying to tell you."

What a comfort it is to know that we needn't explain ourselves to others in our little club. To simply give a mention of this experience or that symptom or some other shared MS reality.

Whether in the same place or in a community space, I've often written or said something which is greeted with the MS nod . . . and I return one in kind.

Employment and Identity
10/28/2015 Cork, Ireland

During tough economic times, finding and/or keeping a job is difficult for typical people. For we of the compromised myelin, the idea of finding new employment is daunting, while the thought of losing our jobs is downright frightening. Getting and maintaining a job while living with MS is also an important part of staying active and contributing to society as well as, you know, paying for things.

Identifying oneself *as* (not just *with*) one's career is not simply an 'American Thing'. I've seen shingles with "John Flattery, Butcher," "Stephen Crumb, Attorney at Law," or "Millicent Weaver, Accountant" hanging from shop fronts and roadsides around the world.

"I am a teacher," "I'm an electrician," "I am a stay-at-home mom" are all far more flattering than "I am MS." And, of course, we all know that we are not our multiple sclerosis. Still, MS intrudes on our careers, thus into the very place by which many of us define ourselves (or at least how we define our successes).

For some of us, MS has crept slowly into our professional lives, and we have employers who have helped us stay an active part of the work force by adjusting our work (or the workload of the actual tasks we perform). For others multiple sclerosis symptoms simply stacked up too fast and too soon for us to navigate them in terms of our professions and we had to leave our jobs due to our condition. Still others—and I wish they were fewer—have found the workplace a hostile environment once we couldn't pull our weight and we were unceremoniously shown the door.

The loss of a job—which means income, may mean insurance, and certainly means a sense of pride and worth—can be a blow to more than our bank statements.

Research presented at the European Committee for Treatment and Research in Multiple Sclerosis (ECTRIMS) in 2015 throws light on the cost of multiple sclerosis and employment—The Earnings Gap.

According to the Swedish study, people with MS begin to feel the effects of the disease in their paychecks a year before they are diagnosed.

Researchers used Swedish national registry data of all residents in 2004 aged 30 to 54 years and identified 2556 individuals diagnosed with MS in 2003–2006. These were matched with 7599 people without MS according to sex and age.

With expected differences for manual workers versus office workers, by the time we are diagnosed, people are averaging 15% less than our counterparts and just five years after diagnosis we earn a staggering 28% below our matched counterparts.

Manual labor and lower education levels saw larger differences than office workers but to my surprise in the report, managers with MS earn only 68% (that's a 32% reduction) compared to the non-MS cohort. This is thought to be due to lack of flexibility in working hours of managers. The head researcher, Michael Wiberg, MSc, Karolinska Institutet, Stockholm, Sweden told ECTRIMS attendees that further research will continue to examine more specifically the type of job environments that allow continued presence in the labor market for patients with MS.

This report was only one of eighteen studies presented that year on the economic burden of MS presented.

Incomes go down, expenses go up. Our identities take a hit and our place in the world can feel diminished. The economy may rather move on without me, but I believe we all have a great deal to contribute to our communities, our professions, and the greater good. Perhaps two years of international hybrid work-from-home during the COVID-19 pandemic will open the eyes of corporations and employers to the fact that we are of more value than they had previously thought.

When #YouDontLookSick But Are
11/25/2015 Dublin, Ireland

A few years after I was diagnosed with multiple sclerosis (MS), I found myself in a medical marijuana dispensary in a state where it was legal. Doctor's prescription in hand, I was checked in through one security door and then another. By the time I was let through the third non-descript door into the dispensary itself, I was beginning to feel slightly uncomfortable (though the staff were quite cordial and affirming given the security of the place).

As my eyes adjusted to the dimly lit waiting room with its dated hodgepodge of donated living room furniture and low din of pleasant conversation, I found myself side-by-side with people with cancer, survivors of tragic burns and crippling automobile accidents. There, alongside chemo patients, AIDS patients, dying patients was me . . . the guy with MS.

About a year later, trying to get beyond the medicate to alleviate phase of living with MS, I took part in a research study on pain and chronic conditions. My disease was causing me fairly serious pain. Still getting the hang of living with MS, this pain was also causing deterioration in my quality of life and what is commonly called, "suffering."

My study group happened to be all men; one who had lost a leg, mid-thigh, to a landmine in Vietnam; another who had fallen off his roof one winter and broken his neck, thus paralyzed from armpits down but could use his arms; and another who had lost an eye to cancer but had been disease-free for a number of years . . . and me, the guy with MS.

This past week, while on holiday in Switzerland, I was fortunate enough to be introduced to a local impresario in a small, mountainside village in the country's northern canton. He and his family welcomed our band of weary travelers into their home, fed us, watered us (quite well) and offered all sorts of local entertainment. Your Man also had visible (albeit well controlled by medication) symptoms of Parkinson's disease.

Our host was kind enough to have read up on me as our mutual friends had sent him my book and other writing. We sat and talked about the world as well as the things that only those with such conditions can understand. We sipped local damson brandy late into the night and early into the morning . . . Yer Man with Parkinson's and me . . . the Guy with MS.

These are, of course, just a few of the pages as I flip through my mental photo album of experiences while living with MS. My life is far more than just my disease and the ways I cope with it. They are, however, very vivid memories colored by the way these groups of people acted and interacted with one another and with me.

There were no secret handshakes or blaring beacons of diseased welcome. Rather I found a kind sense of knowing—like the look in their eyes that veterans of wars may share—and a gentle acceptance from these groups of unlikely peers. No one tried too hard to avoid or attack the subject. None tried to commiserate or empathize with similar or excaudate symptoms. And certainly, I never heard "But you look so good" or #YouDontLookSick.

I don't blame the well for trying to buck us up or make us feel 'normal' with such phrases. The language amongst ourselves may sound quite similar but, "You're looking well, friend" or "I like the hairstyle you've chosen" is not #YouDontLooksick or "I couldn't even tell it's a wig." It's an insider's lingo but we'd love for others to study its inflections and nuances and maybe not punctuate it with patronizations or sympathy.

You see I have a degenerative, often debilitating, chronic neurologic condition. In other words, I **am** sick. It's not who I am or all that I'm about but when I'm not feeling or looking well (and trust us, we know when we're not feeling or looking well) I'd rather my friends say something like, "Is there anything I can do to help?" or "Looks like you're having a rough day." or even "Jaysus, Lad! You look like Hell!"

Those who know and love me get it and I'll give those who don't know me a pass. I just find it comforting when volumes are spoken without much more than a look of acknowledgment, a knowing nod toward my walking aid or even better, a smile so bright that it burns away the aura of illness and says, "There you are, my friend. I see you inside that wreck of a body and you're still you."

I Miss the Office Party
12/22/2015 Kerry, Ireland

Ho, Ho, Ho! Where's the V.O.?

Gifts are wrapped. Tinsel is strung. Brussels sprouts creamed and ugly jumper collected from the cleaner. Let the holiday festivities commence! Yet, something is always missing for me this time of year.

Even if I've only every technically worked in an office for one short period of my life, I miss the office holiday party most.

Like many people living with chronic illness generally and multiple sclerosis specifically, I've had to first cut-back, and then end my working life. Sure, I have found new things to fill my time, to make ends meet, and to make me feel of some worth to society, but I miss working with people and then celebrating with them.

Be it a swanky gathering at a glitzy venue or a simply pot-luck lunch in the break room, the chance to make merry with the people with whom I've worked, was a time I cherished. To sit down for a meal or to chat around a punchbowl and not talk about work was a wonderful thing.

I learned new foods, about other peoples' traditions, took home ideas and made friends out of colleagues. All of this for a few pounds out of old Mr. Fezziwig's purse or out of our own in other cases. Just like Dickens' character, Scrooge, from *A Christmas Carol*, I too look back at the office parties of my younger days with joy and with melancholy.

Of course, to be able to dance again would be nice. But it is the camaraderie of old workmates and bosses, the collective sense of satisfaction in celebrating a job well-done and the time when personal and professional touch that I miss the most. To laugh with an Admiral or coo at snapshots of an assistant's children and to shake the hand of someone working through their own difficulties; to not be supervisor or supervised but to be happy humans together . . . that's what I miss.

I don't dwell on such things. In fact, I don't think of them much at all in general. At this time of year, however, it's one of the blaring things that are missing from this new life with MS. A life without so many things (is also a life with so many great things) but this time of year this one sticks out.

Being part of a global MS community has been important work that I take great joy in seeing as an achievement. I'd love to sit down to a bowl of gin punch with every reader and raise a glass to the season and all the joy that is in it.

On Being an Expert Patient
04/11/2016 Kerry, Ireland

It's not often that I think of myself as an MS 'patient'.

Like many of you I try to think of myself as a person living with multiple sclerosis. I'm not afflicted by it, I'm not an 'MSer' (though I do understand why many identify with this moniker), and please don't ever call me an MS Sufferer. Not to be politically correct about it, but I'm only an MS patient when I'm in the direct care of my medical team.

Yesterday, I was in to see my general practitioner (GP) about a health issue (nearly) completely unrelated to my multiple sclerosis. Our discussion about my general health turned to MS and his ability to help with one of my potential MS decisions.

He asked some questions about my MS and then the discussion turned a bit more general about the disease.

He brought up some topics of which he was peripherally aware—such as Vitamin D, diet theories, the price of MS drugs (and prescriptions on the whole in the USA) and the relatively high prevalence of MS in our specific area (though we are a small town of less than 2000 people, we could rattle off nine people we knew who have MS and most not originally from the town).

The chat soon went from doctor-to-patient to a patient-to-doctor chat.

Now it must be said that while well-educated, running a respected practice and nothing like a Patrick Taylor character, my doc is still a country GP in rural Ireland. He is also one who is willing to do extra research into a topic for the sake of his patients.

My ability to speak from a researched perspective, to paraphrase from recent research papers and answer his questions in apposite medical language led my doc to refer to me, with a smile, as an "expert patient." His tone and the direction the conversation continued confirmed that he meant the title as a compliment and not to say that I was some kind of an MS know-it-all.

I believe that we are all relatively experts on our own condition and the way that MS is affecting our own bodies. I also think that it is important that we educate ourselves about the broad facts of the pathology of multiple sclerosis. It is immediately obvious the change in professional attitude I am afforded when I speak of the *hormone-like vitamin D3* rather than just vitamin D, when I use medical terms like oligodendrocytes (the myelinating cells of the central nervous system) or properly pronounce Progressive multifocal leukoencephalopathy (PML).

Not that all of us need to be experts in all aspects of this disease; we have doctors and researchers for that. I do believe we should educate ourselves to the fullest in order to ask the correct questions with our doctors and be able to hold a conversation which allows those professionals to give us more than the Readers' Digest version of an answer.

If we prove that we have done our homework, I have found that we are treated differently, we are thought of differently and we are spoken to differently. I suppose it's the equivalent (in my former career) of someone saying, "This food is bad" vs "This dish is not to my liking." One will get you further than the other.

Being a patient is only a very brief experience in my life—I'm only in the direct care of my team maybe six or eight hours a year. The information I glean in those few short visits helps me to live my life with MS the best that I can. By being an expert patient, I am able to get more, learn more and process more in the short time I'm allotted with my docs.

The Empty In-Box
05/16/2017 Kerry, Ireland

Even though I've lived with the diagnosis of multiple sclerosis for over 16 years, there are things I experience now and again that are the very same as those first few months after MS came into my life.

One of the most devastating experiences relative to MS in the beginning was my sense of a lack of connection to the world around me.

I'd been working at a job for a number of years which had me flying city-to-city, day after day, week after week, often for weeks on end without being home. I had important contacts to maintain through ten time zones and it seemed I was always e-mailing or on the phone with someone

I was always connected to someone, somewhere.

Then, after I had to lose my job, before the days of social media, there was nothingness. The phone didn't ring, the fax machine (this was a while ago now) and the e-mail inbox was empty. For the person I was—a man who identified himself *as* his job—this was a huge blow to sustain. It could be said that I didn't suffer the disconnection well.

Perhaps it is because my writing has become such a large part of my life and the lives of so many around the world, I feel just as 'connected' as I did in those days before MS. Perhaps you may feel like the connections made through social media have reconnected you with the world on those days when physical contact is difficult (or worse).

Just like those early days of MS and having to medically retire, an empty in-box can leave me feeling adrift in the sea of MS fog.

I think we all respond to deadlines, to expectations, and to schedules.

On the difficult days, the days we are forced out of our everyday routine by MS, it can be easy to drift without aim through a day, a week, or even more. The blip of the e-mail reception alarm can feel like a wakeup call after hitting the snooze button on the alarm clock. An incoming question or note requiring a bit of thought can be a beacon in that MS fog.

It's not just the something coming in that matters that much. In fact, I'd argue that it's not the *in* that matters at all. It's the expectation placed on us and that we place upon ourselves to respond, that makes these connections important.

An empty in-box, or mailbox, or answering machine can be difficult to contend with because it says that no one needs to hear from us. It's the reply, the need for us to do something—even if it's only to respond with "Thanks, I'll read that when I get the chance" that makes the connection so important.

I guess it's like that MS window about which I once wrote ". . . through it I will be able to see the beauty and wonder that is our life, and I will remember that even though I may not be able to be as active in it as I would like, I am still only a pane of glass away from the whole magnificent show." I guess that the inbox is something like that pane of glass.

Connection, real or perceived, is an important factor in living a healthy life with any chronic condition, multiple sclerosis included.

My Batting Average
07/25/2012 Seattle, USA

Baseball has been in the headlines here in my adopted hometown of Seattle this week. Not because we are in a race for anything but the bottom of the West Division, but rather because of the trade of one of the game's greatest who has become an enigmatic legend in the game.

Ichiro Suzuki, the eleven-year patroller of "Area #51" in our ballpark's right field, was no longer seen as an asset to our team and was swapped for a couple of minor leaguers who will likely be nothing more than occasional players in The Show.

While I could write pages on my thoughts of the deal (and mostly the year-plus events which led to the trade), this is about life with MS.

But, if baseball teaches me anything, it teaches me that baseball offers lessons to be learned. The most important, and relative to the deal for this future Hall of Famer, is that failure is part of the game. Not just *part* of the game, failure is expected far more than success.

A batter who fails 7 times out of 10 for his career will go down in history as one of the greatest of all time (a lifetime batting average of just .300 will likely land him in Cooperstown with the first ballot). A team that is errorless for only 20% of its season straight will set club records. I could go on.

My point—and I want to make it quickly as I'll be heading to the ballpark to see Ichiro's last game in Seattle this year—is quite simple. Failure is to be anticipated, accepted and, after learning the required lessons from said failure, moved on from.

I need to remember that when MS keeps me from doing (or doing well) what I expect from myself. I need to remember that when I slip into the dark place of focusing on what I can no longer do rather than what I can. I need to remember this lesson every day of my life, MS or not. I need to remember my failures are just part of my MS Batting Average.

I'm going to slap on some sunscreen, don my cap and go watch a bunch of really talented guys swing and miss, fly-out and get caught stealing. I'm going to go and celebrate failure today because the guys who lead the record books in homeruns are also at the top of the strike-out list.

Out of Sync With Life
09/08/2017 Cork, Ireland

You know what it's like when you're watching a video clip on your computer and the voices are just a little bit out of sync with the pictures? Yeah, that's what MS has felt like to me recently. Like the smallest kid in the marching band carrying the largest cymbals—one shoe untied and slightly out of step—I can't seem to match pace with the world around me.

The dogs need a walk—I need a nap.

I have enough energy to do a bit of weeding in the garden—the rain falls.

I've the energy to cook something—but haven't had enough to go to the markets for ingredients.

My energy levels are up so I might try to do something—my pain levels are also up and making it all but impossible.

The heart may have amorous inclinations—the body sees the bed for a whole other purpose.

I'm so tired I can do nothing but lay down—my brain is so active trying to find undamaged pathways that I am unable to sleep.

Our weekly blog is due—my fingers won't cooperate to write the damn thing.

The summer sun is shining—I'm on medication that makes me sensitive to the light.

A good day gives me a bit of energy to do a few extra things—I spend that energy doing the required tasks that have gone undone for days.

I crave some human company—I can't string four words together to form a sentence, let alone a full conversation.

My head is in the game—my body is still in the clubhouse.

Just like trying to follow along with a video that's half a second off from the sound, I find it unnerving, difficult, and rather exhausting to keep up with the translation. It feels like I should 'reboot' myself, but that's not how MS works.

I share these observations and the difficult times because I know you'll get it and I also know that when I'm honest with myself and with you, we are all more at ease in sharing the good and the bad. It's not always good . . . but it's not always bad, either.

Feeling Useless in a Time of Need
04/01/2020 Kerry, Ireland

We all remember where we were when the planes hit the towers in New York.

In the days after 9/11 we all did what we could do. Families opened their homes to stranded travelers. We queued for hours to give blood. Chef friends from around New England went to Manhattan to help feed the army of responders.

I, on the other hand, was recovering from a dose of Mitoxantrone as part of my fight to find a multiple sclerosis equilibrium. The chemical in my system meant I couldn't give blood, I had to all but sequester as the drug kills off the immune cells for a couple of weeks, and MS had recently made working impossible. I was on a short-term disability which would soon turn to long-term and then permanent.

Those were days of quiet desperation for me. Alone, without social contact or much in the way of connectivity (I'd just moved into a new apartment, so the cable and internet hadn't even been connected yet) and recently sidelined from my work life, I felt burdensome to a society in need. Inadequate on so many levels.

Now I'm more acclimated to my life with MS. I know my limitations and I've found a way to be of use to society within the bounds of those limits. But now, I am sidelined again.

As a nation and the world cries out for help to pitch in during the COVID-19 crisis I am, once again unable to answer the call.

Within 24 hours of the call for retired and otherwise employed healthcare professionals to help out in Ireland, 50,000 people raised their hand. I was trained as first aid responder during my time in the US Coast Guard. My skills would be rusty, but there would be something I could do . . . but no. MS.

Again, my sisters and brothers from behind the cooking line who have had to hang up their aprons because of restaurant and hotel closures are shedding their toques and donning hair nets in hospital and nursing home kitchens to support tired kitchen staff and help feed amassed healthcare workers who are making Herculean efforts. Thanks to MS, I couldn't stand at a professional stovetop long enough to make an omelet.

Local sports clubs are delivering food and medicine to the elderly and otherwise medically fragile. I no longer drive much due to, you guessed it, multiple sclerosis.

Even the places many of us have found to be of use by volunteering for MS organizations, churches, synagogues, mosques, sports clubs, scouts, and the like, have been closed or their activities severely curtailed by the response to this virus.

I suppose the topper to this whole experience is that I am now one of those with a compromised system who must self-isolate in order to 1) keep myself from acquiring the virus and 2) not become a further burden on a healthcare system set to be overwhelmed as we've seen in other parts of the world.

This isn't the first time I've felt a missing sense of purpose. It's been almost 19 years since the feeling has been one that I know others with MS and various health conditions are sharing. There is no comfort in knowing that others are coping with a drop in their sense of worth. There is even less in knowing that many of us are also scared for the same reasons everyone else in the world is.

In a conversation with the president of the Multiple Sclerosis Society of Ireland during the early days of COVID-19, I think I put it about as succinctly as I've ever stated anything before. "It's hard, when you try to raise your hand and help and are told that the best thing you can do for society is stay the f*ck home."

We laughed about my bluntness, but that's how I feel.

Everyone must do their part to stem the spread of this virus. The best thing I can do, it appears, is to stay out of the way of those able to help in ways I'm no longer can.

So I will. I owe it—we all owe it—to the frontline heroes as they battle to keep people alive and safe.

Unplanned Obsolescence
06/08/2020 Kerry, Ireland

I remember the toaster my family had when I was growing up. It wasn't a fancy toaster—two slots, stainless with black trim, and a darkness setting knob which seemed more about form than function. It was a wedding gift to my parents from 1965.

It was a workhorse of an appliance and I remember it being taken to a repair shop at least a couple of times before I moved away from the homeplace.

Imagine that—taking a toaster to be repaired in this day and age. It's cheaper to chuck it and buy a new one. Replace/not repair is part of the economic principle of planned obsolescence. It's better for the economy if we keep buying the same products over and over again in order to keep demand up and manufacturing on a steady increase.

Many products are designed to wear out and be replaced rather than repaired for life-long use.

As I look around at the varied manner in which countries are trying to re-open their economies, I see many people with multiple sclerosis feeling like we've been forgotten. Like the world is trying to move on without us. It's like we've become obsolete.

Whether it was called 'cocooning', 'shielding', 'self-isolating', or some other term, people with MS and other conditions that may have left us particularly vulnerable to COVID-19 were asked to keep ourselves distant in order to keep ourselves safe and not add to the burden of overcrowded hospitals.

Things began to look like they were getting better, and then they got worse, and then . . . well, the whole thing is complicated. But nothing has changed for those of us with MS and other complicated conditions. We may still be vulnerable. We still have compromised immune systems. We, in many countries, are still being asked to take particular care of ourselves and sharply limit our contact with others.

The world around us is trying to tumble through and find its new normal. It is adjusting to what its citizenry can and cannot do, how it can do those things, and at what pace. But that world is figuring out what normal is going to look like and we're still asked to "Stay out of the way."

We've been put at the kids' table while the grown-ups have their planning sessions in the dining room. Without a seat at that table, the contributions that we have been working so very hard to still make to our societies will not be considered. We risk becoming obsolete to the way the world will work on the other side of this pandemic.

We could be looking at an unplanned obsolescence from behind the windows of the houses we've been asked to spend as much time in as possible.

It is more important than ever that we engage with patient advocacy organizations around the world to ensure we are not left behind. It wasn't that long ago that people who were diagnosed with MS were told to quit their jobs, go home, and ready themselves for a wheelchair. Those days are, thankfully, gone but they should not be forgotten.

We have much to give, we can be active participants in the world, and we should be considered a resource not a burden. It might be easier to rebuild an economy without considering us, but it is a richer world when we are able to participate in the design, construction, and running of whatever next looks like.

I'm not ready to be a toaster headed for the scrap heap just yet.

Have I Become a Kettle Boiler?
05/21/2020 Kerry, Ireland

Like many, my wife Caryn is working mostly from home these days. She works at a residential facility for adults with intellectual disabilities. Though she's now going on campus once or twice per week, most of her work is being done remotely.

She is quite particularly good at her work and is sought after for her professional acumen.

Having her carry on her job from the dining room table, where she's temporarily put out her shingle, has made me keenly aware of a couple of things:

1. My wife is a smart woman and knows her profession well.
2. My loss of various elements of employability have come keenly into focus.

We all mourn, move through, and often re-mourn losses or have to cope with a cascade of one thing and then the next being taken by multiple sclerosis. I know that. I've written about that, and I've come to accept it as part of my life. What I don't think I'd given much time to is what the accumulation of all of those losses means, particularly in the professional vein.

I have often seen postings or heard of positions for which I was once qualified. I have seen jobs for which I would love to apply, interview, and be chosen.

I miss the challenges, the collaborations, the relationships, the successes (and even the failures for the lessons learned). I have also come to accept that those things—at least done that way—are forever in my past.

But having Caryn exercising her prowess, while making me proud, has made me a bit envious.

As if on cue, I recently listened to an extended radio interview with Brian Cox. Mr. Cox is a seasoned actor of Irish ancestry raised in Dundee, Scotland.

Of his grandparents' generation, 'imported', if you will, from Ireland, it was mostly women who worked in the thriving jute mills of the time. The men were mostly displaced farmers and chronically unemployed. Generations before Mr. Mom and cooperative parenting they were known, colloquially, as "Kettle Boilers."

Some days it feels like that's about all I can do for Caryn boil a kettle for her afternoon cuppa. Perhaps I'll rest in the afternoon so I can make the dinner, try to get some writing done, or brush one of the Wheatens. Compared to her important work with people who are in crisis, it feels like I'm letting the side down.

I know that's not the case, but in the glare of her outstanding work I am once again reminded of the shadow which MS has cast over that once-important part of my life. I know I have plenty to offer in other regards, but sometimes it can feel like I have drifted into the zone of Kettle Boiler.

Lost in Translation
01/11/2021 Kerry, Ireland

I've heard it said that you aren't truly fluent in a language or assimilated into a new country until you dream in that language with those cultural references. When it came time to choose a language to study when I was at school, I chose Latin . . . not a lot of hope of me dreaming in that dead language.

The same might be said for the translations (conversions, really) we were asked to make upon moving to our little corner of the EU.

It mightn't be language that we're asked to translate but the number of visitors asking about Celsius temperatures or Euro prices, you'd think it was as foreign to them as my three years of Latin study those 40-plus years ago.

At some point, we stopped multiplying by 9/5 then adding 32 and just got on with accepting that 18°C was a fine day. Couple metric measurements with the currency exchange rate and my brain was never going to get around figuring the price of petrol in US currency. We just got on with living our lives in this new normal.

Sound familiar?

How much energy haven't we wasted re-explaining what we mean when we say we are "fatigued?" How many times do we have to explain before (during, and after) being invited to an event that we'd love to come but cannot commit due to ever-changing symptoms? How often aren't we looked at as if we're speaking a foreign tongue as we, yet again, walk someone through what it's like to live with MS?

I'll always remember the look someone gave me when they asked how much a neighboring house which was for sale might cost in US Dollars. "I don't know," I answered, "we don't pay for anything in dollars."

Admittedly, I got a bit of a look from my wife, Caryn, as well. I might have sounded as annoyed with the question as I actually was.

At some point, we stopped living in their world (at least completely in that world) and had to get on with living our best lives in the one where MS is most-days baggage we must lug around. We are limited in the energy we have just to get the days tasks complete; we haven't anything in the reserve tank to keep explaining why, what, or how we are doing something. It's just our language now.

I began to feel, at times, that I was doing the Chronic-Speak version of talking slower and louder when trying to communicate across the MS language barrier. I searched for one-syllable words from their lexicon in my MS thesaurus. More often than I'd like to admit, after repeated attempts and failures, I figuratively threw up my hands at the 'foreigner's' lack of understanding and moved on.

We can only be expected to work so hard for so long at translating our experiences to those who are not living them. Living with one foot in both languages/measurement systems is like having one foot planted on the dock while the other is in an untethered boat. We've all seen how that slapstick scene finishes.

I'd rather not have crossed the border into this chronic life with multiple sclerosis. But I did and it was a long time ago now. I've decided to live my best life here in the land of MS. That means I'm going to speak and think in ways that will help me live that best life. I'd say, "I'm sorry" to those who want me to keep translating my reality and converting my experiences for their benefit, but I don't have that kind of time. Let's face it, there are those who wouldn't understand anyway.

Chameleons
03/17/2021 Kerry, Ireland

I had the great good fortune to meet a group of women in the late 1980s. They all hailed from the furthest upper-left corner of the continental USA. They were a joy to know, and they called themselves "The Fabulous Northwest Babes," and they were FABULOUS!

These women were strong, smart, talented, and beautiful in their own way. They were as comfortable in gowns at black-tie events as they were down at the local dive drinking cans and shooting pool. One of them referred to the group as being "Social Chameleons" and she wasn't too far off. They may have been able to shift colors depending on their surrounds, but each was confident in herself and steadfast in her core beliefs.

I learned a lot from the Fabulous NW Babes, more than I had thought.

Living with a chronic condition—particularly one like multiple sclerosis which can exist almost completely in the land of invisible symptoms—can have many of us putting on different colors in order to meet the expectations of those around us. We slip out of one suit of clothes and into another disguise depending on the business, social, or personal situation we enter.

It's a learned ability, not something anyone told us we would need to study. I suppose everyone adapts a level of the chameleon's ability to fit the landscape in which they find themselves. This shifting of persona in order to meet expectations is fine as long as two criteria are met:

That they are our choice to don, not colors cast upon us by others.

That we realize that they are costumes we wear, not reflections of the true person within.

Early in my post Dx days, I found myself trying to squeeze into old situations using the old costumes. They no longer fit, and I felt like I wasn't the only one who noticed. As things progressed, the world looked at me differently and decided for me what look would make *them* most comfortable.

I was the patient for some, the sufferer for the media, the charity case for former colleagues, the one who couldn't keep up for false friends, the hero for those who knew it could happen to them. These were not my choice of colors, not the look I was comfortable with, but I accepted them as possibly my only way to mix with the crowds I once had.

The lesson I needed to remember from my female pals was that changing color is all well and good as long as you realize who you are and why you're changing hue. I wasn't really shifting shades or trading tints of my own accord. Rather I was walking into pools of colored light cast through someone else's gel.

I wasn't being true to this new me, partly because I wasn't comfortable with him, partly because I believed what much of society was trying to tell me; that I was no longer the same person I was before diagnosis.

Looking back over a life with MS, I see that I've amassed quite a wardrobe of looks. I feel lucky that I have not worn most of those outfits for a long time. The colors just don't suit. They are no longer to my taste. Thankfully, the ones I slipped in and out of without much regard for the damage they were causing are seldom off the hanger. I now know better what fits the real me.

The Letdown Effect
07/30/2021 Kerry, Ireland

'Tis the season for holidaymakers.

All around the northern hemisphere, people are making their way to beaches, forests, camping meadows, resort towns and amusement parks. Schools are out, summer is here, and we're all stressed out as we try to find a way to properly unwind.

How many of us haven't experienced the self-inflicted burdens of making sure that everything at work is sorted for our vacations, the pressure to make it the *perfect* getaway, and anxiety that either something will go wrong while we're away or that the boss will realize we're not that important to the organization? Then, after we finally make it to our place of recovery and recharge, spend the first several days away in bed, in pain, extremely fatigued or even sick with one illness or another.

It's happened to most of us in our work life, and now it has a name, "Let-Down Effect."

While the Let-Down Effect has been studied and associated with upper respiratory infections, migraine, flu-like symptoms, and fatigue with respect to pre-vacation related stress, the physiology behind the concept translates to those of us with MS and other chronic illnesses all too well.

Many of us—be it in advance of vacations, the holiday season, or just trying to power through our daily required tasks—put ourselves through stresses beyond what a typical person would experience during those same periods. Our version of the Let-Down Effect happens far more often and the effects can linger well beyond a couple of days.

During periods of acute stress—and how often do we do this to ourselves as we try to push through the fatigue—hormones such as cortisol, nerepinephine and adrenaline get us through. These are the fight-or-flight hormones, rooted deep in our ancestors' instincts, which helped us to survive and evolve. They have been and are, of course, important to us in many ways.

Like the exhaustion and recovery period after running to escape a saber-toothed cat, however, the body must pay a price for chemical self-dosing of a stress high. Here enters the immune system down-regulation.

Multiple sclerosis is considered to be one of a host of diseases that are autoimmune and/or chronically inflammatory. People with these conditions can often experience flares, attacks, and exacerbations post-stress identical to people falling ill during vacation. This may be due to chemicals called prostaglandins, left over from the stress response, which can cause inflammation . . . and we know what that means to MS lesions.

The obvious, though often unrealistic, answer to the repeating cycle of stress and let-down would be to reduce stress, stop pushing through, and live life on a more even keel. There are actions we can take to regulate if not mitigate the Let-Down Effect. For the holidaymaker, they include controlled stress decompressions. As we live with these stressors more often, I usually focus on prevention.

Breathing exercises, meditation, a quiet walk with the dog can all help regulate hormones on a regular basis. Supporting the body with foods rich in vitamin B5 (legumes, mushrooms, dark greens, avocado, eggs, tomatoes, etc.) may support the healthy stress response. Foods such as sardines, walnuts, seeds, olives, and their oils have shown benefit to regulating post-stress chemicals in the body.

Perhaps most importantly (and the holy grail to many of us with MS) are good sleep patterns, regular exercise, and something that makes us laugh every day.

I hope you have a chance to get away somewhere nice this summer and that you won't fall victim to Let-Down Effect.

Living With a Chronic Disease is Full-Time Work
08/11/2021 Kerry, Ireland

Whether we work away from the home, work in the home, work from home, or can no longer work for pay, the factory whistle blows for my 'MS Job' in the moments before my eyes open each morning.

My subconscious reviews the previous day/nights endeavors and hands over to the dayshift. It lets 'awake me' know how 'sleeping me' (often not-asleep me) handled the overnight work of living with multiple sclerosis.

My eyes adjust to the light or dark of a North Atlantic morning and I review the schedule of the day and assess where the disease is fanning old embers or lighting new fires that I have to deal with. There is no commute in this job. No annual leave, no sick days, and few fringe benefits. It's been a 'diagnosis to grave' job since as long as it's been around. It's a job we'd all like to quit, but as it's an incurable condition, we'd rather not be sacked, either.

Like taking calls and making decisions while driving to the office, I 'work' at living with my symptoms. I rise, ready myself and endeavor to summit my every day. Unlike the man or woman who puts in double-shifts or extended hours because they live to work, this is work to simply live.

For many living with a chronic illness is a second job layered over their career, their home life, and all other aspects of their 24-hour existence. For others, like myself, the disease has taken away my ability to contribute to and receive payment for the work

I did. For work I loved, and work for which I was respected. Our multiple sclerosis is a jealous employer and ate away at our employment of passion and pay—either quickly or over time—and now it is our job to live as well as we can within the borders of shrinking endurance and ability.

I was forced from my dual employment of MS and career after only a few months of struggle. I tried to reenter the work force on a number of occasions, there was an ever-increasing understanding that what I had left in the tank to give to clients was worth less to them than if I kept it for myself and my family.

Once I navigated ships on the high seas and through narrow passages, cooked for most of society's strata, closed multi-national deals and worked five time zones in one week. Now my navigation task is through the murky and always-changing waters of MS. It takes three times as long to cook anything for just myself and Caryn. And now the hours I used to spend managing my work life is spent on insurance paperwork, medical appointments, and energy budgeting/fatigue management.

While I know how much work it can be to labor under two masters, I envy those who have found a way to keep MS as a part-time employer. I hope it will always be the case for them.

As for me, and many of us, stepping away (gracefully or not) from work in order to work for ourselves (in the most real sense of the word I can think of) has allowed me to recapture at least a bit of normalcy in a life which is anything but normal in our former understanding of the word.

My days are now spent working around, alongside, and against my disease. My reward isn't seen in a weekly paycheck. Rather, in a sense of job well done when some once upon a time simple now difficult task is completed or when there is energy left-over at the end of the day for something more than a dive into bed.

Those are the days when the nightshift has an easy night of it. They are the nights I am able to run and jump in my dreams. That's a good day's work.

Set a Timer
11/08/2021 Kerry, Ireland

The first four or five years of living with MS were spent getting my head around what the disease multiple sclerosis was doing to my body. After that I focused on the 'getting my heart around living with MS' phase. Now it feels like I've made another adjustment. At some point in the last half decade, I moved from the theoretical to the practical. From tactical thinking when it comes to living with MS to a more strategic approach.

Part of the living with MS phase included something I called "The Morning Inventory." I would lay awake in bed before rising and test out the chassis.

What could I feel? What could I not? What could I move? What could I not? What was the same as yesterday, last week, last month? What was different?

After preflighting my body, I'd go through my schedule for the day. What had to be done that day? What *had-had* to be done? What could slip a few hours or days if needed? What would I really *like* to get done in my waking hours? Speaking of which, how many of those did it feel like I might get that day?

Finally, I'd overlay the two mental lists (oh, for the day when I could still keep a mental list going in my head . . .) and see how my body and my diary for the day matched, what I could expect to complete and what would have to be moved.

It was a good system but like much of living with MS, it's been a learning process and I've now evolved to a more practical test to evaluate my potential for the day. I set a timer.

Each morning—at some point in the morning—I make a cup of coffee or two (or three on *those* MS days) and most afternoons it's a cup of tea. I'm a bit of a snob when it comes to my coffee, so everything is measured to the milliliter and gram for the process. I use this scientific quirk to help evaluate my day's abilities in practical fashion.

I set the kettle to boil (it's an electric kettle, so 500ml of water takes the same time to boil every time) and begin to scoop, weigh, grind the coffee beans (by hand, thank you very much), and get them into the cafetiere. How far I get in that process before the kettle pops is an indicator of how my fine motor skills are doing that day.

If I spill beans all over the counter and onto the floor, well, that's a pretty good indicator as well . . .

Then comes the timer.

Once the boiled water has cooled slightly (I told you I was a snob about this sort of carry-on) into the pot it goes on top of the grounds and my 4-minute clock begins.

I have a routine of what gets done next. It's not complicated; I get a cup from the press, I wake the dog and let her out the back door. I open the curtains. If it's to be warm, I open the doors. If it's cool, I grab a jumper (sweater). I turn on the radio and my laptop . . . those sorts of things.

I see how far I get down my routine list of tasks before the bell rings to let me know that my coffee is ready to be pressed. Seldom do I get all the way to the electronics. More often than I'd like the trip from countertop to press and back takes my full allotted time. Most of the time, however, my abilities fall somewhere in the middle of that list.

Which side of the middle and how I feel once I sit down to that first, restorative sip of bean juice is, I find, an accurate indicator of what my day can hold and how I'll likely feel at the end of it (and wherever 'end' might fall on a particular day).

My inventory was a theoretic assessment of my abilities on any given day. It worked for me for a while. My 4-minute drill—with the welcomed reward of a hot cup of Joe to contemplate the outcome—well, that just seems to be a more practical foretelling as I progress in my life with multiple sclerosis.

10 Ways to Avoid Becoming Invisible With an Invisible Disease
11/22/2016 Kerry, Ireland

My name is Trevis L Gleason and I live with multiple sclerosis, MS. MS is a neuro-degenerative disease of the central nervous system which can affect all aspects of life—the visible and the invisible.

I must admit to you that this started as a lament to the very real prospect of becoming invisible to the world as a result of a relatively invisible disease. I have seen many friends fade-away into the mist of chronic illness and I felt myself slipping into the edges of that same mist.

There is much that I am no longer able to do or do as well as I once did. This realization prompted me to take a look at what I can still attempt—things at which many have succeeded. Sometimes it can feel like the big, broad world is moving on without us. It becomes our job to find a place to latch-on so we are not left behind.

I hope that you find this list helpful, and I invite you to add your suggestions for keeping yourself engaged.

- **Keep Working** – We work for more reasons than a paycheck. The routine of getting up and getting out would be reason enough to keep employed. The social interaction, the feeling of being of use, and, of course, the needed money are additional reasons to stay on the job. If you need to adapt your work, step back a bit or move down the ladder by a rung. Keep going for as long as you safely can.

- **Find Support/Self-Help Group** – Living with a chronic illness is difficult. No one knows that better (or knows the little tricks for doing it well) than people who live with your condition. There are groups as varied in personality, regularity and intent as you might possibly imagine. Find a group—even an on-line group—that shares your sensibilities and your goals.

- **Engage Your Condition's Patient Advocacy Organizations** – If for no other reason than to find the above groups, get in touch with your patient advocates. There are often several different organizations for each disease. Find the one which, again, shares your goals and offers the services you require now or may need in the future. These organizations are also a wonderful outlet for volunteer energy. Trust me on this one, the energy you expend volunteering for your cause will be returned many times over.

- **Exercise** – The evidence of physical benefits of exercise on many diseases is still fairly new. It wasn't that long ago that people with our conditions were told to not exercise for reasons of fatigue. Those days are long gone. A strong body recovers better and faster not to mention the positive mental response of exercise. The social aspect of group exercise or simply getting out with others cannot be forgotten either.

- **Call Old Friends, Meet New People** – As time passes and we may, indeed, not be able to get 'out there' as much, it is important to keep reaching out. The older we get, the more we realize that most of our friends have something wrong with them as well. Reconnecting with long lost pals can be made easier via social media outlets. Just make sure that you are interacting with people face to face as well as online.

- **Find a Mental Health Professional** – We become pretty good a coping as we go along. But like practicing the wrong musical note over and over again until it's a habitual mistake, we mustn't rely on our own skills alone. Sometimes we get stuck; sometimes we don't even know the signs that we may be headed for the quagmire. A good rehabilitation psychologist can help identify common pitfalls as well as specific issues which to monitor and offer coping skills. You don't have to do it alone.

- **Adapt Your Passions, Don't Abandon Them** – When the things we love become too difficult we needn't give them up. Many can be modified if we keep the true function in mind. If you loved giving elaborate dinner parties because of the joy of having friends around for a meal, turn it into a supper club where everyone brings a course or dish to fit a theme. If you loved running half-marathons for the comradery, volunteer on the next race committee. Teach beginners how do to something at which you were once an expert. You'll be around people who are just discovering a passion that you've developed for years, and the entry level skills may be something you still possess.

- **Learn Something New** – For someone with a neurological condition or just to combat the effects of normal aging, learning a new skill can improve cognitive outcomes by volumes. The social aspect of learning in a group also feeds several of the previous points listed. Don't be afraid that you're not good at whatever it is you're taking on—you're a beginner in a group of beginners. Learning can be fun and it will keep your brain younger.

- **Adjust Your Financial Plan** – No one knows what the future will bring, but it's likelier than not that our future is going to be different than the one we had planned. Just like you might rethink the layout of your home, we must re-examine our financial goals and plans. It's never too late to start and the old adage was never more true than when planning our financial future—"If you fail to plan, you plan to fail." Those advocacy organizations may be able to help with this as well.

- **Don't Be All About Your Disease** – Finally, don't let your whole life—or even the majority of it—be about your disease. It is part of you, but it's not all of who you are. Just like you might tire of someone only talking about their kids or dogs or job and seemingly nothing else, don't let your condition and how you're coping be the only topic of conversation. You are more than your disease. You are a wonderful person. People like you for a variety of reasons. Remember that and you'll have plenty to talk about other than how you're doing that particular day.

When the seas are rough, I hope that these tips help to keep you tethered to the wider world around. Just because we now live with a disease that may be difficult to understand for others—and difficult for us to live with—you are still you. You are enough. The world likes having you around, so stay connected.

CHAPTER 5

Head and Heart

YOU MIGHT REMEMBER THAT IN THE FIRST CHAPTER of this book I said, "it took me a fair good few years to get my head around the idea of multiple sclerosis, the disease, and what it was doing to my body and mind" and I promised the conclusion to that thought.

Well, here it is, "Only then could I get my heart around the concept of living my life with MS."

I have not attained some form of mountain top MS enlightenment, nor do I succeed in every (maybe not even most) of the MS-burdened aspects of my life. I have, however, observed the successes and failures of others in our community as well as being acutely aware of my own failings. Living a life with eyes wide open to possibilities and pitfalls, learning from both my own and others' mistakes, and finding 'MS Senpai' (a Japanese term used to describe a person of more seniority and experience who is mentor and example their juniors) from around the globe.

In moving from Head to Heart, I became more able to let go of things which had become impossible (or at least far more difficult). This freed up physical and mental energy to focus upon the possibilities and make at least some of them a reality.

When a Positive Attitude Isn't Enough
07/08/2006 Seattle, USA

If thinking happy thoughts could, as in the story of Peter Pan, make us fly, many people with MS would be floating out of their chairs and scooters. We are, by some quirk of nature, mostly positive-thinking people who sometimes even find a silver lining to the cloud of Multiple Sclerosis.

The thing is, a positive attitude does little to cure MS. I know that we feel better emotionally and that there is contention by some that a positive outlook can cure some people of some things. For this writer with MS, it just ain't so.

"My name is Trevis and I live with MS." That is the way I start most of the speeches I give on the topic. Nothing is going to change that fact; I have MS, I live with it. I live as positively as I can. I have had ups and downs and when I'm up I know that there will be another down. And when I'm down I look for an up. That is what I live with. That is what most of us live with. That is what it is to *live* with MS. It's like living with your mother-in-law (no offense to mothers-in-law).

So, we live with MS, now what?

I get just as tired as many of you hearing about the mountain climber who says he can climb again because he takes a certain drug and has a positive outlook on his life with MS. Or the woman who "Won't let MS get her down." and has started a new life doing the new thing and is "Better off because of MS."

First, I say "Good For You!!!"

I am very happy that they have come to a sense of peace in the belief that by controlling their attitude, they are in control of their disease.

Second, I think that it is rude as hell!

I don't live on some mountain top in Tibet, nor do I purport to skip my way through a life with MS having thoughts so pure they make the angels blush. I do, however, believe that I have a damned fine attitude and that I do what I can to live the best life I can—MS or not.

Don't get me wrong, please. If it works for them, fine. Just don't make other people feel like we are doing something wrong and that if we were to do the same thing and have a better attitude, our MS wouldn't be so bad. I think that is disrespectful to people who are really struggling.

MS is an insidious, degenerative, progressive and fickle thief. It robs things from some people while leaving others nearly intact. It takes what it wants, when it wants it, and we have very little control over it. It takes our future and makes us reexamine what we hoped to do with it.

There is a peace in accepting that things have changed and getting our hearts around what has been lost.

Attitude is something that can help us to live our lives with MS to their fullest. Attitude is not something that will cure us.

How Stress Factors Into the Equation
10/18/2006 Seattle, USA

I love the line fictional president Jed Bartlet used about stress on the television series *The West Wing*, "Stress is something they invented to sell flavored coffee." As a former multi-tasker I'll admit, I laugh a little at people who get flustered at every little thing. As a person living with Multiple Sclerosis, I find myself slipping into those shoes myself on more occasions than I prefer to admit.

Many people speak of stress as a trigger for exacerbations. There was a time when people with MS were told to avoid all stressful situations as it would make our symptoms worse. Later (around the time I was diagnosed, five years ago) the revelation was that stress had nothing to do with the disease.

I don't know about you, but I think the truth lies somewhere in the middle of that pendulum swing.

While stress may not be a causative factor in the disease, as it was once contended, I have to believe that there is something of a connection. Let's face it, MS is a disease by which some part of our immune system malfunctions. Few doctors would disagree that stress (and I suppose that each of us has a different tolerance for this emotion) has an effect on the immune system. How many of us have gotten sick on vacation due to the fact that we stressed ourselves getting everything ready to be gone for those two weeks?

Stress has different effects on different people. For those of us with MS, stress may influence our disease. That's my opinion and I'm stickin' to it.

When MS Gets Me Down
09/14/2010 Seattle, USA

This just in, MS Sucks!

It sucks energy and time and emotion and well . . . it just plain sucks.

Today, for me, is one of those MS Days that we tell people about in glib, flip little sentences like "Well, there are good days and bad days."

The sun has made itself known to Seattle on a September day, not a normal occurrence. And I cannot get myself up, mentally, to go out and enjoy it. My morning slurred into noon, which then required a kip (it was one of those "lie down or fall down" things).

Now, I find a list of things that hasn't been done, likely won't get done, and I'm feeling a failure for it (not a *total* failure).

What is surprising is how this logy, fatigued physical state can get me down emotionally. MS got me down today even when reading the expectedly inflammatory comments to one of my writing pieces

This is not MS Depression.

It's just the sick-and-tired of being sick-and-tired we all know so well.

We all live with MS here, be it the person diagnosed or our families. We've all had these wee bouts with fatigue-induced malaise. We've all come up with our own coping mechanisms. My fallback tricks of coffee and a cookie, watching the dogs play, feeling the sun (or rain) on my skin . . . they're not working today.

Today, MS has me down . . . tomorrow, I hope will be better.

When It Just Won't Let You Think Straight
09/17/2010 Phoenix, USA

I have spent the past couple of days in a part of our country which still finds triple-digit the norm this time of year. I DO NOT, nor does my MS, find anything normal about 104°f, "dry heat" or not!

I head home at the weekend, so I hope this will all pass, but I'm experiencing a kind of MS-Stupidity with all this heat.

My tongue can't find the words, my reaction times are off and I just feel a little silly.

The physical stuff, a doughy face, slow responding arm and even slower leg, I expected and can understand. This whole in my head space thing is very new to me.

I've found myself being the last one to laugh at something funny or to chime in on a conversation. It's like I'm a half-step behind the whole world as of today. To be honest, I just looked up and saw that I had almost completely rewritten a sentence above just now . . . It's *that* kind of thing.

I'd better sign off before I simply write the first sentence, again.

In Your Head
01/18/2012 Seattle, USA

Athletes know the consequences of letting an opponent 'in your head'; letting an adversary's actions, attitude or banter alter one's personal game plan. How often do we let multiple sclerosis get in our head?

"If I do X then they'll do Y and then I'll have to go to Z, and I didn't want to go to Z. But what if they don't do Y?"

It's obvious how this might make a linebacker or cyclist a decisive few tenths of a second too slow to react . . . Why would I bring it up in the context of MS when we usually measure our reaction time in minutes rather than fractions of seconds? Well, some of my friends' comments to me made me realize that some of us are avoiding our dreams because MS has toyed with us for too long.

It's one thing to have a contingency or two in our hip pocket; it's a whole other thing to second guess ourselves and our plans because of the different paths which may or may not converge in our course.

Now, let me make this perfectly clear—I am not one of those "Attitude is everything" or "Think positive and all is well" kind of people. I guess I'd call myself a pragmatist and that's how I look at life with MS too. I have let MS get in my head before and there's just not enough room up there for both of us!

If you think/feel that "MS won't stop" you, I am happy for you and I hope that it doesn't. I know that MS has stopped me, will likely stop me again and again and again. It's what we do *after* we are left staggering in the path of our former plans, shaking off the surprise and dusting the last attack (or progression) from our trousers that show who we really are.

It's not that we made ourselves stronger than MS, it's that we've become more resilient and are fortunate enough to recover that makes us strong.

It is not shameful to not do something because multiple sclerosis comes to call. Yet, not allowing ourselves the opportunity to do something because MS *might* make it difficult is allowing the adversary into our head. And let's face it, MS is already in our head (and our spinal cord)!

Multiple Sclerosis doesn't feed on the energy we give to planning for stuff. But MS wins if we don't plan or do something we desire because of what it *might* do. As long as we plan realistically for where our disease is 80% of the time (I'm a big believer of the 80/20 rule), then we can expect to accomplish our plans most of the time.

Letting MS affect our plans is one thing which we may not be able to control. Allowing Multiple Sclerosis to stop us from planning is giving it more power and authority than I'll stand for in my life (anymore). How about you?

How do you keep MS from getting in your head? Possibly more importantly, how do you get it out if it gets in there?

The Stress Connection
07/11/2012 Seattle, USA

While off-camera with some of the MS experts I've interviewed, the topic of stress came up. My nurse practitioner mentioned one study that had been published this past summer that I hadn't heard about. I decided to do a bit of sleuthing and I found the paper she of which she was speaking.

MS experts in Louisiana studied over 120 people living with multiple sclerosis using stress management treatments. These therapies included relaxation techniques, problem solving skills, cognitive restructuring therapy, enhancement of social support, help with sleep issues and increased positive activities throughout the study period. Patients were either treated right away or wait-listed for a period of 24 weeks as a control.

The most interesting information to come out of the study, as far as I'm concerned, was not only that the treatment group *felt* better—but that "77% of the patients undergoing stress management therapy remained free of lesions while they were in treatment compared to 55% of those in the control group," reported Dr. Jesus Lovera, the study's lead investigator.

So, controlling stress in our lives might actually slow down the progression of our disease (as measured in MRI enhancing lesions)!

One key to this study was that after treatment with stress management strategies ended, the lesion relapse rate returned to the same of the control group. Researchers hypothesized that many factors, including the need for longer (maybe even indefinite) therapy, inability to sustain the skills taught and possibly even the supportive nature of the testing relationships, may have been a factor.

This is just one, small study into the idea that we might be able to control some of the activity of our MS though active stress reduction.

I look forward to hearing more about this type of research and, in the meantime, will return to the breathing practices my yoga instructor recommends for every day, try to reduce stress but most importantly, I will actively meet life's stresses in my daily life with MS . . . once this international move thing is done and I can relax a bit!

Successful Failure
09/09/2013 Kerry, Ireland

I've heard it told that Mission Commander Jim Lovell never said the words "Houston, we have a problem . . ." which were made famous in the Ron Howard film, *Apollo 13*. What is true is that he, along with NASA, considered that the heroic teamwork that averted disaster in space was a "Successful Failure." I had one of those this weekend and I think that I'm going to start looking at life with MS that way.

On a weekend when thousands were gathered to ride their bicycles to raise funds for our cause and when nearly three-times the number of residents of our little fishing port town gathered to run half, full and ultra marathons, I decided to get my feet wet.

Caryn and I tagged onto a local surf shop's lesson for the morning.

Herself—through growing up and living her first three-plus decades in southern California—has only recently taken up the sport in support of a local Surf-To-Heal group for children with autism spectrum disorder (ASD). I was just along for the craic, as they say here, of just trying to stay on a board in the icy, North Atlantic breakers.

My fat arse was jammed into a black and red wet suit (thankfully with no white or I'd have looked a nephew of Shamu the whale!), I tethered myself to a padded, nine-foot training board and dove-in—both literally and figuratively—and rode into the challenge.

While others in the group complained about the cold water on their feet, I only felt the cold on one foot, due to MS numbness in my other. Quite frankly, the cold water seemed to give me more energy than I had anticipated.

The three to four-foot waves propelled other students a few hundred yards from break to shore. Eventually, all of them got to their feet for at least a few moments. I—not having set the bar that high for myself—was far beyond content to have (sort of) reached my knees on one occasion. The joy I had wasn't in standing or not standing. It came from the attempt to ride the surging waves in whatever fashion I could.

Frankly, I think I 'caught' at least as many waves as the lads trying for the brass ring.

Sure, I found it an unorthodox way to get a saltwater sinus flush, and I've a few sand scuffs from some of the larger waves that won our battles. I was the kid who was just happy to be in the water. I was the guy who sometimes has to use a walker to get around the house. I was, according to my Aussie surf coach rule, the best surfer on the day.

His rule? The best surfer of the day is the one having the most fun.

How true a rule to live by: Have the most fun!

I'll be out there again. I may or may not make it all the way to my knees one of these days. I'll fall off the board, I'll take a wave-beating which will leave me sore and tired and scraped and bruised. I'll be cold and I'll be wet and I'll maybe even be not as good at it one time over the next.

But not attaining goals, falling, feeling beaten and sore and tired and bruised are just part of living life. They're part of living life with or without multiple sclerosis. I look forward to the cold, wet beating I'll take the next time because winning at life isn't about staying on the board. It's about getting back on after you've been swept off. It's all about making success out of failure.

Autumn is a traditional time for challenging oneself in many parts of the world. I'm going to try to challenge myself in as many ways as possible in the coming months before real and figurative winter set in.

Détente
10/07/2013 Kerry, Ireland

In the spring of 1983, I represented my school in our state's model United Nations. After a long day of sessions in the General Assembly, I was awarded first prize in the debate on denucleariza-tion. That time in world history, the topic, and experience inform my thoughts today.

I've decided that I have entered into a cold war phase with my multiple sclerosis.

First I experienced symptoms of MS. Then I was diagnosed with the disease. I suffered from MS, I fought MS and I have learned to live with MS; I've just been looking for the right metaphor to describe how I'm living with multiple sclerosis.

Détente: that's where I am now.

Like many of you, I had MS before I was diagnosed. In my case, my doctors and I believe I experienced those for at least fifteen years. When I could no longer explain away, ignore them, or wasn't misdiagnosed is when I begrudgingly went in for what turned out to be my diagnosis.

I'm not fond of the term 'suffer' when it comes to living with this disease—even though I find it a term used a great deal here

in Europe (The term "MS Sufferer" has even been used to intro-
duce me here). I would be disingenuous (to myself, to my partners
and to many in our community) if I did not admit that suffering
is exactly what I did for the first several years after my diagnosis.

Only when I was at the bottom of a very dark pit—much of my
own digging—did I realize that I was going to have to fight back.
My blog has been part of that fight. I'll not lie to you; fighting can
be a draining business.

I guess I fought back in anger, I fought to regain, I fought multiple sclerosis for all that it had done to me and to those around me.
Then I realize that the MS is in me. The disease is my good soldiers
fighting behind my body's own front. MS is an enemy within and
to keep fighting (at least fighting with the same bloodlust and hate)
had stopped being healthful and had its own risks.

That's when I called a truce and began to understand what it
was like to live with MS.

It has been a cold war of sorts and it has become—not unlike
JFK recounted in his famous inaugural speech—"a hard and
bitter peace."

Now that I have given myself the permission to hate MS without hating the body in which it dwells, now that I've stopped beating myself up for what I can no longer do, now that I've abandoned
those who were never on my side; that ceasefire has developed into
my Multiple Sclerosis Détente.

While another president (presidential candidate at the time of
the quote) famously said "Détente . . . Isn't that what a turkey has
with his farmer—until Thanksgiving Day?" I have to say that this
way of living with MS works better for me than running, headlong
into the fence all of the time. The effort was a very important part
of my journey with this disease, but I've expanded the pen as far
as I can and I'm just not going to keep focusing on the CANNOT
when there is so much that I CAN.

As I mentioned earlier in the week, some see this shift in my
attitude toward living with MS as negative and giving in. I look at

it differently and, as we always have, welcome opposing opinions at every stage. I (more often than you'll ever know) say that "I'm not an expert on multiple sclerosis. I am, however, becoming an expert on living my life with MS."

That's all I'm really striving for and if that means 'giving up' or 'giving in' by some people's definition, I'm fine with the label. I, however, feel better, live better, and have a better outlook on the rest of my life knowing that I've come to an agreement with MS and I'm holding up my end of the bargain.

If you find yourself in one of these places in your life, ask yourself if a détente, in lieu of all-out victory (or all-out war) is an acceptable place to live with your MS?

On Being Healthy With a Chronic Disease
04/04/2014 Kerry, Ireland

"Dad, I'm sick . . ."

Funny that of all of the conversations I had with people around the time of my sudden diagnosis with multiple sclerosis 13 years ago later this month, of all the times I told the story of my attack, of the recounts of the process, of recurring mispronunciations and misunderstandings, the one thing I see as the most inaccurate telling was the one time I used the word sick.

Perhaps it's that I'm only now spending the majority of the day out of bed after a travel-induced crud that had me clawing for breath, coughing-up Technicolors and sweating through bedclothes like Regan MacNeil on a devilishly hot August night. Perhaps my fever fried a few brain cells and I'm not yet thinking straight. Still, I don't think of myself (because of the MS, at least) as being sick.

I flippantly summed it up in answering one of your interview questions of me about five years ago when I wrote, "As far as I'm concerned, I'm a healthy person with MS."

Yes, MS is an illness. But I don't feel ill. Multiple Sclerosis is a disease, but I don't feel diseased. Some call it a 'condition' and I guess I'll flip a response that yes, I do feel conditional about it . . . .

Part of my body—my immune system—does something to another part of my body that it's not supposed to. That something happens to be destroying an important part of my electrical wiring which allows me to function as the rest of my species has evolved.

Still, I have a hard time thinking of myself as sick.

I eat the way I do to try to live as well as desired and perhaps a bit longer. I exercise to a level and as I am able to keep my body strong enough to react well to the things life (and MS) throws my way. I find things which make me happy and I feed them. I search out the negative parts of my life in order to prune them away.

In short, I practice many of the healthy things that healthy people use to get and stay, well, healthy.

It might just be that I am recovering from being what I would call really sick and I want to distance my day-in-day-out condition from that feeling. Perhaps I've deluded myself into believing that my new normal is just as normal as everyone else's. Quite possibly, "The lady doth protest too much, methinks."

As winter's grip is loosed and nature's energies seem renewed, I beg the question of wellness and illness, of sickness and health of your consciousness over the weekend. I think it's a good topic of conversation to have with those close to us and a powerful one for quiet ruminations.

I Don't Want to Have MS Anymore
07/30/2014 Kerry, Ireland

So, I'm sitting at my desk doing some MS research. I'm combing the latest news from clinical trials, the most recent news stories; I'm poking around all of the patient service and advocacy organizations' sites. Then it hits me; I just don't want to have MS anymore.

Don't get me wrong; I know that after a diagnosis and without a cure, not living with MS means not living. I'll choose the latter; thank you.

Still, living for an extended period with MS (and it will be 14 years in the spring, not the 18 I counted last week—stupid cog fog) I find multiple sclerosis like a heavy bag of something that I have to carry around.

The bag wasn't always this heavy. Sometimes it's still heavier than others but it's always an awkward shape and size. I shift the bag from one hand to the other like a grocery sack that was packed too full and try to shift the burden. I sling it around and stop by the road to rest now and again, but the bag of MS is always with me.

The days when the bag would fill and then empty some are gone forever. Now it just gets progressively more full, more awkward, and more difficult and tiresome to carry though each day.

But still, we marshal on.

Today, rather than sit down with my bag at my side to rest for a while, I wish I could just leave it and walk along sans bag for a while. Well, forever really but let's not get ahead of ourselves.

I'm not whining or complaining too much—and even if I were I know that this community would understand what I'm talking about. I'm just tired of having MS. I'm not tired of living, I'm not depressed, I don't need to take a pill or a nap. I'll be fine . . ..

I just wish I didn't have this thing to carry around for today. You know what I mean?

Finding a Post-Diagnosis Life
01/30/2015 Kerry, Ireland

For some, diagnosis with multiple sclerosis was a systematic ticking of boxes as a series of odd things started happening. For others, there was a fight to convince the medical profession that there was something wrong. Still others—myself included—were diagnosed swiftly during the onset of a major exacerbation.

Everything changes with the words "You have multiple sclerosis." Our place in the world shifts; that's home world, work world, and the whole world. We go, in our minds at the very least, from Point A to Point MS in a relative flash of time.

For many of us that journey is only temporary as we get our lives back on track. Many make lifestyle changes, take medications and/or change the course their life was on. Others struggle to retain and remain. Some of us are simply derailed by this debilitating, neurodegenerative, progressive thief.

I often say that it took me three or four years to get my head around multiple sclerosis—the disease. Only then could I get my heart around the concept of living with MS.

I had set out for today's writings to be about staying in or trying to re-enter the workforce after a diagnosis and I realized that the more important topic is finding a new life after Dx.

Very few of us live the same lives we did before MS. Many take advantage of the need for change and make positive changes. Some of us are forced into decisions we either never wanted to make or foresaw only faintly in our distant futures.

It can feel like we've been blindfolded and spun around with our old goals in hand and are left to search out a place for them like an absurd adult game of Pin-the-tail-on-the-donkey. The problem is, of course, that MS changes continuously for many of us and we are spun around over and over again as we progress and have to find new places, new goals and new donkeys every time.

While my MS Mission Statement is to "Find my limits, to press them and then to live within them," some days, I just hope I don't look like the ass I'm constantly chasing in order to pin my aspirations.

A Day Without Thoughts Of MS
04/15/2015 Kerry, Ireland

Monday I was supposed to write a blog and send it in. That did not happen.

We don't, as many of you know, own a car here in Kerry. We do rent a car now and again when needed and this week is one of those times. So I piled the happy dogs into the hired transport, took Caryn to work on Monday and then stopped at a lovely and secluded beach on the way home.

We drove down a shaggy laneway to the strand and I set the pack to running about in the sand. I collected my assistive devices of choice for the day—a sturdy walking stick and another cane for support—and set out after them.

My intention was to let the Wheatens run it out of themselves and then head home to attend to my writing assignment. The chasing of wind-blown leaves and sea foam, the bit of a chat with a local farmer driving his tractor down the beach (sometimes the shortest way from one field to the next) and watching some kite surfers taking advantage of 2-meter waves and a stiff breeze made our quick stop far longer and more enjoyable than planned.

Little is more joyful than watching our dogs playing on the sand. There is something about the feel of it on their paws that mimics the sensation I once had as a child feeling the grains of silica between my toes. They run, jump, turn, twist, and they wear me out just watching them.

Mind, the fields that abut this beach—as many in Kerry—afford sheep and cattle better views while grazing than most of us could ever afford to live with. The smells from said livestock made for some dune climbing for the dogs as well. I, on the other hand, was fine just sitting on a dune or two and watching their struggled efforts to climb only to watch the sand slip beneath them and have to start all over again.

And time began to slip away too.

Owing to the aforementioned intended composition I began to look for metaphors about living with MS that I could take home with me. I won't say that they were few but at each one I was met by some other feat of canine play that took my mind away from thoughts of multiple sclerosis scribblings.

And that was it. Sometimes it feels good—Really Good—to just not think about MS.

Sure, I was using two walking aids to make it just a few hundred yards down the beach. Granted I was happy for the passing storm clouds and the fresh breeze to keep my system from overheating (in fact it was a bit chilly headed back into the wind). Nothing ever takes my MS symptoms away to the point that I'm not at least aware if not actually thinking about them.

I actively stopped thinking about ways to connect my experience with MS for the simple reason of writing about it. I decided to stop thinking, to start looking around at the beauty rather than some bend-to-requirement meaning and just enjoy. How freeing it was.

MS can throw too many unexpected obstacles into our lives. What was the sense of trying to turn a lovely experience into some MS lesson to share?

So, not only did I stop thinking about MS that day on the beach, I stayed longer than planned, took a short bit of a side trip on the way home and didn't even try to write anything about MS for the next two days. Yeah, Me!

I May Appear Well-Adjusted, But I'm Not!
08/12/2015 Kerry, Ireland

I dragged myself from a warm bed into a dark, cold morning today in order to make my way to Dublin for a meeting with Ireland's best MS bloggers. I got to sleep later than I'd hoped to as I made sure that all of my preparations were in order.

These things take more time than they used to for me and far longer than they might for a person not living with multiple sclerosis.

As I dragged my suitcase through the coal-black morning to catch the first bus out of town, I was greeted by many sights and sounds that the writer in me thought could be turned into blog topics or metaphors for living with MS.

Construction equipment sat idle in a carpark awaiting dawn for a full day of work with able-bodied men. Navigation lights in the harbor flashed at differing frequencies marking unseen shoals and safe channels. A dark, night-like sky was sprinkled with bright points of light and though the moon was mostly obscured by the shadow of our planet, I could see its tilted shining sliver as well as the shaded majority like some cosmic blackened eye in the pre-dawn sky.

My still tired brain worked on ways to turn what I was seeing into fodder for the blog mill. At every step I found something that reminded me of MS in one way or another. Not all MS, not even my MS but the general journey with the disease for which we've all been handed an unwanted ticket.

I don't dwell on my illness—well as much as someone who writes about living with MS as much as I do can not dwell. That said, I can't escape what the disease has done to my body and mind. I am unable to simply forget that it's there and I am still not comfortable with all of the aspects of living my life with an incurable disease.

Certainly, living with an incurable disease is better than the alternative. I know that fact clearly and I do get on with my life at least as well as most. Sometimes even people who share a diagnosis with me will admire how well-adjusted to MS I seem to be.

I'm not!

It's not an act; this trying to get on with living the best life I can. It can be, however, an occasional case of fake it until you make it that makes those outside the bounds of my tired, aching, uncooperative body think that I'm coping better than I really am.

I'm learning my way through every day, every set-back and every disease progression and sometimes I wish that I didn't have to study so hard and that I could skip the homework from time to time. Perhaps we all feel this way from time to time. Perhaps that we do and we find in this community others who simply understand is why we've been at this blog nearly ten years now.

I am not the only person who thinks this way, who feels this way nor the only person who is experiencing MS the way I am. From time to time, we all seem to find something in these pages that clicks. Something that makes us almost shout aloud, "I have that too!"

It's just that today (and so many other days as well), I wish that I didn't have to think about MS. You know what I mean?

That said, I think those navigation lights are going to make for a good article, one of these days.

A Moment of Paddy Zen
09/17/2015 Kerry, Ireland

"On a crisp, autumn morning such as this, when I look out and ponder things like, 'If I were to go and collect bulbs of wild garlic from along the bohereen with an eye to setting and tending to them in pots or in my garden beds, would they still be 'wild' garlic or simply a cultivar I'm keeping for my own entertainment?' That's when I know that I've attained an appropriate level of stress in my life."

I found myself jotting down the above this morning in the eye of a mounting storm of bustle and fuss. It's not that I don't have stress in my life. It assuredly isn't that I've attained the 'monk on the mountaintop' phase of existence. But perhaps I have learned to take steps to reduce the stress that MS can pile on top of all the other stuff.

I'm negotiating with an Irish publisher to have *Chef Interrupted* published here and in the UK, I have two MS Ireland events to MC (and for which I must write scripts), an article deadline, a local festival event to manage and the 1996 French Master Chef of the Year is coming to stay with us for six weeks. Stressors? Perhaps . . .

I was quoted in an article for an autumn issue of MOMENTUM Magazine. In it I summed up one of the most important lessons I've learned living with multiple sclerosis: "Were I to dig down into the sack of coping mechanisms that I've gathered over the years, I think that coming to the realization that control is an illusion has served me best. The only things over which I truly have any control are my reactions and my responses. I respond more thoughtfully, I react less harshly, and I assuredly laugh at myself more heartily than ever in my life."

I've come to realize that I get less worked up—less stressed about things—when I accept that I don't control much in the first place. I've taken myself out of figuring out the how, when, where, and why and focused on the "Now what?" And it feels so much better.

Maybe a little bit of the Irish idiom (or Paddy Zen as I've come to think of it) "Ara, sure. It'll be grand" has sunk its way into my being.

When Caryn and I were having immigration issues which may have seen us deported back in 2013, "You'll be grand" and "It'll be right on the night" were uttered with such frequency that we began to believe it ourselves. And it was true.

We learned how to fake it until we make it during that very stressful time and I think some of that way of thinking has settled into my being. I know that it's made for a better life and I also feel the lower level of acquired stress has helped my MS.

Stress is our body's chemical reaction to difficult situations in the world around us. It changes how we think, act, exist and experience the world. It's not a matter of not entering a stress-filled room. It's how we react when the door closes behind us.

By the way, I planted the bulbs of wild garlic in a large pot. Next year, after they've had a chance to take-hold, I'll replant some and set them free in a wild patch of the garden and we will have come full circle. And all will be well with the world.

Glass Houses
02/02/2016 Kerry, Ireland

One night over the winter in our little town a small group of over-watered lads tossed a rock through an old, thick, and very large shop window. This plate of glass was wider than my outstretched arms could span. It was a shame to see it replaced by a more modern 3-pain window for strength and economy should it be broken again.

As with so many other experiences of living with multiple sclerosis, it got me thinking . . .

Many of us lived lives of large pane glass windows when the drunken hooligan that we've come to know chucked a rock through our crystal existence. A sudden rain of shards showered some while others found cracks in their window expanding until one day it just all fell in.

We have all learned to reglaze our lives with new windows but, like my neighborhood shopkeeper, we have learned to do so in panes rather than in expanses of plate.

Perhaps some started with fewer symptoms and recovered fully from them. They may have imitated that keeper and rebuilt with only a few panels to replace the broken window. Many of us, however, began with neat and tidy, even frames of smaller panes of glass. In doing so, we prepare for the next time when MS tosses and breaks something. The damage that next rock brings will then affect smaller parts of our lives.

Our lives become stronger as we make repairs to shore-up the empty casing with solid structures around our fragile bits.

The longer I live with this disease, the more I find myself reducing the size of those panes.

Sometimes I feel like my life's window now looks something like those that let light into Hagrid's hut in the *Harry Potter* films. It's now a hodgepodge of small—and often damaged—salvaged pieces of glass that I've been able to cobble together to a) keep the damage from incoming rocks to a minimum, b) allow me to see the wonderful world of which I am still a part and c) let that world's light in when getting out into it is just more than I can manage.

The funny thing about these small-paned windows that I've had to continually repair and replace is that they have their own unique beauty.

Gone from my life are the wide expanses of fragile plate glass windows. In their place I have leaded together bits of glass of my former life, of lessons gleaned from others who live in my community and from the discarded shards for which someone else saw no use.

My windows are more resilient now. The rocks still go through now and again and I've had to board up some panes until I find just the right piece of glass to fit. Some of those holes are still boarded up . . . but I refuse to close the shutters all together and abandon the light to reduce the burden of maintenance.

I suppose, now that I think of it, that the light reflecting from the faceted and often uneven panes of our lives' windows may be quite beautiful to behold from the outside too. Perhaps the work we do even inspires those who still have the fortune of viewing the world through vast expanses of unbroken glass. I give thanks for the entire MS community for helping me see the beauty of life through my imperfect windows.

Explaining MS: A Chef's Take
09/13/2016 London, England

I miss much from my former career. I was good at my job, I was respected for my work, and I associated with some of the best people I've ever come into contact with. I've said before that it is by remembering the skills from our former lives and putting them into practice living with MS that we can be most successful after multiple sclerosis.

I was thinking of one particular lesson I learned and passed along to my staff that I thought might be helpful to some who are having a difficult time with others understanding MS.

In the midst of a long-term consulting gig, a woman who'd been hired a few weeks after I started came to ask me a professional question.

"How is it that you get so much out of this kitchen staff and you never raise your voice?" she asked. She'd worked in many restaurants and under many chefs. They must have all been screamers (yes, there are still a few of those left in my former industry).

I explained my management philosophy to her and realized that it was the first time I'd ever put it into words.

I told her that I felt that if there were something that one of my employees was doing incorrectly, it was my fault . . . the first time. If I'd told someone what to do and how to do it and a mistake was made, I had likely not made my point clearly and in a way that this person had understood.

Mistakes obviously happen. If, however, someone was doing something incorrectly and thinking it was right, we would have a meeting—a first meeting. I would spend extra time to make sure that my point was understood and I'd have the employee repeat and even demonstrate what I was trying to get across.

Once the person had ensured me that she/he had understood, then we were back on track.

"You don't want to have a second meeting with me about the same thing." I told the woman.

You see, the second meeting was simply to remind the person of our first meeting and that they had assured me that they understood what I expected from them. I would convey to them that if they did not grasp what I was trying to say, they should have asked me to clarify. I would then give them the opportunity to get whatever information they needed from me to be successful.

"The third meeting," I advised, "is you collecting your final paycheck in my office if it happens again."

Harsh? Perhaps. Important to my health and sanity? Yes. Imperative in salvaging a harmonious working environment for the rest of my staff? I believe so. I'd like to think that this method worked, in some way, even for those who had to have that third meeting.

I have to wonder if some form of this tough love wouldn't work when we're trying to live our lives with multiple sclerosis.

If someone doesn't understand what I'm going through, perhaps it's my fault for not explaining my limitations properly. My fault the first time.

When someone puts demands (actively or passively) on us after we have laid out our situation, maybe we should make sure they really understood. I like to think that it was just an error in communications and I'm perfectly willing to take the responsibility for the error.

If, however, we've had that first meeting, if I've explained and they have signified they understand and it happens again, then we have a problem. No, they have a problem.

I don't have the time, energy or inclination to waste my precious resources explaining and re-explaining my MS to someone over and over again. If you say you understand and you don't, this is not my fault. It's not our fault. We shouldn't be made to feel like "Oh, yeah. You told me but I thought it would be different this time."

I've sadly had to have the third meeting with a few people in my personal life over MS. Some try to make me feel bad for the episode, but I know that we are not the ones at fault. We know our bodies, we know this disease, we're not the ones who have the problem.

Don't let anyone make you feel like less of a person because you have this disease. Don't let others decide your course of action in living with MS. You are the boss. You run your kitchen. It's not easy . . . but it's easier than living with people who disregard you and your situation.

Are there people with whom you think you should have a few meetings?

The Importance of Stretching
12/14/2016 Kerry, Ireland

I've said in more than one blog that I consider myself to be a healthy person who happens to live with multiple sclerosis. 'Healthy' perhaps but I've found myself significantly out of shape of late.

With all that 2016 has brought upon me, I decided to ask Caryn's help in getting onto a stretching program to help with the things that MS has thrown my way.

The National MS Society has set out the following guidelines for people with MS as we get into a stretching routine:

- Stretch on a daily basis when possible.
- Include muscle groups that are tight or in spasm.
- Do slow, gentle, prolonged stretches to the point where you feel a gentle pulling, but not pain.
- Hold stretches for 20-60 seconds or 5-10 breaths.
- Avoid bouncing movements.
- Use assistance as needed: a partner, towel or strap (talk to a yoga teacher or PT about what you can use to help you stretch—and how to use it).

These tips come from their page on staying flexible. Most of the stretching I've been doing has included some form of assistance—be it a chair, the wall or often, Caryn herself. My balance has become something of an issue so having something or someone to hold while stretching has been helpful.

Also helpful for when balance is even more of an issue is an illustrated manual called *Stretching for People with MS*.

This manual has plenty of drawings for stretches that can be done seated or even lying down. It has specific stretches for some common areas of spasticity and other difficulties for people with MS. I've even dug out my physical therapist's notes from after my hip replacement to help ease some stiffness in that area of the old body as well.

How out of shape am I? Well, let's just say that the day after those first stretches felt like I'd gone a few rounds with an Olympic boxer. But I'm keeping it up. I'm feeling the benefits after only one week.

My balance isn't any better, my stamina is the same, and my spasticity hasn't eased in effected areas. I do, however, feel a bit looser and more flexible. I enjoy the routine of taking a half an hour out of the day to look after myself and I look forward to the other anticipated benefits as they come.

Even if they don't, continued progress along the line that I've already experienced would be enough to stay the course.

An MS specializing physiatrist once told me, "Everyone should stretch every day . . . MS or not." It's just taken me a little while to come around to heeding his words.

'Tain't What You Do, It's the Way That You Do It
01/19/2017 Kerry, Ireland

Resilience can mean the ability of a person to solve problems and bounce back from difficult situations. That, at least, is the definition a group of researchers from the University of Washington gave to resilience when they surveyed a cadre of 1,574 people with a range of chronic conditions which included multiple sclerosis, muscular dystrophy, post poliomyelitis syndrome, and spinal cord injury.

In their report of the study titled "Resilience and Function in Adults with Physical Disabilities: an Observational Study," Samuel Battalio, BS, and colleagues found that people who self-reported significantly higher levels of satisfaction in the social roles (such as work and family responsibilities) of their life as well as higher quality of life led them to believe they had significantly higher resilience to the things their conditions threw at them.

It reminds me of the 'Sy' Oliver and 'Trummy' Young song, *T'ain't What You Do, It's The Way That You Do It*. The song states "That's what gets results." And ain't it the truth!

The information for this study was collected from mail-in surveys as part of an ongoing study of people as they age with disability.

In short, if we have something in our life that keeps us active and engaged we are more likely to recover from adversity; figure a way around a problem. And let's face it, that can be most days when you live with a chronic illness like MS.

I read this study when it came out and put it on the back burner. In coming back to it, I realized that I had been one of the cadre of research subjects for this particular study.

Every year I receive a thick booklet of questions to answer as they relate to several aspects of living and aging with my disabilities. I think I'm about 12 or so years into being a part of the study. It was nice to see some of the results of the project published.

The take home message from the study is that as much as we work on our physical being, follow our healthful diets, take our prescribed medications and engage in whatever complimentary therapies we might, it is imperative that we also maintain an active part in the world around us; both broadly and closer to home.

Wishing you and your family the best of health . . . because that's what gets results.

Set Pieces vs The Real Game
11/14/2017 Kerry, Ireland

It seems to be the season of team sports at the moment. Professional, club, international; from basketball and rugby, soccer to international rules, American football, hockey and beyond. It's a great time of year for the sports fans.

In typical form, I can't help but see a lesson about living with MS in it.

Most of us know that the hour or so that these teams spend on the pitch (or court, or ice, or field) for a match is only a sliver of what each player, coach and team put into the effort. From physical training to tactical plans, elaborate Set Pieces (that's what they call what I know as 'plays' in American sport), and beyond, we only see a bit of what these athletes go through to make themselves and their team the best.

In particular I've been thinking about those training sessions in the team room with whiteboards covered with Xs and Os, circles and slash marks. With multicolored arrows and scribbled notes on the edges, these are the basis for a team's Set Pieces— their play book.

The best of tacticians draw up plans for how to make it past the opponent's defenses and to score. But it's when the opposing side break up one of these set pieces that we see the great athletes and teams rise to victory.

It's the same for us.

I do my morning inventory, I consult with my MS medical team as needed, I work through plans for difficult times with my wife, Caryn. I try to do my stretches and eat 'right'. But no matter how well I plan—no matter the plays I've rehearsed—MS sometimes gets inside my defense line. That's when we have to play off-plan. That's where all-star players are made.

The way MS finds the holes in our line that we didn't even know exist makes this breakdown in play more common than I'd like to hope. Just when we think we've figured out a way around (or under, or through) something MS has put in our way the next 'MS Thing' gets in our way. We have to rely on past experience and lessons learned from the times before in order to win the day.

I've said before that smart people learn from their mistakes. A wise one, however, learns from other people's mistakes. It's like studying video of the opposing team playing a rival. We learn how others have succeeded or where they have failed under similar circumstances. That goes into the planning that makes up our playbook, but it also gives us insight as to how to make it through (or at least hold the line) when things fall apart.

Whenever a play falls apart and MS gets the upper hand, I'm glad that I can look around and see so many people on my team. Knowing that we've been through much of this before—together or alone—makes those first steps through a broken play a little bit easier. Thanks for being on our team.

Being Flexible
06/27/2018 Kerry, Ireland

It's a good idea for everyone to stretch every day. It's particularly important for people living with MS to have a regular stretching routine. I've said that before, I try to live by my own advice, and I'm saying it again.

Not quite a homograph, but we also need to stretch ourselves in mental/emotional/intellectual ways as well . . . as long as we don't keep searching for the edge of the envelope only to fall off.

The same can be said for the concept of flexibility and living with MS. It's important in the physical interpretation of the word, but we must also find a way to incorporate flexibility into the way we live our lives with this ever-changing disease.

We've learned that plans need a secondary (and oft tertiary or even quaternary) back-ups in the case of disease or symptom activity, particularly in summer months when many of us experience Uhthoff's Phenomenon when the temperatures climb.

Even if it's not for the heat, we have become yoga masters at bending schedules.

Starting times are made squishy, small tasks become major undertakings, we move deadlines closer to accommodate MS-slip, and we take pains to advise our hosts of potential issues well in advance. Like a distant relative's uncouth pet taking up your spot on the sofa, MS is something with which we must learn to bite our lip and soldier on.

I have learned the art of the tactical retreat—the fall back and regroup—approach to life as my MS progresses. It's a helpful tactic, but just like the ounce of prevention being better than a pound of cure, advanced and flexible planning is far more efficient than being forced to pull-back and reassess.

I don't like having to be this flexible—to put so bloody much effort into things others take as a given. The alternatives, however, are far less attractive still.

They would leave me either falling off ridged schedules with no place to go, or not engaging with the world around me by not accepting invitations at all. Then we're back to the physical stretching and flexibility analogies. If I don't keep doing it, things will become increasingly difficult to the point of pain and the loss of ability.

Not an option.

So, I'll stretch my body. I'll stretch my mind. I will keep trying to reach my shoelaces, and I'll continue to make plans and live the best life I can . . . even if it's not the life I'd choose first.

Happy In Spite Of
08/30/2018 Kerry, Ireland

I said to my wife, Caryn, the other day that, "The worst part is that I'm used to the pain now." It's sort of like when I was recovering from my hip replacement surgery and off pain meds for 3 days after being discharged because the medical team couldn't decide what meds would be best. Once I finally got medications sorted and on board, I realized how much pain I'd been in.

Which, by the way, was quite significant.

Don't get me wrong, the symptoms that I (and we all) experience are real, they are difficult, and often debilitating. I'm not one to sugar-coat; sometimes they're just bloody awful. But coping with them, and then becoming used to them, is the part I'm lamenting a bit today.

We are the athletes making the near impossible seem every-day, the actors making simple recitations of Shakespeare as if mundane conversation. You mayn't realize it, but you're doing this living with MS thing very well . . . even if you don't always feel like you are.

We've gotten used to living with pain and soldiering on. Rocking an assistive device like a fashion accessory. Using six times the energy to do the simple things everyone does with ease. Putting on the damned happy face because other people need to see it, not because we like wearing it.

It's like our grandparents telling us they had a great childhood even though they were poor, but they didn't know it because everyone else was too. It's the children shrieking with delight as they stretch a double into a triple at a stickball game in a run-down slum or score a goal with a half-deflated soccer ball in a warzone.

They get on with finding the joy in life—with being happy—even though there are so many reasons for them to be anything but happy.

That's what it's like to get used to living with MS. It's the getting on with it despite the disease. Making a happy life out of a difficult one. Finding a way to make a silk purse out of a sow's ear.

And we have, by unfortunate necessity, become pretty good at it . . . a lot of the time. But not all of the time, and some of the time not very much at all.

But we do try.

In my memoir, Chef Interrupted, I wrote a passage that many people with MS have come to me and said that it touched them very close to home. It takes place when a dear friend with MS stayed on in my cottage for a week after her husband and the rest of my houseguests had departed.

"We also relished the fact that we didn't have to carry around the burdensome cloaks that, even for those closest and most dear to us, are thick and heavy and serve only the purpose of shielding them from our symptoms. These garments of disguise do nothing for the person within; they only weigh us down with the responsibility of caring for other's feelings and reactions, often to our own detriment."

It may have been one of the happiest, if most difficult parts of that winter in an Irish country cottage. Our disease was front and center in a way that we often have to hide from others. At the same time, the joy in shedding those cloaks, and the simply joys of doing things at our own pace were pure heaven.

So, we get on, we live, and we try to live well. I am not happy that I have to work so hard to find happiness in my life with multiple sclerosis . . . but I am happy that I can find at least a little bit of it in each day.

Realism: It's Not for Everyone But it Works for Me
11/31/2018 Kerry, Ireland

The outpouring of good will and commiseration from my readers recently was something of a surprise to me. It's not the first time that I've jotted off what I felt like was a throw-away piece that was likely too personal to resonate only to find that I'd bowed a harmonic which resounded throughout our community.

It is usually when I am at those personal places in my writing that I guess our community hears their own thoughts in the words I've written. It's when I let down my guard that readers can see the bruises I too have behind my raised gloves.

It's not pretty to see, I'm sure of that. I've taken many square punches from our opponent. It has landed blow upon blow that have staggered me and even sent me to the canvas on more occasions than no one but my wife, Caryn, would know.

Some people don't like to see the marks of abuse that MS has rained upon us; even other people who have the disease shy away or deny. I get called out, regularly, for being too negative about my life with MS. I'm not enough "Butterfly farts and unicorn piss" (my words) for the 'attitude is everything' crowd.

The thing is reality is reality.

I have to speak the truth in the bad times otherwise how would I be believed in the good ones? How would people take me seriously in this community? MS does things to me. MS takes things from me. I learn to adapt. I take back what I can. But I am diminished from one point in time to the next. Fact.

For me and my Pack, I get on just fine. I do what I can when I can. I stretch my limits but not at the cost of falling off the edge of the envelope anymore. Our Wheaten Terriers know that they're not going to have me at their side when they run along the beach, but I'll be within sight and with them in their soaring spirit.

Caryn understands and accepts that she has had to take on much of the load when it comes to matters requiring cognition. She comforts me in my corner of the MS boxing ring . . . but knows that she must stay behind the ropes when I toe the line for my next round.

I do live a good life, even with MS awaiting me when I answer the bell. And I don't think of myself as an underdog in the fight. I am outmatched on every scorecard save one—spirit.

MS won't win on that judge's card, though MS has hit that pretty hard from time to time, too.

I guess what I'm trying to say is that I don't candy-coat my life with MS, and it has come to my attention that my Life with MS community is just fine with that.

The Buddy System
2/18/2020 Kerry, Ireland

"You have an incurable, likely degenerative and progressive neurological disease. We don't know exactly the course yours will take—it could be relatively benign, or it could get quite aggressive. Any questions?"

That's not *exactly* how most of us found out of our diagnosis, but at the time it may very well have felt like that's how vague and uncaring our doctor's words were. And then what???

Someone asked me the other day, in an interview, for any 'tips' I might have for people living with a new diagnosis of multiple sclerosis. I've been at it so long that I had to check many of my comments as I can sometimes be a bit jaded about what the disease has done to and taken from me.

I wanted to be as helpful as possible, so I thought about it for a while and said, "Get an MS Buddy."

I had to explain further, but I thought back to my first years trying to get my head around MS and how difficult that whole process ended up being. Then I met a few other people with the disease through the National MS Society. Whether or not they knew it, those people helped me to navigate my course simply by treading the path along with me.

It's sort of like the second-grade field trip where you're assigned a buddy to make sure you get on the bus, meet up for lunch, and return home safely. You needn't spend the whole day with your buddy—you can of course—but the object is to have someone with whom to check-in from time to time to make sure you're alright.

That your MS buddy is also living with the disease can be helpful as he/she may have come up with a work-around for one aspect of MS or another where you might be a bit stuck. They may have a different perspective on the same issue. Or they may just be a sounding board off which you can bounce ideas.

Though I've had several of these partners as I've traveled my time with MS on my back, I also know the comfort of virtual MS buddies (the National MS Society has several ways to connect with someone online). Some of these virtual pals we meet online in the MS cybersphere. Others we lose physical contact with as we move around in life, and our in-person buddies sometimes become virtual ones.

The buddy system is co-beneficial as we also act as guide/confidant/mentor/friend to our buddy in return.

A doctor, a friend, a spouse, or partner can never quite 'get' what it is to live with multiple sclerosis like an MS buddy can. Not that all of those other people in our lives aren't of utmost importance in a healthy life with the disease.

I'm just saying . . . if you ask me for one tip, I'd have for someone who is a little lost on the field trip of a life with MS, it would be to find a buddy, and you'll never miss the bus again.

Newton's Third Law
10/15/2020 Kerry, Ireland

Newton's Third Law of Motion states that for every action in nature there is an equal and opposite reaction. It's been around since he published it in 1686 and I likely first studied it in the late 1970s.

When I say "studied," well . . . I learned about it, understood it, and then like many aspects of theoretical scholarship, I moved on. But wouldn't you know it, Newton's Third Law came to mind as I read responses to an online query I'd posted a few weeks back.

Using a couple of questions from Bernard Pivot's *Bouillon de Culture*, I asked of the Life with MS Facebook community what their favorite and least favorite sound or noise might be. The answers were all over the board, but what struck me was how many of the same sounds/noises appeared on opposite sides of the love/hate line for people.

While for some the revving engine of a motorcycle might be of utmost annoyance; that same sound was a favorite of some who had once ridden or raced motorbikes. The same with the sound of birds early in the morning . . . for those with sleeping issues, the noisy avian signaled the end of another sleepless night while for those who enjoyed their mornings, they were a joyous chorus.

There were even votes from each camp for silence. Some saw it as still and relaxing while others found it lonely and foreboding.

For many answers there was an equal and opposite response.

While the survey question was intended as a bit of diversion from our normal MS conversation on the page, it, of course, brought MS to my mind.

It reminded me of how some people's worst fears about what might be are comforts to others who have already experienced and adapted to them.

I remembered a woman admitting to me that she was happy to be in a nursing facility while it is high on the list of fears for so many—MS or not. I recalled the number of times I've heard or read that "ending-up" in a wheelchair was the ultimate dread knowing more than a score of people who view their chairs as a tool of freedom and mobility rather than something in which they ended-up.

We all see life from our own angle. As an old friend used to say, "We all direct our own film and view it through our own lens." What I experience and how I relate that to my life is based on every other experience I have had and those I have learned of from others. The same is true for every one of us who live with multiple sclerosis or any other condition of life.

If one person finds a room full of laughter and conversation stimulating, and another finds themselves overwhelmed and confused; it's the same room, they are with the same people . . . it's simply an opposite perception of the same experience.

We all know that MS is a different disease for every person. What I'm coming to realize is that part of the reason it seems so very different is that we experience even the same encounters differently.

I suppose it's like having a severely affected left hand. If you're right-hand dominant, symptoms in the left would be annoying and unpleasant, but nothing compared to the left-handed person's experience of the same symptom.

We all live our own lives; we all have our own symptoms of multiple sclerosis. The odd part is that even when we have the same symptoms we experience them differently—even oppositely—than another person with the disease. No wonder it's difficult to explain to those who don't have it!

As an aside, no one in my unscientific survey found the 3am retching of a dog or cat outside of their bedroom door as a happy sound. So, at least we have that in common!

No Shortcuts
01/05/2021 Kerry, Ireland

Last week, we were staying in a hotel for the first time in nearly a year. Hotels weren't open then, nor are they opened now. Both trips were 'medically essential' trips for follow-up appointments. As we hadn't been off the peninsula since the last time we had to make that trip, we decided to stay over, enjoy the sights (albeit mostly closed sites) of Cork City and make a mini city-break out of the trip.

As it was only a one-night stay and I was obviously out of practice at staying away from home, I didn't do my usual full-unpack upon arrival. I HATE digging through a suitcase for some item or another.

So, picture the scene (but don't picture it too closely) I'm in the shower, face lathered-up for a shave and I note that my razor is still in my Dopp kit hanging on the hook at the back of the bathroom door. It's not a 5-star resort hotel in which we're staying, so the door isn't *that* far from the tub, so my first instinct is to reach for the bag on the door and the razor in the bag.

My second instinct was to ask myself, "What the actual hell are you thinking?!?! No!"

Like many of you, my balance isn't only not what it used to be, it's not what it should be for someone my age. It hasn't been since my diagnosing attack (even though I've done all the physiotherapy, exercises, and yoga they said might help) and it's never going to be again. I know better than to take the shortcut of a quick lean—even when a wet tub isn't involved—to grab something just out of reach.

I don't reach too far on dry land even.

I don't expect to bend over and grab the things that I drop (and boy, oh boy, don't I drop some things!). I don't turn too quickly; I don't even stand up or sit down in a rush because I'm just not that sure what I'm feeling (or not feeling) is my actual orientation in time and space that the hard objects all around me occupy.

Like many with MS, I've learned the hard way that short-cuts between point A and point B often, for me, have a required hard stopover at point A.5, e.g. I'm on the floor looking up at point B.

I'm not complaining. I'm just sayin'.

I suppose it's the same issue that anyone a decade or two my senior would know well. It's one of those elements of a relatively young life with MS has me living well in advance of my neuro-typical counterparts. My older friends and our parents know the trials of which I'm writing. They've been adjusting to the long way around life but they've done so at the normal pace of advancing years and at a socially acceptable pace.

For someone in their 50s ("Um, *middle-50's*" insists my wife, Caryn), I have to care for my body's place in the universe and gravity's effect as though I am someone 20 years older.

I turned off the water, used the handrail in the shower to lower myself to a pre-placed bathmat and carefully took the razor out of my bag. I placed it on in the soap dish in the shower, then remounted the raised tub to complete my shower and shave. No shortcuts, but no fall, no bruises, no damage. Just a few extra minutes taken up by my morning routine.

Minutes that I've also learned to add into just about everything in my day. But that's another story.

Lessons from COVID-19
03/18/2021 Kerry, Ireland

In a recent conversation with a friend from America, he referred to the public health restrictions we've been adhering to over here in Ireland as "Draconian." While they have been strict and it has been a long year of them, I hardly feel like they measured up to the ancient Greek standards of Draco!

In fact, after a good few years of taking medical advice onboard, researching, reflecting, and incorporating them into my life, I feel like the public health advice here (when properly adhered to) has not only been sound but also that it has made a massive difference in the spread of the virus. Just like many parts of my life, I've taken a look at the whole thing and I realize I've learned some lessons about life during a pandemic that will benefit me as I try to live my best life with MS.

GET OUTSIDE EVERY DAY

Even if the weather is nasty, even if you're tired, even if you just don't feel like it. Every day get out for at least a bit. Be it your constitutional a mile walk, a trip around the garden, or simply sitting on a porch or balcony under an umbrella for 20 minutes—get out and get some air (and sun if it happens to show its face). It really is a mood enhancer and if the sun is out you get the added benefit of Vitamin D.

STOCK THE LARDER

One needn't hire a trailer and head to the club store for cases of tinned goods to have a well-stocked pantry. Dried pasta, rice, Asian noodles all make a great base for a quick meal. Dried and/

or tinned beans, tomatoes, clean-label pasta sauce, tinned sardines and/or tuna. You're on to it now. Frozen veg is better than canned. Canned is better than none at all. Then spice it up. Salsa, curry, harissa, and the like. And don't forget the incredible edible eggs!

TALK TO SOMEONE OUTSIDE THE HOUSE

It's easy to fold into a house-bound routine. It's even easier to let days slip by (MS or Pandemic) without talking to the outside world. Be it a phone call to a friend, a chat over the garden fence, or a chinwag with someone you meet on your walk; talk to someone. During my pre-surgery lockdown last spring, I only got as far as a few houses from my own and there was no one out on our bóithrín. It was then that I realized the importance of another voice.

STRETCH

With restricted movements of public health guidelines or multiple sclerosis, our literal and figurative range of motion can shrink. Just like fresh air and a chat with a neighbor, a daily stretch of our muscles will keep body and mind in far better health. If motivation is lacking or the simple act of stretching is hard, make it a partnered affair.

SLEEP HYGIENE

When one locked-down day seems to pass into the next without much notice, it can be easy to binge watch on the streaming services, get stuck on one screen or another, and really muck-up our sleep patterns. Following a nightly routine, turning off the screens early, and sticking to a set time for lights out and for waking are just some of the recommended tips for good sleep hygiene.

We've another month or so of Level-5 restrictions where I live. After that the health professionals will reevaluate the situation and will make recommendations to the Government. We don't know what will happen then, but we're sure not to go back to 'normal' that soon. Even with fewer restrictions, the list above will be an important part of our lives for a good few months. After that, I know there will be times that MS keeps me closer to home than I'd like and the lessons of COVID-19 lockdown will serve me well there, too.

Life on a Rheostat
06/21/2021 Kerry, Ireland

There are loads of analogies—and I've used my share and then some—likening multiple sclerosis, the disease, with household electronics. Frayed wires, corroded phone cables, and the like, can all correlate to what our bodies are doing to their own communications system. The same can be said of the symptoms of MS.

Buzzing, tingling, shocking. The manifestations of the disease, in the multitude form of its symptoms, can be easily related to electricity. Out on an early morning walk the last day, I came upon another but this one relates to living with MS—the disease and its symptoms.

I try to get myself and our wheaten terrier, Maggie, out for a walk most mornings. On doctor's advice and for my own sanity, we started on this routine last winter. It's been good for both of us in more ways than I can list. This morning in question, I had a tall stack of things that needed doing and the prospect had even shortened my sleep.

We left the house much earlier than usual.

The sun was up, but a thick layer of sea fog blanketed the town, turning the day a sun-faded slate, like the roof tiles of an ancient cottage. It was one of those matter-of-fact mists . . . the sort of gray that can't be bothered to do more than hang in the air and wait for you to walk into it and soak yourself.

As we walked, I expected the morning to brighten as the sun climbed its way up from behind the coastal mountains which I knew were there despite their invisibility behind the nature's damp curtain.

But the day didn't lighten. It stayed an even, muted version of itself for the hour or so we walked until we were properly wetted. It was light enough for the time of day we'd left the house, but it hadn't changed with the progress of hours. It was as if someone had turned nature's dimmer switch from early summer to foreboding medieval battle scene. That's when the analogy struck.

Living life with multiple sclerosis is a life in which our disease controls the rheostat. It dims and brightens our days but, thankfully, hasn't flipped our switch to dark.

As with my damp walk with Maggie, once I got used to the level of light in our day, I sort of didn't notice it much. If I thought about it, sure it seemed dimmer, more somber, a bit dull. But the tone of the sky didn't inhibit our enjoyment of the seaside stroll (seaside stumble, more like it, but I'm on a roll there, people!). Our morning didn't brighten into those we'd experienced together on that same walk before. That didn't make it less of a joy, just a different type of one.

Life with MS isn't the same life I had without the disease. Is it better? Is it worse? Yes, and Yes, are my answers to those questions but the more correct answer would be "It's just different."

Our eyes get used to the new level of light and we just get on with it. We enjoy it for what it is. We try to make it better. We squint at the hard stuff and we try to find solace in this new, dimmer light.

It's one of those axioms about living with MS for a while that doesn't make sense until you have lived with it for a while. Things are different—most *everything* is different. That doesn't mean it's bad. It doesn't mean we can't find fulfillment in this new level of light (I do try to think of it as a level of light rather than a level of darkness). We adjust and we get on. Not as well, perhaps as before, but we keep going none-the-less.

Multiple sclerosis has dimmed the lights on us. It's now up to us to find a way to avoid bumping into things and brighten our world from within.

Missing the Eclipse
06/24/2021 Kerry, Ireland

The recent solar eclipse over the norther hemisphere skirted our home. We hoped to see a 25% bite of the sun missing just before midday and prepared with recommended pinhole camera viewing devices, the most technical of versions worthy of a 2nd grade class project, we woke with great expectation of the rare and wonderous site.

My observations today have less to do with the partial eclipse than they do with the experience around the rare occasion of our moon's shadow passing overhead.

The comparison of the light of the day being blotted out by MS would be an apt one if our planet, our satellite moon, and our star aligned as frequently as multiple sclerosis can; blotting out some or all of our day's radiance.

What did come to mind on more eclipse days I've experienced was how our much-anticipated viewing of a solar Packman was obscured by a thick layer of cloud that seemed to sit over our peninsula.

Be it a wedding, graduation, birthday, dinner with friends, even a trip to the shops after months of pandemic lockdown, a chronic illness can cloud over the day and make a much-anticipated outing less enjoyable or take it right out of the realm of possibility. Like a layer of 'overcastness' rolling in from the sea. MS has stolen my joy, obscuring a much-anticipated event, more times than I care to remember.

Sometimes, with great care and planning, we even take into consideration how the gray of the disease may cloud our plans. We understand our disease and we change our activities to rest up and recover from a party. We pre-cool before a workout. We spread large preparations over a longer period than most would consider necessary because we know that, even if they don't always work, the only way they might work is if we plot and scheme.

Like the terrestrial weather can blot out our enjoyment of the celestial, be they meteor showers, solar eclipses, blood moons, or a simple evening of watching the sun set over the sea, life with a chronic illness can be one disappointment after another if we let it be.

We were all let down by the weather on eclipse day. We were saddened to miss our chance to knowingly witness an event which would have frightened our ancient predecessors. We felt a bit done-in by nature. But those of us living with MS learn not to be disheartened when plans are scrubbed or experiences diminished.

Somehow after months, years, or decades of living with a disease that takes away our abilities, we've learned to make whatever we can of an event and take some joy in the beauty of a cloudy day.

The "To Don't" List
09/02/2021 Kerry, Ireland

To pass the time during the third wave of COVID-19, I found myself dipping in and out of several diddly little tomes. A bit of craic here, some sage advice there, mindlessly entertaining drivel now and again. Funny, it seemed to me to find a sage bit of advice in a book called *Grumpy Old Wit.*

Even more absurd was that the piece of wisdom passed off as "Grumpy Wit" was attributed to management guru, Tom Peters.

"Create," goes the quote, "a 'To Don't' list that contains tasks, rituals, and meetings that you should never waste your time on again. Then stick to it."

While I'm confident Mr. Peters' list is intended for important executives and the high-powered leaders of business and industry, I think there is a solid plank in this acumen upon which to build a strong platform for living my life with MS.

I know of the importance of a To Do list. I was even fairly good at managing myself and others using graduated, running lists of

priorities for multiple outlets and locations in various time zones
. . . back in the days before. Checking things off from such lists (or
confirming that others had) gives one not only a sense of accomplishment but requires accountability to ourselves as well ensuring
that things don't fall through the cracks.

All well and good in both the business and the MS worlds . . .

The idea of looking back at attempts I've made during my decades
of living with MS and jotting down those which were a complete
waste (along with those with a little or no net return) seems a great
way of turning negative experience into positive outcome.

Modes of exercise and/or weight loss that didn't work for one
reason or another would be a good start for me. Then on to various coping methods which were either unproductive, or worse,
harmful would be up toward the top as well. But beyond the
obvious, I think there is a lot of ore to mine in the discards of our
previous attempts.

It could be some attachment to puritanism in our DNA, but
we seem too often to regard ourselves at fault if something doesn't
work for us. We think we mustn't have tried hard enough or for
long enough if an attempt falls flat. Rather, I'd argue, some things
just don't work, or work anymore.

Furthermore, some things just aren't worth the return on
investment—monetary or otherwise. I think back on the long-term side effects of treatments for attacks and I'll put those on the
list. Perhaps not as "to don't," but rather "Only if . . ." as their echo
can still be heard reverberating on my health.

Perhaps the most difficult, but possibly the most important,
subjects to place on our running To Don't list will be the people
who have made the difficult parts of our life with MS more difficult
and/or made the good parts of life less good.

Like trimming dead and dying limbs from a tree in order that
it might continue to thrive, adding toxic people to my list of things
to not engage again may be the most difficult of all. They may be
the hardest to untether from our habits. But they are likely also

those which would be imperative to catalogue and, paraphrasing Mr. Peters says, "Stick to" as to avoid them sticking it to us, again.

As I reflect on this idea, it may seem a bit harsh—"never waste your time on again" is a pretty damning list to put something/someone on. If I think on it for more than a passing moment, however, I can see the extent of energy, pain, and self-doubt which would have been saved if I'd recorded endeavors and antagonists, attempts and bête noire which led me down paths better not revisited.

We've a finite reserve of energy and an ever-dwindling expanse of time upon which to spend that energy. Why then, please tell me, would we think it positive to step again on stones we know unsteady and have before sent us unceremoniously skidding on our backsides? No more. I'm making an MS To Don't list . . . and I'm sticking to it!

The Stories We Tell Ourselves
11/02/2021 Kerry, Ireland

"Act as if ye have faith and faith shall be given unto you. Put another way: fake it 'till you make it." It's a line written by Aaron Sorkin for the character of best friend and Chief of Staff to the eventual President on *The West Wing*. Caryn and I binge watched the entire series in the waning months of a previous American administration.

The line stuck with me in recent weeks, and I realized that I'd gone beyond "Fake it 'til you make it" land and have been living in a world of stories, fairytales, and outright lies to myself for a good while now.

It's difficult not to be hard on oneself when you come to this epiphany, but I came to the parallel truth that most of us tell ourselves the fables we need to get by. I'm not the only one, and I'm not even close to sure it's a bad thing.

I began walking it back from the edge when I stopped saying "We all tell ourselves the lies we need to hear." These felt like lies on the kinder end of the spectrum of falsehoods; the "It'll be grand" end. If they were lies I was telling myself, they were of the paler variety and they felt more parabolic than outright fibs.

Those who have read my writings know that I look at MS as a life sentence rather than a death sentence. That means that I have decided to get on (and keep on) with the living part. In order to get on with the getting on I seem to have a particular proclivity for averting my eyes from the difficult realities and skirting painful ones.

It's the MS version of telling myself that the old dog went to live on a farm where he's able to run free with his friends.

The difference between fairytale and outright lie shares a delta with need to know and ought to know.

The tales we tell ourselves help to soften the edges of our MS reality. "Maybe tomorrow" and "It won't last" are the "Once upon a time" introductions to many of these MS stories I tell myself. In them, the dragon is slayed, the protagonist rescued, and all is set right in the world. In their telling, I can put aside my fears, overcome obstacles, and the new normal is just as good as the old normal.

Most of the fantasies I inflict on myself are of the Tooth Fairy level of diversion. They are little distractions that do no real harm; they help me through a bit of trauma. They're something I hope to grow past in my own good time. Those are the benign stories I forgive myself for telling. The sinister tales are those which I use not to divert, but to deceive and delude myself.

Those are the dangerous lies that are towards the darker side of the spectrum.

So, for the sake of sanity I'll still tell myself stories to get me through the rough patches. I will not, however, (alright, I'll try not to) let the fantasies slip into the land of lies for this is a place from which I mayn't ever escape.

Fearless
10/29/2020 Kerry, Ireland

I've heard it said that one should never get in the way of an angry grandmother with a cause—they've the experience of a lifetime, the zeal of the converted, and they just don't give a damn what you think. They're the epitome of fearlessness. True or not, I know I'm going to sidestep any possible encounter with Granny Vehemence and her knitting club.

On the eve of a routine but invasive cardiac procedure, I find myself without any fear and I have to think it's because of my experiences over nearly two decades living with a diagnosis of MS.

The thought first came to me when I reflected on an operating theater chat I was having with the anesthetist who was about to put me under for what turned out to be an 8-hour surgery. As her assistants connected me to various apparatuses which were to monitor my life signs and keep me on this side of the light, we talked about the hand-made hazel walking stick I'd used to amble into the room.

We'd lived in nearly as many places in the world as the other, we talked of our different life experiences and, I'll admit, a bit of flirting as well.

As one of the leads came online a nurse requested the doctor to have a look.

"We have a new champion, ladies and gentlemen!"

My pulse rate and respiration were lower (in the good, relaxed way) than any patient she'd ever had on the table in her career. I was cool as a cucumber as I lay ready for an operation which may very well have altered the rest of my life significantly. Breathing easy and showing no more stress than being on a beach watching the tide go out on that warm July morning.

Tonight, I feel just as calm and, while I'll never give MS credit for teaching me anything, I will admit to being a good student.

We've all been through our share of ups and downs (and further downs). We've learned our way back to some semblance of normal even when very little is the same as it had been before. I've taken more punches than I've dodged, and I've spent more time face-down on the mat than I care to admit.

Multiple sclerosis has stolen from my life some of the aspects I once held in highest regard. It has ripped them from me, slipped them away while I wasn't looking, and walked away with them as if it knew I was unable to give chase.

Still, we are here. Battered, bruised, and beaten-up, but not bowed. Not today. Not by MS . . . not by whatever the world cares to throw at us.

Financial difficulties: check. Existential crises: done. Physical challenges: you're joking, right?

Like a hardened steel saber, we have been taken from the furnace, beaten by disease's hammer, plunged into the icy waters, and back again more times than anyone would believe. Like that sword, however, we are stronger, sharper, and more likely to keep an edge for the experiences.

I am stronger now than before. I am better able to cope than ever before. I will stumble, but I will carry on. I will fall, but I'll get up again. I will be beaten back, but I will not stop.

So, go ahead, Life. Bring It! I have MS . . . and I am fearless.

CHAPTER 6

Falling off the Wagon

*L*IVING LIFE WITH MULTIPLE SCLEROSIS (*or any chronic illness*) *shouldn't be a scorecard type affair. I know I wouldn't want to look back on the points total between myself and my disease. Particularly with MS, however, there are times when we appear to be winning and those when we're knocked back a few paces.*

The unpredictability of the disease—the symptoms, the attacks, the progression, the outcomes—makes living a life in tandem with MS maddening. Until there is a cure, however, living with it is preferable to the alternative.

I've become accustomed to new stuff that happens as my life and my disease progress on their parallel track. That doesn't mean I'm not surprised, taken aback, and even angered when the thief takes another sense or ability from me. I suppose the most difficult realizations have been when I catch a glimpse of myself in a mirror or passing a shopfront window.

I may have grown accustomed to what MS has and continues to do to my body and mind. That doesn't mean I'm not startled by it now and again—and I hate it all the more for the surprise.

Knowing When to Say "When"
06/12/2006 Seattle, USA

It's an old issue for me: acceptance of where MS has taken me, how far it has progressed. It seems so long ago now that I bought my first cane. I don't know if I'd have one today were it not for the persistence of someone close to me who was getting really frightened at the number and severity of the falls I was taking.

We seem to wait to use assistive devices, especially for that first one, until about 30% after we really need it. That number is anecdotal and based upon conversations with loads of people with MS.

We wait and we wait, we fight and fight. We feel that if we give in to our need that we are somehow giving in to the disease. We think that if we fight the good fight and stumble and fall and pick ourselves back up, we are better people for it.

NEWS FLASH: The disease is progressing whether you are using what you need or not. By putting off the use of what you need, you are actually fatiguing yourself unnecessarily and could be *worsening* the symptom!

I know you don't want to give in to MS, nobody does. Using something to help you get around is hardly giving in. I offer that *not* using something to get around, but rather limiting what you do because of your lack of mobility and fatigue without a device, is the giving in.

Sure, I make these statements as a man who has been using a cane for nearly five years now. In fact, when I came home from Ireland and wasn't using my cane every day, I realized that no one in Seattle knew me *without* my cane. But I also make the statement as a man who has a walker in the closet for the days when the cane is not enough.

Was it hard to buy that God-awful thing? YES!

Is it a comfort to have on the day or three per year when I need it? Yes again.

I urge you, no, I implore you. If you are in need of 'the next thing' to help you live your life to the fullest with MS, get the damned thing! It will be hard to do, but you'll thank yourself the very day you do.

Wrung Out
04/02/2010 Seattle, USA

MS is a disease that, no matter how well we plan, takes us by surprise. Go to bed fine only to wake up with part of our body not responding to a call to action. A simple battle with the circulating *bug du jour* and a fever puts you down like a crumpled boxer in their corner. Vertigo can make a turn of the head into a cyclone-spiral to the floor . . .

MS can really wring one out . . .

I'm currently on a planned slide into anemia after my treatment on Monday. I've been able to pretty much plan a lighter schedule (ok, who am I kidding??) knowing that I'd be far from 100%. Still, there are things that *should* get done by me. It's just taking a little extra effort.

It got me thinking about those times when our requirements wander beyond the should and into the must.

How, when MS makes even the simplest tasks Herculean, do you manage to get done the things that must be done? How do we make decisions when we're all fogged up with MS doing the thinking? How do we negotiate with ourselves and put things into the Should Do or the Must Do columns? And when do we just let go and put ourselves first in the Must Do column and take the rest we so desperately know we need?

An Attack
06/25/2010 Seattle, USA

You're going along, minding your own business when, all of a sudden, POW!

These things happen to all of us now and again. We hope, with the use of our disease modifying drugs, that they happen less often and that when they do they may be (maybe?) less severe.

The funny part is, I had an appointment scheduled with one of my neurologists smack in the middle of it. I, of course, knew there was something not right going on with my body. The new symptom, a constant numbness of my left thigh, was not something I'd experienced before and it had lasted for more than four days. The feeling of bumble bees in my feet and legs are with me more than half the time now.

Going through the familiar exercises, standard for a neurologic exam, shed new light on the state of my condition.

The-Hold-your-hands-out-at-arm's-length-with-your-eyes-closed test revealed my left arm sagging by a good foot once I opened my eyes again. My left foot would not answer the call to duty when the doc pressed it down, imploring me to resist his force. I don't even want to know what my gait looked like as I rallied (or so I thought) for the walking test unassisted . . . Caryn's face as I returned to the exam table was evidence enough that all was not well.

So, what to do?

I'll reschedule my next MRI due to be in the autumn to the next couple of weeks. I'll make that appointment with my specialist and read up on my options. It's time to make a decision what the next steps in my course of MS treatment will be, and it's not going to be an easy one.

While I've not taken the relative calm of my MS over the past years for granted, I will say that this calm has allowed me to keep it on the back burner (for the most part of most days). It has now decided to bubble up and make a bit of a mess on the stove. I guess it's time for Chef to pay attention and get his kitchen under control.

Am I Just Getting Old?
07-19/2010 Seattle, USA

"Is it _____ or am I just getting older?"

How many times have we, people with MS or other chronic illness, asked ourselves that?

We forget things, we seem confused, large crowds set us out of kilter, simple mental tasks overwhelm . . . Is it MS? Is it normal aging? Is it *something else*?

It is a valid question for us to ask ourselves and our medical team. Many of us have moved on from our initial, knee-jerk reaction of blaming everything on our MS. It's easy, with the help of friends who say, "Oh, I forget things too . . .," to write these things off as something other than Multiple Sclerosis taking its toll on our executive function.

It is easy, it may even be the likely cause. It may, however, not be wise to be dismissive.

The way I gauge my progression with most things MS is by comparing myself and my symptoms to my neuro-typical friends. If everyone seems to be misplacing their keys as often as I am, I'm good. If, however, I cannot seem to get one project started if three need attention . . . that ain't good.

I am constantly surprised when I hear of people talking, with real concern, to their doctors and getting a brush-off as to the severity of a symptom. Let's face it, most of us are not just crying wolf about our MS. We don't bring something to the doctor's attention unless it is of real concern (ok, some people do . . . or should that be all of us do at some time or other but not typically?)

If you feel like your cognition is slipping, it is important for you to get that checked. Most neurologists (and nearly ALL primary care providers) are not qualified to make the call of our mental impairments. For that we have neuropsychologists.

There is a battery of tests that can help identify, not only if, but how our mental functions are affected by Multiple Sclerosis.

These tests are not cheap, and many times are not covered by health insurance. They are, however, an important tool to ascertain and subsequently track any mental deficiency that may become part of our life with MS.

So, if you can't find your mobile phone now and again, simply call your number from a landline and you'll find it. If, however, you're having trouble remembering your phone numbers . . . well, you get the point.

A Moment Alone
04/13/2012 Seattle, USA

So often, multiple sclerosis is a disease of which everyone in my life seems to be a part. Friends and distant family walk or ride on a Team Gleason around the country, colleagues (past and present) always ask about my health, multiple blog communities around the world keep track and comment on my musings about living with MS. This week, however, I took time (or, rather, it was forced upon me) alone with my disease and had some pretty hard choices to make.

With the help of anti-fatigue meds, I spent a few days in Boston advising some folks from my old professional world. Even padding the travel with a recovery day and scheduling as little as possible, I came face to face with the brick wall of our disease; I was mortared with fatigue that was reinforced by weakening limbs and anchored in numbness.

Excusing myself from what would have been a relaxing evening meal with colleagues who've become the dearest of friends, I sequestered to my quarters and dined on room service and retired early. But not before I became aware of a reality which had been subconscious for quite some time.

Business travel is just not in the cards any longer.

I used to be able to fool myself by padding my arrival with a day to recover and clearing a couple after my return. I made sure meetings didn't start too early, didn't go overly long, and I had time enough for a rest (or maybe even a cool shower) in-between. When the few days on the backside turned into a week and my capabilities during a visit decayed in half-life fashion, I countered with caffeine, with sugar, and with that most addictive of cocktails The Denial-tini, shaken (hard) with a jigger of bravado and garnished with a blind eye.

This night, however, alone with my MS and struggling my way through the 87,474th hotel room service club sandwich I've ingested in my career, I admitted to myself that this was—for all intents and purposes—the last of this type of trip I am to take.

I'll still travel to speak for our cause, to volunteer when I can and—I hope—to promote my upcoming book next spring. The idea, however, that I can hold on to the imaginary thread which I have attached to my former professional self has turned into a noose. I must let it slip from my grasp in a way the other parts that were "Chef Trevis."

Like the gambler who has finally seen how much the loan shark has stolen from his family's coffers, I have looked into myself and have finally come to understand what everyone around me has seen as truth . . . and it is a relief.

Not to worry. I'm not going to stop my writing. Quite the contrary; that I was unable to write due to my exhaustion over this past week was the straw which broke my conscience and let me see my reflection clearly.

When Pseudo Exacerbation Meets a Real One
08/13/2012 Seattle, USA

"So," as David Mamet so aptly put it in his film *State And Main*, "*THAT* happened . . ."

Pseudo Exacerbation. It doesn't mean that the symptoms are

not real; it's rather that old damage is being aggravated. Those old symptoms that are caused by the damaged areas in question flare up for a couple of days or until the cause—heat, fever, stress, etc. passes.

Actual exacerbations—known as Attacks, Flares, Episodes or even just 'Things' by some—are the result of new damage to the nervous symptom. They are usually characterized by new symptoms or worsening of existing symptoms for periods of more than 24-48 hours and are not associated with the above-mentioned factors.

Well, the stress of travel, time-zone change, and heat brought on a Pseudo Flare for me last weekend. It wasn't something that I didn't expect. Seattle has been rather cool this summer and I was heading into the teeth of a Michigan August for a weekend family wedding. I planned long, cool showers, lots of hydration and plenty of rest as part of the trip.

Despite my mitigation efforts, I was surprised when a whole new batch of symptoms I'd never experienced started. My right side, always the stronger side since my diagnosing episode in 2001, began to spasm and twitch during the wedding ceremony!

My leg began to give-out and I was very happy to have opted for the forearm crutch rather than the cane. By the time Caryn and I got home on Sunday night I was in a full-on exacerbation.

On the plane ride home, I did something very uncharacteristic of me; I told Caryn that I was going to need help.

I'm not back to my old self, but I can tell you that, with help, I am feeling much better than I was and have hope for more recovery.

I may not be 100% this week or next, but I'm going to give it a go.

Creeping Symptoms
03/21/2013 Kerry, Ireland

I know a guy with MS whose symptoms started with a slight tingling at the end of his index finger. That tingling turned to numbness and it crept right up the musician's finger, hand and up his arm. When I last saw this lad, his arm was all but useless to him. Multiple Sclerosis doesn't always (or even often, to my knowledge) work that way, but I've had a new and creeping symptom similar to this.

A few days ago I took our dog Sadie out into the back garden for a pee. It was a bright, cold day and I enjoyed the feeling of the sun on my face as Herself searched for just the right spot to empty. By the time I came back into the house it felt like I'd been wearing toeless sandals on my left foot. The first and second toes beyond my big toe were very cold. They were cold to the point that I mentioned it to Caryn.

It was as though I had holes in my shoes, but I let it go . . . until later in the night.

By the time we got into bed, the cold feeling was replaced with a deep ache that radiated from the ends of the toes through to the joints and felt as if I may have broken them a few days before.

Morning found them about the same, but by afternoon, a burning line of tightness extended from the toes, across my foot and up the outside of my calf muscle. At about this time, the pain at its original toes had changed to hypersensitivity and even socks were painful to feel against the skin and the line up my calf continued to burn.

It's been over 72 hours now and it's been accompanied with some fatigue and—I'm sure Caryn will confirm—a shortness of temper and a quick finger on the frustration trigger. Though I'm officially secondary-progressive, I'd have to say that this is a defined worsening of symptoms. Damn!

I'm just going to see where this one goes. I'm not going down the worry path that has me using a walker to get to the bathroom. I'll just note, try to get around, hope that it won't get worse but plan for if it does.

My Shrinking Gray Matter; Brain Atrophy
09/10/2013 Kerry, Ireland

The more we find out, the more I hate this disease. Don't get me wrong, research into all aspects of multiple sclerosis is a good thing. I'm not going to lie to you though, I hate MS.

A recent study released shows that we may be losing brain mass to multiple sclerosis before we even know we have MS. This new study seems to show that deep MRIs of patients presenting with clinically isolated syndrome (CIS)—that's basically having a first 'attack' and one lesion showing up on a scan—have already lost brain volume compared to healthy controls.

The shrinking of the brain was once thought to only be a sign of advanced disease in MS. This new study seems to show that we have MS before we have MS . . . and that it's not just all about inflammation and lesions.

This data, if proven by other studies, may promote doctors to advise general brain health practices for all of us from diagnosis.

Will eating more brain-healthy foods cure my MS? Will brain exercises keep me from losing what I have? Will my new mediation plan change how my multiple sclerosis looks in the future? I have no idea. But it can't hurt!

Blood-brain barrier, lesions, axonal damage and atrophy are very scary words and concepts. We associate brain loss with dementia, senility, and Alzheimer's disease . . . and now with the earliest stages of Multiple Sclerosis.

We have all learned to move it or lose it with our body parts. It's time for us to consider doing the same with our brains.

Good Days and Bad Days Are a Moving Target
10/18/2013 Kerry, Ireland

When someone bemoaned their ability do to a "Bad leg" during a yoga class I once attended, we were all treated to a lesson about what is bad and what is good. The leg isn't bad; it's affected by MS. It is my leg.

Our legs, our limbs, our bodies are inherently good.

Since that day I have strived to focus on the good as much as possible. I'm not a Pollyanna but a pragmatist. To me the truth is that it doesn't matter if it's a good day or a bad day; it's about what I do to wring the most out of that day that matters.

What may seem like a bad day one day because of slow limbs and mind-numbing fatigue could be good relative to a day MS has kept me in bed. The days I can walk Sadie for a few hundred crutch-aided yards may be a fantastic day even if that is all the energy I have for hours or days to come.

My MS is different from anyone else's. We all have different disease activity and symptoms and damage and external circumstances. We also have different coping mechanisms and management skills. So, it is up to each of us to find the best way to make the most of the good days . . . even when they aren't actually that good.

The North Atlantic rains are lashing our little garden right now and, even if they weren't, my legs have taken on a spate of pins and needles so that walk with Herself isn't in the cards. At the same time, through my rain-washed window, I can see a long and spindly late-autumn sunflower dancing to the wind.

These are not the big, dinner plate sized flowers I knew before moving here. They have faces about the size of a child's palm and long and resilient stems. This flower bounces to the rhythm of the breeze and its petals of school bus yellow are flicked by drops of wind scattered rain.

It looks a combination of animation and high-speed photography as leaves and twigs and other less resilient greenery blow past.

Sometimes I feel like the bits of the garden that are being blown around by the storm. Most times, however, I try to be the flexible one who makes standing against the wind look like dancing—badly choreographed—and refusing to break.

It might not be the best day for my legs or for that sunflower. It's not the day, however, that frost will burn those petals or slow legs will drag down my heart.

I can see that flower and the rest of my garden from a warm and dry room though a clean window and my heart tells me that it is a good day.

Do we need more than that to define a day as "Good" or "Bad"? Days will be different, one to the next. Mine is not to determine whether the glass is half-full or half-empty. My task is to get done what I can with only half a glass and some days it feels like less than half.

Good day or Bad day—just like the lesson of the bad leg—it is MY day. Mine to do with it what I can because if I don't do that, it matters not if the day is good or bad it will have been a waste.

And, surely, a wasted day is the last thing I can afford.

Like Having Acne at 70
07/03/2014 Chicago, USA

No seventeen-year-old kid is happy about an outbreak of acne on the eve of a big date. But at least they're prepared for it. It's not something a couple, dressing for their 50th wedding anniversary party has to worry about. But that's how I felt this week when my progressive MS—you know, the kind that's supposed to be post-inflammatory, steadily declining and WITHOUT ATTACKS— jumped up and slapped me in the face with a full-on exacerbation.

It's been years since I've had such an acute onset of something new. Usually, it's just a few days or weeks of a new thing creeping into my consciousness when I—all of a sudden—realize that it's become an issue.

I'm not a silver lining guy, as you know. But there was some-thing about slipping into the Secondary Progressive MS (SPMS) world that made me think "At least I won't have to put up with *that* anymore . . ."

Oh boy was I wrong.

I apologize to my RRMS readers if I have adopted anything that resembles apathy for the challenges you face. We all cope the best we can. I've been so focused on the slow drip of water torture that is Progressive MS that I forgot how to cope with the brutal club of an MS exacerbation.

I Want to Feel Regular Tired Again
09/24/2014 Kerry, Ireland

We picked up our pack of Wheaten Terriers from the boarding kennel the other day. They'd spent two nights sleeping over while Caryn and I took her parents up to the airport at the end of their stay.

The boarder absolutely adores our dogs (okay, ALL dogs) so it's almost a vacation for them. They play in the fields, they romp with other well-mannered furry guests, they get a bath to wash away the layers of mud, muck and grass stains all earned in a day's play with the Pack.

They are so excited to see us they jump around the back seat of the rental car and bite the air flowing in through the partly opened back windows.

Then we get home . . . and they crash.

I remember the days of being tired for a reason. I worked or played so hard that I fell asleep in a chair in the garden. I'd just get into bed and be asleep in moments due to exercise, exertion, vocation, or avocation. There were days when my muscles hurt from chores in the yard, when my mind was numbed by study, or my spirit sapped by good work for a great cause. Those glorious days ended in well-toiled, whole-person exhaustion.

I miss being tired for a reason.

We all know the debilitating fatigue that can come with MS. It's one of our most common symptoms and we've had many conversations about it.

Sometimes I just wish I could be tired for a reason other than brushing my teeth or walking across the room. It's one thing to earn a good weariness. It's a whole other thing to have it doled out like some perverse charity by this anti-benevolent disease.

The Pack slept through the night and I'm not even sure they rolled over in their beds. I, too, had a deep, anesthetic-like night of rest. I just wish it had been earned rather than just an MS sleep.

Am I the only one who misses being tired (or sore, or confused or whatever) for a good reason other than because of MS?

Everything Changes One Day, But One Day Everything Changes Anyway
05/18/2016 Prague, Czech Republic

Our sleepy little town on the edge of the North Atlantic was changed 46 years ago when Academy Award winning writer/director, David Lean brought Hollywood here for nearly two years to film *Ryan's Daughter*. Next week will bring change again as cast and crew of *Star Wars* come to your town to film for a fortnight.

In 1970, we had not a single restaurant in this town and no tourists to feed anyway. Today we are Ireland's #1 Foodie Town and can feel more like a tourist town with a farming and fishing problem rather than the other way around. Who knows how Luke Skywalker's visit will alter the place?

Nothing changes a place like a blockbuster film.

My Wheaten Terrier, Sadie, has always been my little girl even though she turns 11 this summer. Wheatens are known for being energetic and puppy-like for life. Well, they're puppies until one day, they aren't.

A fortnight ago she was playing with her little sister, Maggie, and she pulled-up lame. She's better now but Sadie has changed; she's slower and more deliberate in her movements like she knows she's more fragile than before. That sunny afternoon romp with Maggie was the day that Sadie stopped being a puppy.

We who live with chronic illness know how everything can change on one day. Diagnosis changes everything. At the same time, the change has been happening for a long time as we likely live with the disease for years before we hear the confirmation of that diagnosis.

The day I heard that I had MS sent me into a years-long slide of self-doubt, questionable decisions, and depression. The years leading up to my diagnosis were something of a disease devolution as much of my life was changing all around me in increments as opposed to the seismic change of diagnosis.

Perhaps it was only my perception that completely changed all in one day, one moment, really.

Sadie will find her new normal, and her incomparable puppy spirit will return even if her body—like her Da's—may not answer every joyful call. The Jedi will leave the mark of The Force on our shores, but those same beaches and cliffs have seen invaders for millennia. I doubt the Millennium Falcon is going to be much different in the long view.

I guess it's all a matter of perspective. Yes, MS does change everything but nearly everything was going to change anyway. Maybe it's because it is a different type of change—definitely it is more and faster change—but if we change with it rather than only being affected it, perhaps we can reduce some of the trauma to the soul.

At least that's what it feels like today.

The Art of The Delusion
10/07/2016 Kerry, Ireland

I use the mantra "Control is an illusion" fairly often. What I've come to know is that we can only control our reactions and our responses; everything else is pretty much out of our control.

Today, after a couple of weeks of new symptoms and progression that is hanging on with a grip far better than mine, I have to wonder if I haven't replaced my illusion of control with delusion of normalcy.

I have been appalled by how far I seem to have fallen in the past days. My gait, my strength, my stamina, my cognition, my speech, all have taken a serious hit in the past fortnight. And so has my self-esteem. Caryn has had to take a whole new roll in caretaking as she has kept me from wandering around like a stoner looking for Screaming Yellow Zonkers.

We laughed at it for lack of anything else to do but that's what I've felt like—as if my mind and body have been totally stoned on drugs.

I have been appalled, but Caryn was surprised. Not surprised by how heavy my comedown has been, but rather surprised that I see it as so new and so odd. I've often said that I'm not the only one in the house living with my MS. It seems that Caryn has seen this coming for some time now and it's not new to her.

There is the delusion.

I've been deluding myself that I'm better than I am. While this relapse has forced me to look at the way I walk and talk and get on with my days, I'm simply seeing what Caryn has observed all along. Sure it's more pronounced and all-at-once this time, but she's been watching me pretend that I'm better than I am for a long time . . . and I can see that it makes her sad.

We have a little joke line that we like to say when one of us stumbles upon the obvious in life. "Oh, you're soooooo pretty!" (said with a loving pat on the shoulder and a comforting frown). Think, "Petal, have you seen my reading glasses?" when they're on the top of my head or something like that.

Well, I've been sooooooooo pretty, deluding myself that I'm getting on just fine. I'm not and I'm wondering if there is anything I can do about it.

I happen to have an appointment with my MS team next week. It looks like I'm going to have a lot to talk with them about. I'm in a tough place right now and I know that many of you can understand.

We're going to keep on living our best lives, Caryn and I, MS or not. I guess I'm just at a place where I can no longer pretend that little is the matter. MS is the matter. And I have to wonder if, other than the shock of coming out of it, living in that delusion wasn't a little bit better.

Invisible Symptoms
06/30/2017 Kerry, Ireland

Invisible symptoms of MS are some of the most difficult to explain (and be believed). The National MS Society has a great 2-part video about these symptoms. They've also just printed a piece about some of the less common symptoms of MS in their recent *Momentum Magazine*.

I suppose having someone interview you and ask about these invisible symptoms is quite a bit different than a family member (or friend, or employer, or insurance provider) not believing that we're experiencing these difficulties. Just because they can't see my vision problems or bladder symptoms or know that I cannot feel my left side, this does not diminish their existence . . . oh, how I wish that it did.

I wrote a piece for the MS Society of Ireland talking about the importance of not focusing on MS all of the time. It helps so much to not think about MS whenever we can. When we feel like people don't believe us (or are directly confronted by those who actually don't), we can be forced to face those facts even more starkly.

I can't see atoms, but they're there. I'm not able touch a star, but they are real. I cannot demonstrate everything that MS is doing to my body . . . but it is doing those things.

Some people may never understand that and I really shouldn't bother with them, but sometimes we must and it can be exhausting.

The Disability Spiral: Part I, The Body
07/19/2017 Kerry, Ireland

Overall, this past year with MS has been a difficult one. I've had some setbacks, some rough patches, some progression; whatever you'd like to call it, I've had it. Now as I try to crawl back to find my new normal, I'm finding many things I used to undertake with relative ease more difficult . . . but can I just not do them?

Sixteen years on from my diagnosis, and likely another 15 years past my first MS symptoms, I'd like to think that I've got a handle on how to live with the recurring loss of abilities and work arounds. I'd like to think that, but I'm finding that I'm caught in the beginning of a downward spiral which I must arrest.

By downward spiral I mean that I'm finding many physical undertakings toilsome and even painful. I am now tending to avoid those tasks. By not trying, not pushing, not endeavoring to go past my current discomfort and general malaise today, I may be making it more difficult for tomorrow.

It's the "I can't easily—so I don't—so I can't without great difficulty—so I won't—so I can no longer" kind of spiral.

Surely, I'm not alone in these horns of a dilemma.

Something as simple as daily stretching, as mundane as emptying the dishwasher or as important as brushing my teeth can be taxing today, onerous tomorrow and all but impossible further down the road if we let them get out of hand.

While I still try to push the edges of my MS envelope, I feel like my envelope has got smaller of late. The energy I once expended on finding my limits is now spent shoring up the basics—and with just as much, if not more, effort

But push I must.

That's the thing about spirals; once you've begun down the path it can be very difficult to turn around. Though difficult to keep myself only on the edge of this self-perpetuating vortex, it would be much more difficult to try to make my way back out.

So, then, what to do about it?

The hope, of course, is that this is some level of plateau and I will be able to recover. That's not a given (in fact, as an MS pragmatist, I have to realize it's not even a likelihood), so I must play the cards in my hand rather than lamenting the fairness of the deck.

Self-care and finding ways to enjoy life inside my shrunken world are to be the order of my days. I will strive to do the annoying, the difficult and the mundane knowing that those things aren't climbing mountains, running marathons, or helping a friend move. My days will begin with my all-important MS inventory and I will strive to do the little things and do them well. Otherwise, I may not be able to do them at all.

As I write this, I realize that it's not just the physical aspects of life with MS that may be hazarded with these downward spirals. There is also the systematic disabling of the MS population by healthcare, insurance agencies and the government.

Here's to staying off the slippery slope . . . for getting back up may be impossible for some.

The Disability Spiral: Part II, The System
07/24/2017 Kerry, Ireland

As much as the limits that symptoms of a disease can put on our bodies and minds, the systems of insurance and disability assistance can also cause a spiral.

Health insurance differs not just from country to country but, in America, from state to state. The out-of-pocket costs for everything from seeing a specialist to the price of medications vary widely, as do assistance programs to help with those costs. Sometimes, for some people, the price they must pay for a disease modifying drug—one that will slow progression the disease— is just too expensive. They do not, therefore, take the meds and become disabled thus costing The System more in the long run.

This is a most simplistic example, but a real one nonetheless.

Another example would be needing health insurance because of a condition such as MS but, because we have MS, we are put into higher risk pools for insurance and priced out of the system completely.

Work-related issues are a major factor when it comes to a disease like MS as well.

Many people get their insurance coverage through their jobs, so employment is more than just a paycheck. If we find it more and more difficult to work full days or weeks, we risk losing healthcare coverage. If we lose insurance coverage because we're working only part-time (because we can no longer work full-time) then we cannot afford the health insurance we lost because we can't work.

The working part, the short-term, long-term and permanent disability systems are a difficult labyrinth to themselves.

Can't work because of your MS for a short period of time? Your employer may have a short-term disability coverage that will give you a limited time (usually somewhere between six weeks and six months) that will offer you a salary during the time you cannot work. This sounds great, but the sums are typically minimal and only apply when you cannot work at all.   If you need to cut your hours, short-term disability does not help.

Once you reach the end of short-term disability coverage, long-term insurance may kick into play. These policies may be underwritten by the same insurance provider but are administered by a completely separate branch of the company. You'll have to jump through many hoops in order to qualify. Once approved, you'll be awarded a settlement figure of between 40%-60% of your former wage/salary (averaged over the previous 2 years, usually). This is, again, only available if you cannot work full-time.

As you can see, when it comes to work, there is no system (in the US, at least, in most countries in Europe it's different) where you might receive a supplement if you can't work full-time but can manage part-time in the old job.

The systems of disability coverage can seem stacked with very black and white blocks. Either work full-time and get the benefits that you need or don't work at all and get some of the benefits that you need. If you need help but fall somewhere in between, you're pretty much out of luck. It's a system that can help create disability and then forces us to prove that disability over and over again.

The first steps into the disability system ladder are uncomfortable, but often necessary. The scariest part is how quickly those rungs become a slide and we're all of a sudden on a spiral into the disability system.

Chronic Discomfort
09/14/2017 Kerry, Ireland

Do me a favor. Before you continue reading this, take the largest book you have near you and put it under one side of your bum so that you're sitting half on and half off the book. This will make sense . . .

The husband of a dear old friend with MS got in touch recently. He made contact rather than his wife because her advanced MS has left her body significantly impaired. Her bright and indomitable spirit has overcome much of what MS has dished out. It's people like Jeanne I think of when I feel like I haven't another chapter left in me.

The topic he wanted to discuss was the chronic discomfort his wife has to deal with. It is the discomfort those who have lost use of their limbs and the ability to reposition themselves when they are uncomfortable.

How's that book feeling under your cheek?

The inability to move, coupled with loss of feeling, can lead to injuries such as pressure sores, contribute to Urinary Tract Infections (UTIs) and other knock-on effects. Now imagine (and some of you will not have to imagine) that you can still feel the sensation of discomfort but cannot shift your weight to ease it. As Jeanne's husband stated, "Most folks make constant micro-adjustments without even thinking about it. During the day and night, we alleviate discomfort on pressure points or adjust body positions or clothing, and don't even notice we do it."

Now do you understand why I had you sit on that book?

Those of us with advanced MS may not be able to adjust and either simply try to soldier on through it—sometimes to the detriment of their health—or constantly ask a caregiver to help them with what might seem to be mundane and miniscule.

It's the itch that you cannot scratch; the raspberry seed in your wisdom tooth, the pebble in the sole of your shoe. It's the book under the side of your arse right now.

I know many people who use more advanced mobility aids and, even with empathy and 16 years of diagnosis under my belt, I'd never thought of this aspect of what my friends in chairs might be going through. It must be one of those things that we swallow hard and just try to get on with rather than facing the thought of becoming a burden by having someone help with something seems so insignificant.

I think you can take that book from your chair now. We all get it. I just didn't think of it before now. I'm sorry that my friends may be chronically uncomfortable.

I'm Still Brought Up Short Now and Again
01/24/2018 Kerry, Ireland

Storm Georgina—the seventh named North Atlantic storm of the 2018 season—hit our island last night. One hundred kph winds brought lashes of rain and Smarties-sized hail from the southwest, directly targeting my bedroom window throughout the darkness. My wife, Caryn, was away on business so it was just me and the dogs left in the house to weather the storm.

None of us slept well, hardly at all, really.

At about 02:30 I gave up the reading of a book and opened my laptop to pass some time. Fumbling around for a while I settled on a series of YouTube snippets of an old favorite (my last appointment television, actually), *The West Wing*.

Most of you will know that the character of President Josiah 'Jed' Bartlet in that program had multiple sclerosis.

As tense, dramatic, humorous, and endearing scenes played I remembered why I liked the show so much. Great writing, wonderful ensemble acting, well-crafted direction all made for award-winning television.

Then one clip played that brought me up short.

As the President is being prepared for emergency surgery, the First Lady (the character is a medical doctor herself) informs the anesthesiologist that her husband has MS.

I saw this episode when it aired; I've seen it subsequently in re-runs in its entirety. Seeing just the clip, however, plucked from its dramatic context and flayed bare in quick, raw succession . . . it caught my breath.

I was brought back to my diagnosis with the same, incurable disease. My breath caught in my throat, my chest heaved, my eyes blurred with tears. To say I was surprised, sitting there on the verge of tears in the middle of a dark and stormy night would be litotes.

Sometimes, even when we think we've a handle on living this changed life—a life of lowered expectations and of new normals—some little thing catches us off guard. It might be seeing our reflections walking alongside us in a window. It could be photographs of before MS. Often, it's the unguarded look of someone who hasn't seen us in a good long while.

I recently heard a comedian say that "Pain is the rapid flow of knowledge." Stub your toe on the end of the bed, rapid flow of knowledge to NOT do that again. It feels like those moments that I'm surprised by my reaction to having MS are a sudden and rapid rush of memory of what was before, how far I've fallen, and

it brushes past all of the lessons I've learned over the years as it
flows in.

And it hurts.

To acknowledge this is easy in the bright sunlight that met us
this morning after the storm passed. But in those dark and stormy
moments when it catches me unawares, it's just pain. A pain I wish
I could numb.

When Indulgences Become Unaffordable Necessities
06/19/2018 Kerry, Ireland

When I was young and at school, the term "Latchkey Kids"
really took off. From its origins during World War II, it wasn't used
much until its revival for my classmates. For reasons of necessity,
career pursuit, or a few extra dollars for the niceties of life, more
and more mothers were working full-time jobs as I went through
my school days.

Two-income families are more the norm than one-worker
homes in this day and age, and far more for the necessity or career
pursuit than the extra Bob or two.

This led to an increased standard of living for America (and
many in the world) as we grew into adulthood. Things that were
once opulence became more regularly ascribed indulgences and
might even have been considered deserved pampering and reward
for a hard week's work.

Growing up, the idea of a housekeeper, a pedicure or hot-towel
shave would have been as foreign to my family as the menus that
grace my adult dining table. These were not things affordable,
expected, or really even considered.

Now they are often a norm (or at least more regular niceties)
for hard-working families with a bit of fiscal space for such things.

As with so many parts of living with a chronic illness like
Multiple Sclerosis, we find ourselves at a crossroads of some of

these indulgences becoming requirements at the same time our earning power decreases

Simple (to most people) acts of grooming like trimming toenails or even shaving can require assistance when MS comes thieving. A little nick provided by an MS tremor while attending to the body with sharp objects can lead to infection—and we know what that means for MS! Membership in a health club with a pool might be the best way for someone with MS to exercise and keep cool at the same time the budget shrinks due to the next prescription co-pay. Dust might begin to stack up as energy (or ability) keep us from cleaning chores and reduced income stonewalls our ability to pay a housekeeper to come in and help.

There are assistance programs for many aspects of living with MS. Many people couldn't live a life even close to 'normal' without such financial help. For most, however, this time of crossing need and affordability leaves them with need but too much means to qualify. Also, what many of us experience as growing need may be seen by society as extravagance.

MS is a neurological disease. It is an inflammatory disease. MS usually falls under the category of auto-immune disease. Multiple sclerosis is also a disease of significant financial drain at the same time it reduces earning power.

I'm not whining, I'm simply stating a fact that many of us with MS know too well. Maybe it's an aspect of MS others don't think about, but those of us living at the juncture of increasing need and diminishing resources know it all too well.

When Come-and-Go Symptoms Come-and-Stay
08/16/2018 Kerry, Ireland

I had to take my laptop into the local tech repair shop this week. It has been giving me problems with the touchpad for the last while.

Sometimes it's fine. But other times the cursor seems to stick in one place and I can't get on with the job at hand. When that job is my next book, it can be annoying. That it happens on and off and then on again . . . well that's just MS annoying.

I had to bring it in because, even though it's still an intermittent problem, it was getting more frequent.

I've also had an old, on-again-off-again MS symptom not go off-again for the past few months. And I almost miss that annoyance of intermittence.

Like my laptop, come-and-go MS symptoms—the ones many of us first experienced before being diagnosed—are some of the toughest to diagnose. The tech guy couldn't get the problem to happen while he played with the computer and I didn't really have the time (nor budget) for him to play around with it for the day.

So, I left with an external mouse to try to bypass what he suspected was a faulty sensor in the touch pad. You guessed it, as soon as I got home not only did the problem start again, but the fix didn't fix it either.

How many times have we left a doctor's office with this or that prescription, diagnosis, or even lack of diagnosis only to find that the patch was far from effective?

But that's just one stage of dealing with MS symptoms. When the intermittent symptoms become forever symptoms, they go from annoying to concerning.

Yes, we learn to live with them as part of the constant background noise of our disease, but as an open window is first covered with a screen, then a curtain, then the window closes, we eventually realize that it's also been locked. I'll miss the breeze coming in that window.

An old, dear man used to say, "Better bad breath than no breath," and he wasn't wrong. Weakness that makes me fall now and again (and again, and again) is better than the total loss of those legs. Not knowing if I'll wake with burning, neurogenic pain down my leg or if that pain will go away if I do wake with it isn't pleasant. That pain being my constant companion is even less so.

A pesky dark or cloudy spot in the field of vision is a pain in the arse. When that eye is lost to optic neuritis for good, we lose a level of independence.

MS symptoms come, and MS symptoms go . . . but sometimes they come and they stay. And that's when I found myself longing for the good old days of when they went away . . . even if only for a little while.

A War of Attrition
01/21/2019 Kerry, Ireland

I guess it's worth stating that it's this type of writing gets me in trouble with a slice of the social media pie.

"You've given up." "That's not how *I* think you should live." "Why are you so negative?" And the inevitable "I'm unfollowing you" comments come rolling in my way.

The thing is I have far from given up and pragmatism works for me . . .

Living with, and therefore fighting the good fight against, secondary progressive multiple sclerosis (SPMS) is a whole different thing than other forms of the disease. SPMS isn't the hot-zone we see being waged against relapsing forms of the disease with their new weapons and popular understanding of exactly what the enemy looks like.

Neither are we in a cold war with primary progressive MS (PPMS). This is the fight without the fighting. Without treatments, people living with PPMS tell tales of fear but also with getting on with life under the constant threat of major destruction. It's the chronic illness version of living with Stop-Drop-& Cover drills.

No, the battles with SPMS are a war of attrition sort of messy evolution.

It's trench warfare with small shifts in the battle lines. Its digging and backfilling with tablespoons and crawling along on our elbows while live rounds whiz above our heads.

The bullets they use against RRMS don't always work against the SP foe. Our battle is hand-to-hand, knife in the guts stuff.

Bombs aren't lobbed at us in the form of relapses, exacerbations, and full-frontal assaults. No, ours is more The Somme than The Ardennes. We don't fear the landmines any longer, ours is a slog with Trench-foot through barbed wire and punji sticks.

The mud is caked to our uniforms, the water leaks into our boots and the tedium of life on the Front wears down our spirit.

In many ways, we know that an all-out victory is unlikely. We know that much of the fighting we do is for the benefit of the next wave of troops more than it is for our ranks. If we can just hold our position, loose as little ground as possible, the new recruits may have a chance to not go across this battlefield.

Yup, pretty negative stuff.

But, like they who shall not grow old, the bonds that we have, those who know the difficulties (and victories) of living with SPMS, are strong and they are life-long.

If the people with MS belong to the best club you never wanted to join, then the battalions of us living with SPMS are the elite fighters—the Special Forces—of the MS army. We know the secret handshake. We can look across the crowded room and know the face of a fellow veteran.

In many ways, this is the battle that no one wants to talk about. It's the one the Generals know is being fought, but it's not the sexy one with victories that can be touted to sell war bonds. It is the fight for which we'd been preparing without ever knowing why. It is a quagmire and the only way out is forward.

And so we go . . . forward, together. Bit by bit, side by side, one day at a time, one step at a time, one inch at a time . . . It isn't a pretty fight. It brings to mind lines of one of my favorite Shakespeare soliloquies, from *Henry V*:

But we in it shall be rememberèd—
We few, we happy few, we band of brothers;
For he to-day that sheds his blood with me
Shall be my brother; be he ne'er so vile,
This day shall gentle his condition;
And gentlemen in England now a-bed
Shall think themselves accurs'd they were not here,
And hold their manhoods cheap whiles any speaks
That fought with us upon Saint Crispin's day.

I've Got The Mumbles
07/02/2019 Limerick, Ireland

"Marley was dead, to begin with."

That has to be one of the best opening lines of exposition in all English literature. First, it grabs us. More importantly, however, is the informing of this hard fact. "There is no doubt whatever about that." It sets the stage for the extraordinary sequence of events that follow throughout the whole story in *A Christmas Carol*.

Dickens goes on a few paragraphs later to state, "This must be distinctly understood, or nothing wonderful can come of the story I am going to relate."

Caryn's hearing is just fine. Caryn is my wife and I could go on to say that she has no auditory issues at all, and that she gets on with hearing the world just fine, thank you. I say so because, like Marley's being dead, this too must be distinctly understood . . .

I have found myself having to repeat my statements to Caryn more often than I ever remember. One might put that off to a couple who have been together over a dozen years, are often in other rooms, or are busy doing with so much going on in our lives.

One might, but none of those is the case. It often happens when we are mere feet from one another and in the middle of a conversation. It doesn't just happen with Caryn. I find I'm being asked by others to repeat myself on more regular occasions.

I'm beginning to mumble.

I don't think I'm yet Dustin Hoffman's character in *Dick Tracy*. Perhaps it's more of a slurring of words and a bit of breath weakness. I'm not really sure because, in my head I'm saying the words perfectly clear . . . most of the time. I do catch myself feeling like my jaw isn't keeping up with my tongue and larynx. It sounds like what bad lip-syncing looks like.

It has been my long-held fear of MS that my ability to speak and verbally communicate would be compromised by MS. Some people might think it's a trite fear when there are so many symptoms that MS has and could visit upon me. But to me the ability to get my point across is of great consequence and concern.

We joke about it, Caryn and I (and the publican, the postman, the greengrocer, etc.) We write it off to a mishmash of accents colliding or to the declining hearing of my partner in conversation. But at the end of the day, it's something I'm going to have to work on.

Many of the same muscles and nerves used to speak are involved in swallowing (with which I've had some frightening difficulties in the past). It might be one thing to take a punch to my vanity in having to repeat my statement. Dysphagia, however, is not something to be taken quite so lightly.

The joys of MS. The disease that keeps on giving . . . or should that be taking?

A Good Night's Sleep
10/01/2019 Kerry, Ireland

One of the great conundrums of living with multiple sclerosis is not getting a good night's sleep. Yet, one of the most common symptoms of the disease is fatigue. There are often parts of the day (or entire days) when we can hardly move for the weight of the disease but, come the night, our sleep is disturbed, interrupted for a variety of reasons.

These might not be all of the reasons we might experience poor sleep with MS, but they're the ones I've unfortunately known.

NEUROPLASTICITY—THE GOOD AND THE BAD:

Firstly, there is a very positive reason why we might not be getting sleep. It's not positive that we lie awake for hours on end, but it's a good thing happening in our central nervous systems.

The brain is surprisingly good at finding new pathways around damage. At least for a while, but that's for another discussion. It's known as neuroplasticity.

The unconscious energy it takes to find new pathways to get the signal from its origin, through the mess of a maze that MS leave in our white matter, must stimulate us in some way. We are, of course, very happy that the messages—in the form of electrical impulses—might make their eventual way to the intended muscles. That they keep us awake is why many of us are prescribed sleep aids during times of disease activity.

PAIN:

Not much exhausts the body like constant pain. And MS pain is a particularly painful pain in SO many ways.

You might finally get through a day (or part of a day) and put your feet up and close your eyes to take some rest, only to be kept awake by neuropathic pain or other painful sensations related to MS symptoms.

RESTLESS LEGS:

For many people in the USA who have become used to seeing prescription drug adverts on television, the idea of Restless Leg Syndrome sounded like a manufactured malady for which big pharma was trying to peddle placation in pill-form

RLS is real and for people with MS, especially odd as limbs that don't like to respond to intended movement impulses, seem to take it upon themselves to jump and kick us awake, just when we seem to have drifted off.

FREQUENT URINATION:

If restless legs sound like a pain for sleeping, try a bladder that can't seem to remember that it's already been emptied. Five minutes ago!

Up and down to pee more than twice in a night and you've really mucked-up any chance for a quality, restful sleep. It's such an issue that people with MS practice a level of dehydration in order to get good uninterrupted sleep.

OVER-NAPPING:

Many people with MS have perfected the practice of an afternoon nap. It is important, however, not to sleep too much. Getting into REM sleep during an afternoon rest can set one's sleep patterns all askew and lead to poor sleep during the night.

ANXIETY/DEPRESSION:

While these two states of mental health are separate, they can also be linked. Often the anxieties of living with a chronic disease have to do with self-worth, employment, finances, relationships. I'm not sure why I started a list of what can make a person with MS anxious. That list could be FAR too long.

The same goes for depression, which many think of as a condition that will result in too much sleep. But depression can also create a state of being where sleep can be difficult.

As I said, these aren't the only MS-related concerns that can affect sleep. For all of them there are medications that may help. All can also be aided by non-drug practices. From meditation and mindfulness, to sleep hygiene and dietary changes, there are things you can do to improve the quality of your sleep.

I'm sure there is more to write on the topic, but I had a really crappy night's sleep last night and all I want is a snooze . . .

Independent Reconfirmation
12/12/2019 Kerry, Ireland

Many of us know the occasional (or regular) reopening of our grieving wounds when a new MS symptom, or the reoccurrence of an old one, brings us up short. We step right back on to the first rung of the Kübler-Ross ladder and relive the difficulties nearly as vividly as we did that first time we heard the words "You have Multiple Sclerosis."

For me, as my MS has moved into a more progressive phase, I don't have many of those major attack moments any longer. My systematic shocks come more from finding that I can no longer do something today that I was able to a few weeks or months before. From comparing my today with my yesterdays, to the feeling that the rest of the world is outpacing me and my disease.

In general, I try not to dwell on the gradients of loss.

When I went to a new physiotherapist to be fitted for long-overdue orthotic insole replacements, however, I did get pulled up short by the medical professional who'd never seen me before.

She was very good at her work and professional in every way. I look forward to working with her in the future. She met me at my level of knowledge and language. Didn't talk down to me nor over my head. She's the kind of player I am happy to add to my lifetime MS healthcare team.

But when she explained her observations of my muscle tone, levels of weakness, comorbid effects of my MS, and laid out our plan, I took it harder than I'd expected to.

Not unlike getting a letter from a disability insurance company or from Social Security confirming that we ARE actually disabled, having her play show-and-tell with what MS has done to my lower extremities socked me right in the gut.

She showed me how some muscles had atrophied while others were over-developed due to compensation. I was made aware of my adjustments that had become normal to the point of not noticing them. We talked of strategies to help maintain my loss of functions where they are rather than ways to regain because that's just not possible for some of my deficits any longer.

It was a difficult hour and a half journey home.

I'd thought I was doing pretty well, all things considered. I suppose that the truth is that I am doing pretty well. I'm just not as good as I thought I was. I'm good at masking. I'm good at compensating. Apparently, I'm also pretty good at ignoring (or at least overlooking) some of my body's shortcomings.

I suppose it's much better than always dwelling on what MS has taken from me this time. It was still an unpleasant jolt to have an expert in the human body highlight MS's grip on my body and point out the indelible marks that it has wrought on me over the years.

Eyes on the Horizon
06/18/2020 Kerry, Ireland

Seven years ago, and some eight years on from first collecting her, I brought my dog, Sadie back to her breeder to help me select a new puppy. She was going to have to live with the new addition as much (if not more) than my wife, Caryn, and I would, so we figured it best to afford her the opportunity to register an opinion on the choice.

We all laughed at how, after greeting the dam and getting to know her, Sadie raised her head and didn't even acknowledge the puppies that were now running around her like a swarm on a hive.

She was acting as if they weren't really there, as if she couldn't see them. This is a coping mechanism many with MS will be familiar with.

It reminded me of an old sailors' trick I'd learned as a ships' navigator in the US Coast Guard to avoid (if not always evade) becoming seasick. To avoid the rocking and rolling sensation of the ship beneath your feet; keep your eyes on the horizon.

Levelling our gaze over the affray of roiling/rolling sea to the clean line of the horizon is a way to get on with the tasks required of us. It's a way of tricking the mind to convince it that our world isn't in the uneven state of fluctuation. It is this horizon line that helps me focus on the tasks I need to focus on while on the stormy MS sea.

This isn't the only sea-going analogy I've found for living with MS. I often tell people that the reason I'm fatigued beyond expression is that, like being out standing on a boat all day, my body has been constantly working to keep me upright every moment of every minute.

Many people can relate to the feeling of exhaustion after a day on a boat.

As one who has painted the waves with his breakfast, I can tell you that keeping an eye above it all will not always work. Just as a change in wind or wave can send even the most experienced sailor to the rail, my MS and its wont to sneak up and shift the deck beneath me. It can, and often does, bring me up short. But focusing on the bigger picture—the relative calm in the distance—I have found that I weather the stormy days far better than when I allow my concentration to be taken by MS.

Sometimes, no matter how well I think I'm managing a particular rough patch of MS, the waves still break over the bow, soak me to the skin and threaten to toss me overboard completely. And, like Sadie trying to avoid the rush of clumsy puppies, I have learned to live with most of the annoyances that have come home with me, no matter how hard I've tried to avoid them.

And, too, like Sadie I have learned to growl at them a little less.

The Semantics of Care
02/12/2021 Kerry, Ireland

"When the fall is all that is left, it matters very much." So says Prince Richard in the play *The Lion in Winter*. It's an oft misquoted line to do with how we handle ourselves in the darkest of times.

While the semantics of what we call those who help us get on with our best lives possible may not seem like one of those times that Prince Richard's sentiment would be apt, for many living with MS—that's those of us with multiple sclerosis and those close to us—what they are called means very much, indeed.

November is National Caregivers' Month in America. But is 'Caregiver' really the right term anymore?

I mean, for one, if I have a caregiver (and there are many in my life who offer me care), should I not then be the care*taker*?

By definition a care<u>giver</u> and a care<u>taker</u> can be the same thing, but they are not the same person. If even the English dictionaries have ambiguities like this, how are we, those needing care, let alone the general public, supposed to understand or communicate the subtleties of this delicate topic?

When I consider those many people in my life who afford me care, I mean it in the broadest sense of what MS care means to me. The man who mows the lawn, the woman who cleans the house, the butcher who will deliver if I need, the neighbor who calls in for tea if I'm not seen out of the house for a few days . . . these are all people who offer me care in relation to my disease and its ever-changing needs. But are they my caregivers?

My wife, Caryn, above all is there to offer up care. From my household chores she may need to take on from time to time, to the tasks which are simply no longer possible for me, she is surely a caregiver/caretaker. But she is so much more than that. So, frankly, am I.

The term used more here in Ireland and in the UK for a person who cares is "Carer." Like horse riding rather than horseback riding (because where else would you ride on a horse), this more succinct term feels a bit closer but is still clinical and one-sided.

And maybe that's where I take umbrage. All of these care terms, -giver, -taker, -er, they all imply that one party offers and the other receives; that we are merely recipients.

I feel like I am a participant in the care process. Along with those who help me, I co-manage the level of assistance I might require from one day (and sometimes hour) to the next. This care goes beyond healthcare delivery.

How is it that the accountant I use to do my taxes (because mathematics beyond the simplest equations is no longer possible) isn't considered a carer? Before MS I did my own taxes and now I don't because of the disease. How is that not care in the sense society uses? Surely many professions are used by those of us with health issues because and only because we have those issues.

I want to recognize all the people who offer care to me, but I want to do it without feeling like I am a burden to them or a drain on society. That's my gripe about care terms; they make me feel needy and that's one thing I could do without feeling. We can require care without being caretaken. We can need without being needy.

We receive care from many people. In the care we receive, I like to think that I am an active participant in deciding the level of assistance. Like determining if it's a day for a cane or a forearm crutch, the level of help required changes and, if that help comes from others, we have a responsibility in that care as well.

The term I like to use is Care Partner. The partnership isn't always a 50/50 split. If I'm being honest with myself, it's hardly even 60/40 on most days but I do carry a share of the load . . . even if it's not my fair share.

A partnership also implies an agreement. I agree to pay people to help where appropriate and to simply accept the help and say "Thank you" when it's offered when payment would be insensitive. I agree to ask a little help before it goes to requiring a great deal of support. We can agree to a watchful eye if we're given a little slack in order to try things for ourselves without judgement.

So, others acknowledge Caregivers month in November, and so will I. I'll just thank those who help me without labeling them as anything other than my partners.

Affirmation, Confirmation, Kerplunk
21/05/2021 Kerry, Ireland

I've heard it said, and many anecdotes along the same line, that a person working in the like of say, a chocolate factory, doesn't smell the wonders of Willy Wonka as they go about their daily business. For those of you who have never been to such a confectioners, I must tell you that the heady curtain of complex phenolics (scents) that envelop a visitor is the gentlest of velvet waterfalls. How could someone spending hours on end enrobed in such wonderful sensation not notice??

Scent processing is a very old part of the brain and one very closely related to memory. It's why a dog will remember where it has buried its bone and why a particular smell will send us straight back in time to a place or person with which the smell has a strong connection. Scent is also everywhere . . . EVERYWHERE! If the brain didn't filter it out at some point, we'd be overwhelmed by the experience.

Once our higher brain has remembered, identified, classified, and verified as safe our surroundings by the way they smell, it moves on to the next thing and we sort of stop smelling whatever it is. This goes for bad smells too, but not as much because the brain is trying to tell us that we won't want to hang around for safety or sanity.

The same, it seems, is the case with many of my MS symptoms.

At a recent physiotherapist appointment for what I thought of as a tangential MS symptom, the way multiple sclerosis causes me to walk has really mucked up my feet, I was met with the 'smells' of this disease that my brain has turned down so I can get on with my life.

She was pointing out in my feet, ankles, toes, calf muscles and how my drop-foot, reduced sensation, weakness, and my compensation for them was causing knock-on effects on my gait, muscle mass, and bone/tendon alignments. What a blast!

She took out skeletal models and showed me how my feet were working (or not) and how the adaptations I'd been making subconsciously put pressure on places it wasn't supposed to and how the issues with my feet had a cascade of responses all the way up my legs to my hips and back. Everything she pointed out in a physical manifestation on my body I could relate to an MS symptom or the results of said symptoms. She said X is happening because your foot As, Bs, and Cs. And she was spot on in every observation.

But I'd forgotten about what MS was doing down there.

Not forgetting as in denying that it was happening. I forgot in the way our chocolatier, in order to get on with the day's job, assimilates to her workplace's decadent scent of cocoa. Perhaps it's more like a tabby in a field of catnip trying to focus on a shrew it's eyed for lunch; my avoidance of the symptoms has more to do with survival than making truffles.

We have become adept at living in spite of, alongside, and in stride (albeit a wonky stride) with the disease that takes away our abilities (ironically, the sense of smell being one which can be directly affected as well).

We drove away from the appointment with a prescription for new orthotics for my shoes, stretches for my legs and back, and the reminder that while I might not pay my full attention to some of the symptoms of my MS, they are there and they are having detrimental effect on my body beyond the symptoms themselves.

And I also had a craving for chocolate.

Restricted in Ability to Maneuver
06/16/2021 Kerry, Ireland

My Wheaten Terrier, Maggie, and I were out for our most-mornings stroll down to the harbor. We try to get four laps of the park at the end of the breakwater at least four days of the week. One day we (alright, I) rest the limbs and the others we do what we can to get in or near the sea for our exercise.

Taking our daily constitutional where the elements of air, water, and earth come together is both physically, intellectually, and somehow spiritually invigorating. It is equally relaxing, and restorative. The weather and my MS make our intent and reality columns out of balance, but we'll not tell the accountants!

On this particular morning, when the meteorological outcome of the day was far from sure, we chanced our arm and donned multi-weather gear for our walk.

There was an official looking vessel moored down the piers which hadn't been there two days before (rain moved our rest day up by one). As a former US Coastguard, I guess I still have something of a sailor's eye when it comes to something being different in my home port. Anyway, this small ship was not only 50% larger than any other vessel at the quays, but also flying an international Signal Code flag on the starboard outboard halyard (an appropriate place for such things when sending a signal).

It's been a long—LONG—time since my navigator's days when I could recall each of the flags and their meaning at a glance and form a response without even thinking twice. There are some, however, that you just never forget.

The red-yellow diagonals of the Oscar flag mean "I have a man overboard." You don't forget that one. Nor the solid red of Bravo—"I am taking on fuel/have a dangerous cargo," Solid yellow—Quebec—"I am in quarantine" or the red X on a white field that is Victor and says, "I require assistance." On this ship the blue and white with blue dovetail Alpha flag flying in the breeze was to inform everyone to stay at distance because, "I have a diver down." I remembered that one.

You'll note the personal nature of the flags' communications. They are first-person comments from one ship to another. They are succinct, they are prominently displayed, and they are internationally recognized no matter one's native tongue.

Ships also use red and white lights (at night) and large, black day-shapes (rather obviously in the day) to send signals when out of range for flag patterns to be made out. One day-shape we used to use regularly on my first ship, a buoy tender, was a Ball-over Diamond-over Ball, "I am restricted in my ability to maneuver." When you're working on aids to navigation at the edge of channels etc. you can imagine that we couldn't really get out of anyone's way . . .

And there we are, back at my life with MS.

My walking stick/cane is something of an international signal—a day-shape if you will—to the world that I am restricted in my ability to maneuver. It's a first-person announcement that I might not be able to get out of your way, so don't get in mine. I have spoken with many in the MS community who, even on the days when MS isn't at its worst, take some form of day-shapes with them into crowds for just that reason.

They just didn't know that there was a nautical twin to their signal. If only everyone on land knew what these flags, day-shapes, and lights we exhibit meant, ours would be an easier track-line to follow.

It also wasn't lost on me that the crew of that ship at the pier had forgotten to take in their Alpha flag. There was, obviously, no diver down pier side. And I smiled at the thought of how many times I've seen disabled parking placards hanging from the rearview mirror of cars driving on the motorway, obviously NOT parked.

The Gap Year(s)
08/30/2021 Kerry, Ireland

My wife, Caryn, and I recently acknowledged the anniversary of our meeting. It was at a self-planned, roundy-numbered birthday party. Hers was a fortuitous invitation to the gathering by a neighbor of mine who was a friend and colleague to Caryn. She almost didn't come to the party. I'm so very glad she did.

Of the many things we have discovered about each other, and our relationship, is since my last high school girlfriend, Caryn is the only woman I've dated that was my own age (usually my dates/relationships were with women several years my senior, save for a few occasions). While this may not seem significant, our cultural references come from the same time in our lives.

Now, it must be admitted that our experiences during those times in our lives, hers in Southern California while mine were based in western Michigan, were not the same. We were through the looking glass for a number of events in our lives, but on the same rung on the ladder of life.

There are, however, gaps in my cultural references due to long deployments in the Bering Sea and its treacherous surrounds during my early 20s as a US Coast Guard Navigator. You tend to miss a few Top-40 tunes, television events, and film releases when you're billeted to a ship stationed at an island off the Alaska Peninsula. It's not the end of the earth, but you can see it!

Now and again a tune will come on or a reference to something that occurred during that time and it's just not there for me. It's a bit of comfort to know that there is a reason behind the gap that isn't MS-related.

But . . .

There are other gaps in my cultural reference, one I suspect I share with those reading this page. Not MS cognitive gaps because they usually come and last in short spurts. There is a gap, not a total black hole as I remember much of what was going on internally, from the first few months of 2001 though the end of 2005. Those were the years I call my MS Gap Years.

Like a break before starting college when some in my generation took to backpack around Europe, not reading any news from home while working for a charity in a developing country for a year between graduation and graduate school, or, in my case, spending a couple of years bobbing around in the 60+ foot rolling waves you've seen on *The Deadliest Catch*. I just didn't have the mental bandwidth to register much about what was going on in the world for those 5 years.

It's the time that I often refer to as "Getting my head around MS." As I have shared, those years were a free-fall in many ways. They were a pin-ball machine in others, as I bumped and banged my way to the flippers which eventually put me back on course.

I did damage on that descent, to myself, to others, to relationships, to just about everything off which I ricocheted on my way down. Those things I remember (though probably not as vividly as I responsibly should).

It was a selfish time if I were to look at it coldly. Giving myself a bit of slack, however, it was also a period of self-preservation and grasping for sovereignty of anything over which I still had the illusion of control. I am not proud of how I fell. I'm better now than I was then, and I'll try to be even better tomorrow.

Atonement is a daily exercise.

For the swag bags attendees of that birthday party 15 years ago, my sister compiled the Top 40 of the Last 40. Each person got a 3-CD set of the #1 song on my birthday up until that year. I feel like I could use a primer to refresh and (re)introduce me to the songs, films, and major events of that half decade of my MS Gap Years.

The Evil Magician
09/08/2021 Kerry, Ireland

Abracadabra, hocus-pocus, now you feel it—now you don't!

I was standing at the drinks' cabinet the last evening. Into a favorite Italian glass (with a line at the halfway mark, above which is etched the word Ottimista and below Pessimista) I'd just put three dashes of bitters (it was a night for a Pink Gin) when, Presto-Chango, the glass was 8-feet away from me, on the floor, and in dozens of pieces.

What magic is this?

Between reduced strength, fine motor impairment, and tremor of intent thrown in for good measure, the glass had, faster than the eye can see, slipped, slid, tipped, and been batted across the room before my mouth could even form the beginnings of an expletive.

It's not the first time one object or another has slipped or flipped from my grasp. I have to say, though, this one had style.

After the sweeping and swabbing to clean up the sticky shards I decided to forego another attempt. By the time the broken glass was in the broken glass bin (a requirement for every MS household) I was laughing at the absurdity of it all.

The MS Magician had stuck again.

But this conjurer is not of the children's birthday party top hat variety or the Las Vegas illusionist ilk. The MS Magician is more of the, "And I would have got away with it if it hadn't been for you pesky kids . . ." sort of Saturday morning cartoons of my youth evil magician.

He hides things in plain sight and makes words disappear from the tip of my tongue. While I'm focused on my hands, he swipes the floor from beneath my feet. Some days it even feels like he's put me in some sort of a trance. I could really do without that Cog-Fog trick of his.

With the deftness of a Hollywood B-Movie voodoo practitioner, he sticks pins in me from afar. Showing me he's got nothing up his sleeves, he plucks away one ability of mine or another like a street performer snatching someone's watch. With a wave of this evil wand, I find myself levitating above my body, miss-seeing it as the broken shell that he has transformed it into.

Sometimes this magic makes me laugh.

It's more the nervous titter of an audience volunteer plucked from his seat and not knowing what's next to come most of the time. There are times, however, that I simply roar at the absurdity of the 'trick' and have to give credit when even I am surprised by the legerdemain.

And we'll not even begin to think of how many 'potions' I've had to endure at the hands of the MS Magician . . .

I wish there was some way to turn this metaphor around to close this post. I really do. The fact is that it's not magic that MS performs on my body. It's no illusion. I suppose the only counter to this dark sorcery is to focus on the light. To know that MS only has powers over my physical (okay, and sometimes my intellectual) self. It can only toy with my sense of self and the real person inside this broken shell if I hand it over.

My job is to make sure his spells never reach that far.

An Open Letter From One Man Living with Multiple Sclerosis
11/06/2021 Kerry, Ireland

To whom it may concern,

I'm the guy you saw today. I'm part of a group of individuals you saw today. I am part of the community of people you saw today. We're the ones you had a fleeting thought about. I didn't see your eyes on me, nor did I read your mind, but I know you were looking. We know you were thinking . . .

You see, we feel much of what you were thinking about us. That's how we know.

"He walks (talks, moves, eats . . .) funny." "Didn't I see her last week out and about and now she's using a walker?" "I thought he was sick?" "What's she doing using the disabled parking bay?" "He's awfully young to be retired." "Must be faking it . . ." We've thought and felt many of those same things as we tried to get on with our lives while strapped with the heavy pack of our disease weighing down our physical, intellectual, and emotional selves.

For the most part, we've overcome those feelings of self-doubt, lack of worth, posing, and trying to be 'normal' and live up to your standards of societal responsibility. We've worked hard just to get to the point where we *can* walk funny, drive ourselves to that parking space, and be a small part of the workings of the world around us.

I sometimes feel myself a burden on my family and the society around me. We push ourselves to live up to our former expectations of ourselves, so we really don't need (nor appreciate) you throwing your expectations and assumptions in our path.

When we are laid low by our disease, it's not because of a lack of will, a detriment in personal fortitude, or our desire for attention. We aren't battling, we're getting on with. We aren't Sufferers, though we do suffer. We are fearful of what tomorrow will bring, but don't want to be the focus of your fear that you might 'end up' like us.

That look or thought you had at/about us today was yours and we didn't react, but we knew it was happening.

There may have been pity in it, there may have been compassion. There may have been fear, there may have been understanding. I don't always know what you're thinking when I catch *that* look, but I know that you'd probably not like to share what the thought was, were I to ask.

Don't get me wrong, we do the same thing. But those of who are on the other end of those looks, we tend to think differently about those we see.

"I wonder if they have the same thing I do?" "I wonder if he needs help?" "Good on her for giving it a go!"

You see we've spent so much time rooting for ourselves and our individual community to succeed (often times without much in the way of external cheerleading), that when I see someone else getting out and getting on, I see me. We see Us. Not in the "Oh, I hope I don't get that bad" or "I hope she doesn't get worse" way, but rather, with a sense of appreciation and understanding as a person who is, in a way, that person.

Ours is a knowing glance, a tip of the cap, a nod and a wink intended as encouragement from a fellow traveler who is in on the joke.

When you look at us, we know. Exactly what you are thinking, we don't . . . but we know you are. Please be a little kinder when you do, because we're really trying to be kind to ourselves and it's something that has been a long, hard lesson to learn for many of us.

By the way, sometimes it does get 'that bad' . . . and it's not as bad as you think.

Thanks for your time.

Black and Blue
12/14/2018 Chicago, USA

There are many reasons that people living with multiple sclerosis know about being black & blue. We bruise when we fall, run into furniture, bump into walls, and sometimes we don't even KNOW what caused the shades of discoloration on our bodies.

But there is another kind of black and a different blue that has been helpful to me in living with MS. It's something I had a chat about recently with a group of Gold Circle Sponsors for the National MS Society. They are the Black humor and Blue language.

Many will know of my adage about laughing and MS: If I didn't laugh, I'd cry . . . and I've cried enough over multiple sclerosis.

If I weren't to make a joke from my prone position or flat-out on the floor, there would be an uncomfortable pause in a crowd of friends. If I can laugh about it, however, others will laugh with me rather than feeling sorry for me.

All of the donors at the event had some important connection to MS. Still, my brash (and, perhaps, borderline inappropriate) comments caught a few people off guard.

Hey, it works for me to be irreverent about MS. It helps me cope to have a go at the disease that is taking from me. My brand of getting on with life with multiple sclerosis isn't for everyone, but it works for me . . . most of the time.

What I did rein in on that night was my blue language.

Now I'm going to excuse my use of the more colorful phrases! Perhaps it's because I love the English language—the nuances, the adjectives, and the ability for some phrases to completely shatter barriers. Maybe it's my status as a retired sailor! Add to those formative years my current environment in the land of effing and blinding (in two languages!) has something to do with it. Hand-to-God, I heard the local parish priest once say as I was passing on my bicycle, "For feck's sake, Jerry. Can Your Man not keep his head out of his arse for two minutes on end?"

Whatever the reason, I love to swear.

My wife, Caryn, tells me that when I'm having a particularly bad night of it, I'm known to curse in my sleep in a manner which would make a Barbary Coast privateer wince. In the hallowed early hours of morn my first utterances on my feet touching the floor are often from the more colorful end of the linguistic spectrum.

I'd say that I try to keep my adult language for appropriate times and places, but the truth is, I probably spend my time in the company of those who understand or just don't give a damn.

We all have our own MS demons. We all cope differently. For me, MS has made me black and blue over and over and over again. I think it is only fitting that my responses are of the same palette.

Enough Is Plenty
02/06/2020 Kerry, Ireland

There are two colloquialisms that struck me as deeply meaningful when we moved to this little town on the edge of the beyond. The first made particular sense the first winter we were sans automobile, sans bicycles and sans our belongings (still making their way from America).

"We haven't died a winter yet."

Staunchly standing in the face of difficulties—be they climatic challenges, comestible deficits, or cultural adversities—the people 'back west' are keen to point out their fortitude . . . up to the current point in life, at least.

"Haven't died a winter yet" has become a general commentary about getting on with life in the face of whatever obstacles present.

It's the second which took me a little longer to apply to life, but it has become part of my MS mantra of late. Also, in recent times, much of the world has been forced to embrace the concept of settling as well.

"Enough is plenty" is how the saying goes.

In my life with the diagnosis of multiple sclerosis (which just recently hit the 19-year mark) learning to settle has been a constant lesson. Be it living on a lower income, adjusting to ever-changing physical limitations, wall-walking my way through Cog Fog, or any of the myriad of fences this stupid disease has installed on my life, I have come to accept that the best I can do is going to have to be good enough.

For several weeks people living in states of quarantine were forced to live without, to live with less, live in an uncomfortableness in order to try to stay alive and simply live. That was their little peek into the window of our lives. We do our best to turn cannot into sorta can, can kinda, can sometimes . . . and we've come to accept that if it's enough, it just might be plenty.

Not plenty in the typical sense of abundance and bounty. Plenty as in half a loaf is better than no bread at all (another saying taught to me by our local butcher). Not the plenty that others are not happy with even though it's much more than I can achieve.

A lot of people out there are talking about what they hope people remember from the early COVID-19 months and years. They say the sense of community, the way people took care, the time they were able (all be it forced) to spend with those closest to them and the appreciation of the little niceties, the nuances of life. My hope is that people remember that they can not only get by, but really enjoy life within limitations and without everything they thought once required for happiness.

Good enough is, by definition, good.

Life with MS in the wilds of West Kerry have taught me that enough is plenty and that's no small blessing, because it can be a lot of work just to scrape together 'enough'.

CHAPTER 7

The Unspeakable Bits

*I*N 2011, I WAS ASKED TO CONSIDER WRITING *for the National MS Society's MS Connections Blog. Wanting to be of use but having no desire to simply write content interchangeable with the platforms where I already registered my thoughts, I begged the indulgence of writing about the things that no one else seemed to be writing, the things that worried me and about which I had difficulty finding accurate information.*

I figured that if I wanted to know more about these seemingly 'unspeakable' parts of living with MS and was having a tough time in searching out credible answers, so must others. I wrote about these topics before and after the MS Society assignment. These topics are not printed in the order in which I wrote them, rather in sequence that made sense to Emma and I as we looked at our own MS journeys.

I never enjoyed the research or the writing. I was overwhelmed—and still am to this day—by the comments and e-mailed responses that these pieces evoked.

You may not be in a place where you want to know more about the topics in this chapter. They are the Boogie Men of multiple sclerosis. If you'd rather not look under the bed just yet, know that the information you may want to have later is here for you . . . when you are ready.

My Dirty MS Secret
09/21/2017 Sligo, Ireland

So, a fat guy with multiple sclerosis walks into a pub . . .

As one does when in a local pub for a pint or two, I had to visit the loo. In I walked, made room for the next pint, and then washed my hands. While at the sink, my cane fell to the floor. I picked it up and proceeded to the hand dryer when I realized where that cane handle had just been. On the floor of a men's toilet.

Sure, I washed off the handle of the walking stick and went back to the bar, but it got me thinking; how dirty are the things that help us get around?

While it might not be the floor of a toilet, I have to think that our walking aids must harbor quite a few bacteria. Just for a lark, I took one of those pre-moistened alcohol pads that come with injectable meds and wiped one of my other canes. Let's just say the color of that swab made me think of writing this article.

Most of us wouldn't think of sitting down to a meal without washing our hands. Even in a restaurant or pub, we wash-up before eating. But then we grab the same handle that was out on the street with us, maybe fell to the floor of the car, slipped down from the booth onto the carpet and was stepped on by a hurried waitress, or maybe even worse.

What are we getting back on our hands every time we handle our assistive devices?

It might be even worse for those devices that have porous, padded handles. They might make it more comfortable on our hands, but they would also be more difficult to clean.

Perhaps I'm alone in the fact that I never thought about the sanitation of my sticks and crutches and walker. I hope not as that would make me feel pretty daft. But I have to admit that I hadn't thought about it at all, not until the fall to the floor of the men's bathroom.

As the cold and flu season approaches, I think we are all a little more conscious of hand washing and public hygiene. I'd have to wonder if we shouldn't think about minding our walking aids a bit more as well.

An interesting study might be made of cultures of what's living on the handles of the devices which help us get around in our worlds. I wonder, too, if this creates any elevated level of infection with common viruses and the like?

As our old pal, Rusty, might have said, "Things that make you go 'Hmmmm.'"

MS bladder issues
03/05/2007 Seattle, USA

March is here and you know what that means? Spring training is in full swing with just about a month until the only major team sport without a clock *and* St. Patrick's Day is less than a fortnight away. For this writer (coming off my annual alcohol-free month) they both mean good times and good beer!

That, of course, brings to mind the old saying that you really don't buy a beer, you just rent it for about a half hour. Unless, that is, you have MS.

Bladder issues are talked about covertly, if at all, even within the MS community. Well, if there's anything I like to do, it's getting things out into the open! So, let's look at the bladder issues.

My MS docs and nurses (including one of the few MS specializing urologists in this country), tell me that bladder dysfunction will occur in about 80% of people with MS. When we hear that "No person's MS is like another's," it appears they're not talking about fatigue or bladder dysfunction.

All bladder issues stem from one of two dysfunctions: failure to store or failure to empty. The former can be uncomfortable, embarrassing, and annoying while the latter can be deadly.

Frequency and urgency issues (including nocturia, frequent nighttime urination), can be controlled with a number of prescription drugs as well as diet, exercise and fluid management. Failure to empty, however, may require catheterizations (permanent or self-administered, intermittent).

Without treatment, urine can be left in a dysfunctional bladder causing infections and kidney damage. A dear friend with MS has nearly died, twice, from these infections, as she cannot feel the discomfort of them the way most people can. Catheterizations, in and of themselves can cause Urinary Tract Infections (UTIs) as well.

I have read that UTIs are the most common form of infection among people living with MS. They are the reason I always take my temperature when I'm feeling particularly MSy, as they usually manifest a fever.

Yes, bladder dysfunction can cause some serious, emotional distress when you think about discussing it with your doctors and or friends. It can cause serious, life-threatening problems if you don't.

MS Dysfunction of the Bowel
04/30/2012 Seattle, USA

The very idea that something might go wrong with our excretory system, a very private matter for most people, is so far beyond polite conversation that we may not even discuss it with our medical team.

Truly, MS bowel dysfunction is one of the Unspeakable Bits!

While symptoms causing problems of the bowel are not all that uncommon, severity beyond management seems to be rather rare in MS.

Not unlike MS symptoms of the bladder, bowel symptoms come, mostly, in two opposite forms: constipation (retention) and loss of control. Couple these with the always-possible loss of sensation and we might not even know we have to go nor feel the discomfort of constipation.

As I said, while symptoms of bowel dysfunction from MS are not particularly rare, the severity of the symptoms are usually relatively mild (and may predate diagnosis and have never been thought of as a symptom of MS at all).

Relatively simple (and healthy for the general population) bowel management strategies can be implemented by you and your MS medical team (if symptoms are intense enough, you may include a gastroenterologist). Steps like drinking enough water to stay properly hydrated, eating enough fiber in our diet and taking note of changes in regularity are also very helpful and have fewer side-effects than the prescription medications used to regulate bowel function.

One factor often overlooked which can both cause and exacerbate bowel issues can be the result of another MS symptom, lack of mobility.

The simple act of moving around helps our digestive system work better, work properly. If a person's mobility is affected by symptoms of MS it stands to reason that sitting in a chair or scooter for most of the day will have detrimental consequences to bowel health and function. A few, low intensity stretches each morning can help wake mind, body and bowel.

Shakespeare, in his monologue from *As You Like It*, states that "All the world's a stage . . ." and by the seventh and final age we have returned to childhood once again. While we don't think about it much, we somehow expect that adult diapers may play a part in our final act. We have a hard time, however, thinking that we may require this prop while still "seeking the bubble of reputation."

It is important, therefore, that we not risk our health for the sake of humility. Many bowel symptoms of MS can be easily attended to well before they become severe. Not talking to our docs about our concerns early (before they happen, even) and hiding behind the bathroom door seems rather childish and, let's face it, MS makes us wise beyond our years.

Sex
02/14/2012 Seattle, USA

If we're going to speak the unspeakable, we might as well jump in the deep end. I am going for it in terms of the Unspeakable Bits, talking about erectile dysfunction, vaginal dryness, bladder leakage, sexual positioning, inability to attain orgasm, sex and multiple sclerosis. How's that for speaking the unspeakable?

Sex is a natural, important and, let's face it, <u>fun</u> part of human existence. We think about it, we save ourselves for it, we abstain from it, we revel in it and we embroil ourselves in discussions of its 'proper' place in our society. Sex lives in a unique place in culture as we struggle with the animal nature of the act and the purely human aspects of its affection. Sex is natural, wholesome and a part of a healthy, adult life.

But, like other parts of our healthy life, multiple sclerosis can and does take its toll on our sex lives.

There is an excellent primer on various forms of sexual dysfunction caused by MS and its symptoms. Those dysfunctions include, but are not limited to:

1. Loss of Libido
2. Reduced sensation (or painful, heightened sensation)
3. Numbness
4. Difficulty achieving/maintaining erection (for men)
5. Vaginal dryness (in women)
6. Difficulty achieving orgasm/ejaculation

Feeling like we're speaking the unspeakable yet?

How about some of the other symptoms of MS which can wreak havoc on the ancillaries to a healthy sex life?

"I'm just too tired to_____" can be a regular part of the day for people living with MS. "I'm just too tired to make love" isn't a stretch at all. So, fatigue can lead to sexual dysfunction.

Pain (Yes, doctor. Pain can be a symptom of MS), spasticity, rigidity, vertigo all of these can keep the flames of passion snuffed. Loss of use of limbs (both legs and arms) can be a significant barrier to sex for both the person living with MS and for our sexual partners (and more on them in a moment).

I'm tempted to add something of a societal symptom to our list of sexual barriers. That would be the barriers around speaking openly about sex. For many people living with MS the idea of trying alternative sexual positions, bringing toys into the bedroom (let alone ordering/purchasing such things!) and discussing our sex lives with our medical teams are lines not easily crossed!

Right alongside those societal symptoms would have to be our partners' reactions to us and our MS.

Time and time again I hear from people whose spouses have gone from lover to care partner to care-giver. It cannot be stressed enough how important it is to hold on to the parts of our relationships that are not MS. For the partners who do most of the care giving, respite care can be an important element in keeping a loving relationship from sliding into a patient and aide relationship

Each partner must understand the difficulties the other may be experiencing in their half of a life with MS. How we see ourselves and how our partners see us as sexual beings can easily be altered by MS if we allow it to happen. Like any part of a good, working relationship, we may have to consider our limitations in dealing with sex and MS. *Before* our relationships begin to suffer, we may want to seek professional counseling to help us deal with these very intimate issues.

Of special embarrassment can be issues of bladder leakage, painful urine retention, constipation, and incontinence as they relate to sex and MS.

If MS makes it difficult to walk, we get a cane, or crutches or a scooter, we do not give up on mobility completely. Why then would we think that some difficulties in the bedroom somehow make us asexual beings?

As multiple sclerosis is nothing if not cruel, on very rare occasions MS can cause hypersexual behaviors and sensations too!

As an act of disclosure and to show that I'm genuinely trying to open the door to this conversation, I have some sexual dysfunction caused by MS. If I'm to believe my urologist, I've more 'issues' to look forward to, due to current levels of damage, and let's just say they're not the "hypersexual behaviors and sensations."

There, we've done it. We opened the bedroom door to how MS affects the goings on in the boudoir.

What are your MS and sex issues? Do you talk about them with your partner? Do you talk about them with your medical team? Do you hide from them? Do you fear them?

Damaged Goods
12/19/2012 Clare, Ireland

The approaching holidays can be a bright and wonderful time of the year. It can also lead to some tough times for people living with MS. While friends and family gather to bask in the warmth of the season, we can sometimes feel less-than.

No one would want a gift from the damaged and discounted goods table, why, goes the faulty logic, would someone want us?

For people in supportive and loving relationships, this may seem like an unfounded worry. Even I hear whispers of the little voice of doubt creep into my head in the dark hours when I am alone with my thoughts. And, let's face it, these fears are not unfounded.

Dating and relationship building is tough work in a culture of perfection. We need to whiten our teeth, wear expensive clothes and pretty shoes if we're going to attract a potential mate. How are we going to find and then pursue Mr. or Miss Right if we have optic neuritis or use a forearm crutch?

Being overlooked for a year-end promotion can be easy when the bosses see us in a wheelchair. Family may continue to ask more of us than we can deliver during the hectic holidays, or they just stop asking (or talking to us at all) all together.

For many of us our financial situation has been compromised by MS. Whether it's lower income, high insurance costs or the price of medications, budgeting for gifts can make us feel more like Ebenezer than Elf.

We know it's not logical to think of it this way, but sometimes it feels like it's Christmas on the Island of Misfit Toys and we are destined to be marooned there for the rest of our lives, unwanted, unloved, and damaged misfits.

I have no cure for this sentiment. I can only offer to you the hard-fought knowledge that we do have worth, and value and that we can enrich the world around us. If not given the opportunity, we make it ourselves.

I urge those of you in our community who are finding this time of year to be particularly difficult on any level, to reach out to your local chapter of the Society or to an MS Navigator or to a trusted friend who gets you. They will be able to help you to find resources to get you through the difficult patch and off that island. Your friend will be there with you as you take your next step.

It is strength, rather than weakness, that leads us to ask for help when we feel alone, unloved and damaged. I have been there and can attest that my local chapter made all the difference in the world for me.

My name is Trevis Gleason, and I live with multiple sclerosis. I may have a few things wrong with me, a few dents but I'm far from Damaged Goods, and so are all of us.

MS + Depression DO NOT Have to = Suicide
11/12/2010 Seattle, USA

Hemingway used to refer to the times when depression brought him to the very brink of suicide as "Black Ass Days." Recent events have brought this topic to the fore of our attention in a very personal way, and I feel compelled to address what is often taboo but must be spoken.

People with Multiple Sclerosis die from suicide at a rate 7.5 times higher than age-matched population.

The study was published in 1991 and is based on data collected on Canadian MS patients between 1972 & 1988, a time, we must remember, before disease modifying drugs.

I have discussed doctor assisted suicide before and I see these two topics as very different. Let me explain . . .

Death with Dignity is what some call doctor-supported suicide (I say supported because many of the states that allow for this course of action do NOT allow any actual assistance by a doctor, or anyone else for that matter). The processes by which a person can end their life under these circumstances are well outlined and the patient's mental state is checked along the way.

Depression must be diagnosed and treated before end-of-life medications can be prescribed.

I have supported Death With Dignity laws for a long time. Not because I feel I need one, but rather because it might get *that bad*. The process can be a peaceful hastening of an inevitable (and sometimes painful) end and a way for family to help a dying loved one pass over.

Suicide, on the other hand, I find to be a tragedy.

Alone, in pain, seeing no other options and usually leaving a trail of suffering and blame behind them, suicides are forever a messy thing.

If, by some stroke of fortune, you are reading these words as you contemplate ending your life because of Multiple Sclerosis I implore you to stop.

Life may get 'that bad' due to MS, I'm not saying anything contrary to that. If, however, you feel like it's so bad RIGHT NOW that your only way past it is out of it . . . and this hasn't been part of a plan, a plan you've shared with and constructed with those around you, STOP!

Everyone has their limits, everyone has their "That's Enough" point I would not judge what those are for anyone. Suicide is a permanent solution to a temporary problem (painful, beyond any explanation). There are treatments, whether that is people or medications which can help get past much of what our disease flings at us.

This topic has been burning my brain since it woke me for 3:00 am. I don't know if I've done it justice.

What if I Can't Work?
01/15/2014 Kerry, Ireland

From the very beginning of writing about Unspeakable Bits, I have written from the premise that information is the remedy to fear. I believe that full-heartedly and while it is sometimes difficult to face ugly facts about living with multiple sclerosis I'd rather look at them than hide from them.

One such difficult aspect of living with MS comes if we can no longer work due to our disease.

There are loads of resources out there to help us in disclosing (or not). The government wants to help us stay among the employed. Even with rehabilitee counseling, we get to a place that we just cannot work any longer. As we live in a society that seems to value what we do rather than who we are, this point in a career can be particularly difficult.

As a person who had found his calling, passionately pursued my second career, and quite vainly defined myself by my work, being forced to leave my job within months of diagnosis shook me to my foundation.

The fact was, no matter how my employer, doctors or I looked at it, I just couldn't do the work and all that went with it, any longer.

I am not a silver lining guy. The financial hardships that came as a result of my disability were as crippling as the disease. To say

I was unprepared for the difficulties of such an event would be the understatement of my life. There are some financial holes that MS dug that I may very well never manage to fill-in.

For those who are still working after diagnosis, there is still time to prepare for this possibility.

Some of the things you may consider:

- Do you have short- and long-term disability insurance (either though your work or privately)?

- Are you paying all or a portion of the premiums of disability insurance? (I found out that this has serious tax implications if you make a claim).

- Might you be eligible for a supplemental income policy?

- Do you have long-term care insurance?

- Are your savings and investments structured so that you can access them?

- Do you have savings that can get you through until insurance benefits kick in? (Do you know how long that is for your policy?)

- Should you begin to down-size your home/lifestyle now?

All of these are difficult questions to answer, and I'll suggest they may even be difficult questions to ask.

Your local chapter staff or an MS Navigator can help you define the questions you need to ask, the places to find answers and helpful resources if those answers hard live with.

Even if the answers you find aren't very pleasant, at least you'll know in advance and you can begin to plan around them. You'll thank yourself tomorrow if you begin asking today.

Treating Relapse vs Treating Progression
08/17/2021 Kerry, Ireland

There is an abundance of metaphors about living with MS. I've been writing about my life with MS for over a decade and a half and I've yet to see an end to the list of tropes, descriptions, similes, allegories, parables, analogies, and comparisons that fit. There are low-hanging fruits out there and those for which I've stretched, but we usually tie them together in the end.

After my recent fall, I've come up with another I'll share; this one having less to do with the disease as it's more about how we choose to cope.

I was only out for a walk when I took my spill, so I wasn't draped in protective gear. Had I been riding a skateboard or something (yeah, we'll just let that image slip away without much thought; shall we?) I would have been bedecked in helmet, knee pads, elbow protection and likely those padded Artful Dodger type fingerless gloves you see the kids at the skate park putting to use.

As I wasn't padded up like an 8-year old linebacker for my simple walk down the lane, I was left to betadine and bandages as my only recourse, and therein lay the comparison.

When deciding where to focus our energies and monies in treating our multiple sclerosis, we either tend toward padding in the form of disease modifying medications in hopes they will arrest the progressions, or bandages to help cope with symptoms and relapse after the fact.

I'd not assume to offer suggestion nor solution to anyone when it comes to making the choice for their life. I have studied both research and my personal disease course. I have discussed the options with my medical team and my wife. We've weighed all the options we care to consider (at this point, because there are always going to be changes in options as well as situation) and come up with our plan.

Everyone must come to their own conclusions. An important aspect of the process is understanding the decision in the context of the whole.

The padding approach can be very good at protecting but, like that school kid whose pads weigh more than he does as he stumbles onto the field, they have their downsides, cost, side-effects, relative efficacy, and convenience to name a few.

Bandages, on the other hand, are only useful after the damage is done, but some will protect from further injury . . . a bit. Bandages are usually less expensive than padding, but if you keep banging you knee and throwing a plaster on the cuts, there will eventually be more substantial damage that a bandage can't help.

Even with the padding route for DMTs, breakthrough disease can occur. With the help of our doctors and family, we treat the symptoms and decide if our choice of padding is still right for us or whether we should rethink our protection plan.

If you read this far hoping for an answer as to which is better—knee pads or bandages, the answer is, "Yes." A well thought out decision, based on medical advice, personal research, family discussion, financial planning, and not a small bit of soul searching in order to come to the conclusion with which you are most comfortable is always going to be the right decision.

It's just not as easy as throwing on pads and stocking up the first-aid kit.

Conspiracy Theories
04/23/2014 Manchester, England

I believe that the internet has become the most powerful tool that people living with multiple sclerosis have at our disposal. The access it allows to hard-to-find research, historical data and others living with MS around the globe is an informed patient's dream.

To paraphrase Newton's Third Law of Motion, however, for every action there is an equal and opposite reaction.

For all the good that is out there on the 'interweb', there is an equal (some would say greater) volume of quackery, misinformation, and conspiracy theories.

Just like bad science, if you go looking for a specific answer to something on the web, you're going to find exactly what you're looking for. Seek out that mercury fillings are the cause of your MS and you'll find loads of people saying that you should get your fillings yanked. Think your MS can be cured with a specific diet? There are even doctors out there on the internet telling people exactly that.

How is one to tell truth from snake oil?

I go with two rules:

1. If it sounds too good to be true, it probably is
2. If it sounds too absurd to be true, it probably is.

The third leg of my evaluation process is based on Ockham's Razor. Plainly put, "All things being equal, the simplest explanation tends to be the right one." Conspiracies are usually far, far from the simplest explanations.

I do, however, believe that much of the belief in bad science and conspiratorial notions is bred in genuine fear and frustration. I saw the International Space Station fly over my house the other night and I won't lie that part of my brain went to "We can put people into space, but we can't cure my stupid disease?" My frustration.

I'd have to say that I believe the most prevalent and dangerous theory out there is that They are out to keep us sick. 'They' being a mix-n-match confederacy of pharmaceutical companies, medical professionals and patient-centered service organizations.

When I look at the profit statements of pharma and the upward spiral of the cost of MS drugs, I get frustrated as well. I can't, however, accept that a cure has either already been found and is being kept from us, or that drug companies don't really want to find one because they make too much money from their disease modifying drugs.

Do not get me wrong, MS drugs cost too much and we are being profited from at a rate which makes my stomach turn. Full Stop.

Think about this, however, for a moment and you'll understand why these ideas are out of bounds for me:

There are a million or more people in the USA living with multiple sclerosis. Estimates are 2.8 million of us in the world. About half take a disease modifying drug. Consider the number on the market (a couple of dozen at this writing). A new treatment has, at best, a shot at about 60,000 taking their drug. What company would hide or not look for a cure that all 2.8 million are clamoring for?

The one who finds the cure for multiple sclerosis gets the whole pie, not just a slice. I 100% reject the idea that smart people aren't searching very hard for the cure (and for better treatments).

I know there are those who will say that a certain kind of water has made them better or that their MS is gone because of <fill-in the blank>. Good for you. I'm glad that you found something that you feel works for you. Just don't go around spouting unscientific (or worse, Bad Science) in support of your assertions. You're doing harm to people looking for genuine answers to real problems.

The world is not out to get us.

Discrimination
06/28/2010 Seattle, USA

This morning's announcement of the passing of Senator Robert Byrd is sure to stir up conversations of civil rights and the part he played (on both sides of the argument). It's odd, really, that this would happen on the day I had intended to post a piece about disability rights and the discriminations we may have encountered.

I, sometimes, quip that MS has made me a minority for the first time in my life (some 75% of people diagnosed being women and all . . .). I've tried to limit that remark as I don't want to be insensitive to any other minority. The burden I face is far, FAR less than theirs.

The fact of the matter is, however, that there are real issues of discrimination that those of us who live with chronic illness and disabilities face. For many, the only discrimination may be the nasty comments we endure from time to time. For others, I fear that there may be more than a sharp word or two.

I suspect that many have had to deal with mistreatment in the workplace. Many of us feel like we have shifted to survival mode in our work lives. All too often, our employers are willing to keep us there.

I have to say that my last full-time employer bent over backwards to make things right for/with me. They even conducted a system-wide review of their programs and policies after I left, to make sure that any bumps we encountered would not hinder any future cases (and that was helpful to a friend who later suffered a severe accident.)

There are, of course, other places where we might face discriminations. Housing, hotels, travel in general . . . many of us didn't get our fair shake at something and perhaps we think our MS was the reason.

We All Deserve to be Treated With Respect
9/12/2012 Seattle, USA

I was riding the city bus the other day and we took a route I don't normally see. Along the side of the road, I saw a billboard for a state-wide hotline to report abuse or neglect of elderly people. That got me thinking about the abuse and neglect of people living with disabilities, particularly people living with multiple sclerosis.

The stories of people living through unkind treatment first makes me sad and then these stories make me angry. I am even a bit baffled that some people treat others so appallingly or that others in our community are so used to the dreadful standards that we don't expect anything better. I feel like it's time to address this unspeakable part of living with MS.

We must realize that we are just as good as everyone else in the world and deserve to be treated with common courtesy and respect just like any living soul. If we require extra help or assistance to meet our everyday needs, it is not asking too much to request help (and to expect that it be given without a side-order of guilt).

We needn't stand for people talking about us like we're not in the room. We shouldn't be made to feel a burden and we are most assuredly not to be the targets of some emotional archer's misguided slings and inappropriate arrows.

When I read of a person being told that they are "Lucky I stay with you otherwise you'd have no health insurance" or some other rotten comment I want to vomit. When I read that some member of someone's family calls them "lazy" or a "fake" I shake my head and wonder what's wrong with people. And when someone tells me of a person with MS being kept like an unwanted pet in some room or being abandoned to a skilled nursing facility, I want to cry.

It breaks my heart when I hear people living with MS not feeling worthy of better treatment. So often people say, "It's better to be in this bad relationship than not in one at all." I don't pretend to know the details and intricacies of the emotional tapestry that makes up a person's relationship. To think that being treated badly is somehow better than being alone is a hard one to understand.

Would we stand for someone talking ill of a deaf person in their presence because they can't hear the comment? Do we sit by if a child is beaten in front of us? Don't we call 911 if we see a dog locked in a car on a sweltering day? How is it that we allow this kind of treatment of ourselves? What happened to us that we believe this is it?

People who treat those of us with MS as diminished or some-how less-than are pathetic bullies. When verbal barbs give way to woeful neglect and physical abuse, however, now we're talking criminal.

We are not toys to be made fun of nor are we emotional punch-ing bags. We are thinking, feeling, sentient beings who deserve love and respect and understanding and we should not accept less. MS takes enough from all of us. We needn't give over our dignity to someone who thinks they are put upon by our disease.

Here are some resources if you feel that you or someone you know is being treated less than they deserve:

The National Domestic Violence Hotline (http://www.thehot-line.org/)

Mental Health Resources by state (http://www.findcounseling. com/help/hotlines/)

The Befrienders Worldwide (http://www.befrienders.org/) can help both USA and international readers find help.

MS Friends (http://www.nationalmssociety.org/living-with-multiple-sclerosis/society-programs-and-services/msfriends-peer-telephone-support/index.aspx) is a great resource if you just want to talk with someone who knows MS from *our side*.

Finally, if you're afraid to call 911 because you don't think your case is an emergency, The US Law Enforcement site (http://www. usacops.com) has a listing of all local police contact numbers.

The Know-It-All
05/22/2013 Kerry, Ireland

Have you ever come across the Know-It-All? You know, the guy or gal who has done, seen, tasted, smelled, tried, succeeded at (hardly ever failed at anything), read, studied and/or experienced whatever topic might be at hand? And have you noticed that these KIAs (might as well give them a name, right?) have opinions that are almost always diametrically opposite to yours on just about everything? It seems sometimes that these KIAs can only feel themselves to be right by making the rest of us feel like we are somehow wrong.

How about the MS KIA?

I've run into MS KIAs who will tell me that they have cured their MS—and attempt to make me feel bad for not curing mine. Or MS KIAs who tell me that my disease-modifying drug of choice (or choice to no longer be on drug) isn't the best for me because <fill in the blank>. How about the MS KIAs who know everything about your multiple sclerosis simply because their great-aunt's cousin by marriage six-states-away had MS; someone they never met?

I've run into plenty of KIA (not just the MS type) in my life, and I just don't have the energy for them anymore. I guess it's partly because one of the things I've learned from MS is to budget my energy, and they are simply not worth my energy. Still, a little part of me would love for the KIA to see the error in their ways and understand that there is little in anyone's life history to support such arrogance. Well, that and who gave them the authority to spout off about our disease the way that some people, particularly strangers, think it's alright to touch any pregnant woman's belly without asking?

I've been doing a lot of reading of late, on support sites and checking out various social media sites about MS. There are some very good sources of information, intellect, and emotion out there on the web. There is also an overwhelming abundance of MS KIAs.

Seriously! Where do people get off?

I suppose, if I were to be fair and go back to read nearly eight years of my writings, I might see a touch of MS KIA in myself on an occasion or two! If that is ever the case, I heartily apologize.

I guess it all comes down to a core principle to which I adhere; I don't really <u>know</u> that much. I <u>know</u> that I am a sentient being and I <u>know</u> that I am capable of love. Other than that, it's just my system of personal beliefs that get me through each day.

So, I guess when an MS KIA tells me that they <u>know</u> something that is contrary to something I have grown to believe, it makes the comment more of a personal affront and gets my dander up.

The thing is, changing a couple of words in a conversation can change a MS KIA into a person who at least appearing to care. "You should" replaced with "Have you thought about . . .?," becomes a conversation not a sermon. "I'm sure you've thought about___ what do you think?" works much better at holding my attention than "You know what I heard (or read or saw) that works?"

I guess the biggest one for me is the incorrect use of the word cure. If someone says "cure" and it's not in the context of research, fundraising or hope, it's a near-automatic MS KIA badge from me.

I suppose that one positive thing I've learned about living with MS is that I just don't have to make time for that kind of person, that type of attitude or that sort of emotional drain in my life. I've also learned that I can stop just about any MS KIA dead in his/her path of their illogical argument by saying, "Excuse me, I have to go give myself an injection."

Why Can't We All Just Get Along?
08/21/2013 Kerry, Ireland

I believe that most people with multiple sclerosis are really good people dealt a challenging hand by the fates and who are just trying to get through and help others along the way. Results of the most recent CCSVI study, however, have once again highlighted some rather nasty patient-on-patient treatment.

Over the years—and as social media interactions among people living with MS have increased—I have noticed some thoughtless, some insensitive and some downright rude behavior within the MS community . . . *toward one another*!

The internet uproar over Jack Osbourne's personal decisions on his treatment and even reaction to a pharmaceutical donation to the Society in recognition of his *Dancing with the Stars* performance is another example of people lashing out at one another and at organizations trying to help us.

I suppose we could chalk some of it up to frustration. I know I get frustrated with my MS sometimes and the internet can be a relatively easy and anonymous place to let off some steam in a chat room or on a blog. But some of the comments I have read over the years have been far too sharp and pointy and very directly aimed for my taste.

"MS drugs are poison" or "They don't work" isn't helpful to someone looking for genuine assistance. And the way some people talk about how their positive attitude has helped them conquer their MS makes others feel like they are doing something wrong.

If something **seems** to be working for one person, it does not mean that it would work for **everyone** else, and it assuredly doesn't give anyone the authority to push their point on someone else. But that doesn't stop some people from shoving all the same.

I'm not what one would call a practitioner of any religious faith, but I understand what is intended and I appreciate the thought when someone offers prayers for me through my blogs or social media. I am always taken aback at the disrespectful comments that are hurled back and forth (from both sides of that topic) as soon as religion and MS is brought up. Seriously, I don't mind someone offering healing thoughts for me; do you?

A recent blog discussion about issues surrounding death with dignity had people actually telling others how (and why) to live their lives with MS in a manner that went far beyond impolite and into the realm of arrogant.

Sometimes it feels like there are people just trolling the internet looking for someone to poke. My editor once told me, after a particular set of nasty comments that "People seem to write things they wouldn't say to your face . . . when they know you can't punch them in theirs."

It's one thing to have to hear the litany of insensitive comments from those who have no idea what it's like to live inside of this MS bubble. To be attacked from within our own ranks is beyond the pale.

I'll admit that some may lump me into the category of offender as I have always been what I call a "Hopeful Skeptic" of CCSVI and its liberation therapy. I went as far as asking if getting the treatment paid for by insurance wasn't a form of fraud which some interpreted as a criminal accusation. I do not see it that way, but I have moderated my tone to make sure that it is no longer categorized as offensive . . . by most.

Living with this disease has enough challenges, without us adding to them. I'm not saying, "If you don't have something nice to say, don't say anything." What I'm trying to say is that none of us is an expert in MS. If we're an expert at anything, it's at living our own lives—not anyone else's life—with MS. None of us knows it all, so we shouldn't act the MS know-it-all.

We're all in this boat together. Why can't we all just get along?

Have you run across people being beyond rude online about your MS? How do you deal with it? Do you think you might be guilty of being rude sometimes? How do you keep your feelings intact after a long internet search?

Medical Marijuana
04/24/2013 Galway, Ireland

4:20 was long counter-culture code for the use of marijuana. Being that April twentieth is numerically represented as 4/20, I put out a broad question about the medical use of marijuana (MMJ) for multiple sclerosis to my community on that Saturday and was surprised by the overwhelming response and support for the legal use of the substance.

LEGAL HISTORY

It is important to remember that while Marijuana (*Cannabis Sativa*) has been used as medicine in many of the world's cultures for thousands of years, it is federally illegal in the United States (even for medical use). Though several states (18 and the District of Columbia at this writing) have medical use laws on the books, a 2005 Supreme Court ruling upheld the federal government's right to prosecute patients who possess marijuana for medical purposes no matter the states' law or the patients' prescription to use MMJ for symptom management.

The US government deems cannabis (and its active chemical compounds) a Schedule 1 Narcotic and Congress in doing so, has determined the following to be true of the chemicals in marijuana:

1. The drug has a high potential for abuse.
2. The drug has no currently accepted medical use in treatment in the United States.
3. There is a lack of accepted safety for use of the drug under medical supervision.

Even if you live in one of the states that allow patients access to cannabis, you are still breaking federal law and subject to arrest and prosecution if you use MMJ as medication the way your doctor prescribes.

The inability and/or unwillingness to try MMJ for symptoms due to the legal status of the drug was one I read over and over in the comments on my post. Some posted comments that they would really like to try MMJ as many of their symptoms (particularly pain, spasticity and sleep issues) aren't responsive to many prescription meds. Some people went so far as to say they were considering moving to another state (as some have done to be closer to MS Centers and MS specialists).

SPEAKING FROM EXPERIENCE

The most common MS symptoms named in conjunction with the medical use of cannabis include spasticity, pain, sleep quality, bladder issues, tremor and depression/anxiety.

As a person who formerly lived in one of the states allowing for medical use of cannabis, I have availed myself of a prescription and found relief of one particular, medication-resistant symptom without getting stoned. Now, living away from that state, it is illegal for me to treat the MS spasticity in my neck with MMJ so I am forced to experience that symptom without relief.

My MS doc believes the research only beginning to catch up with what people living with MS have been saying about MMJ for a while now; for many of us, it works.

Some patients wouldn't consider using MMJ, even if it were made legal. Others use the drug for MS symptom management in spite of serious legal ramifications. Most of us, I suspect, simply abide by our state laws and wonder "What if?" as we wait for new treatments and an eventual cure.

HOW IT WORKS

By binding to several different receptors and proteins in the brain and immune system, it is thought that the chemicals in MMJ (known as cannabinoids and include, but are not limited to, THC) have the potential to 1) alter the disease course of MS and 2) curb some symptoms of multiple sclerosis.

No drug treatment is without side effects and MMJ is no different.

The dangers of smoking *anything* are well known (though there are other methods of dosing with MMJ including edibles, teas and vaporizing). Increased risks of nausea, vomiting, sedation and even seizure have been reported due to smoking of marijuana. Though dosing with MMJ is typically considered relatively low, chronic use of marijuana can impair lung function, cause cardiac issues and increase the risk of some cancers.

One of the concerns I've heard from people living with MS is the worry of increased difficulty with walking, talking and fatigue were they to use MMJ. I've found that dosing is a learned art but I (and others I know) have found a way to find relief without getting high and minimizing some of these side-effects.

Some doctors and patients believe that the risk to benefit ratio of MMJ is weighted more to one side while others feel its current legal status makes the conversation a non-starter. The only way to understand these possible benefits fully is with more research, something the Society is currently funding.

MORE RESEARCH NEEDED

Dr Allen C. Bowling, M.D, Ph.D., the well-respected guru of complementary and alternative medicines (CAM) for MS, offers a full chapter about MMJ (sometimes called clinical cannabis) in his book on MS CAM. Dr. Bowling brings up several studies and trials but notes that they have shown a mixed bag when it comes to results in MS patients.

Dr. Bowling, along with the National MS Society's strategic response call for more funding and more testing of these compounds (including both natural and synthesized forms of the chemicals) for use in treating MS symptoms.

The Society's official stance is "That better therapies are needed for distressing symptoms, including pain, tremor, and spasticity, that may not be sufficiently relieved by available treatments . . . Yet there are serious uncertainties about the benefits of marijuana relative to its side effects" and that the legal status of MMJ "further complicates the issue."

Complicates. Indeed!

These things only move forward with open discussion and open discussion is something I would suggest with great caution when commenting about your personal use of MMJ. In fact, I think that's a really bad idea given the state of things. I do, however, believe that an exchange of ideas on the topic is possible without incriminating oneself. Whether you are of the live and let live side of the conversation or you see medical use of marijuana as a step down a slippery, moral slope, we need to have the discussion.

Death and Multiple Sclerosis: It's Complicated
07/13/2013 Kerry, Ireland

People do not die from MS, in the same way people do not die from falling off a bridge. They die from the landing.

It is extremely rare that disease activity creates lesions that stop vital life functions. It is not so rare, however, that disease activity causes issues that lead to death. These deaths are unceremoniously lumped together and reported as a result of "Complications of multiple sclerosis." But what does that even mean?

In a study of 119 Canadian MS patients whose cause of death could be determined, researchers reported that 47.1% between 1972-1988 (that's 56 deaths) "were directly attributed to complications of MS." 47.1%!

On World MS Day 2015, researchers published a further study on MS mortality. I didn't appreciate the timing!

The report, informs us that "New research suggests people with multiple sclerosis (MS) may have double the risk of dying early compared to people without MS, with those younger than 59 at a three times higher risk."

The relatively good news in the study found that people with MS—specifically people living with MS in Manitoba, Canada—live to be an average of 75.9 years. The bad news, the matched cohort without MS lived to be 83.4 years. The other good news was that people with MS seemed to die less often from chronic lung disease, diabetes, hypertension, and ischemic heart disease than the control group.

Sounds like we are, indeed, a healthy population living with an incurable disease. To paraphrase the '60s song, we're in pretty good condition . . . for the condition we're in!

But still, these "complications" . . .

It is first important to understand that there are treatments, exercises, medications, and devices to help us manage the most challenging MS symptoms—even those that can eventually contribute to death. Being that death is something all of us must face in our own time, I have found it helpful to understand how MS *might* be a factor when that time does come. It is rare, but it does happen.

These are the major complications of MS that can cause death:

- Pulmonary involvement
- Severe infections, sepsis
- Aspiration pneumonia
- Suicide

PULMONARY COMPLICATIONS

A National MS Society clinical bulletin on Pulmonary Function and Rehabilitation states that "Just as muscular weakness in the limbs occurs early in the disease and increases as the disease progresses, the same progressive weakening occurs in the ventilatory muscles. Ultimately, respiratory complications are considered the major cause of morbidity and mortality in individuals with advanced MS."

SEVERE INFECTIONS

One of the hazards of advanced immobility due to MS can be pressure sores (commonly known as bedsores). Pressure sores begin as a relatively benign problem, but if left untreated can quickly progress to more serious concerns (including sepsis—basically a full-body infection caused, in the case of pressure sores, by bacteria entering via the open wounds). Many factors can contribute to pressure sores; they include immobility or inactivity, decreased sensation, bowel or bladder incontinence and poor nutrition.

Other common infections which can lead to life-threatening consequences include recurrent and severe urinary tract infections (UTIs) and aspiration pneumonia.

ASPIRATION PNEUMONIA

Dysphagia—or swallowing problems—can cause food or liquid to be deposited into the lungs. The body sees this foreign matter as an intruder and sends its defenses to work. The resulting inflammation and fluid accumulation can lead to pneumonia.

SUICIDE

The reported rates of a person with MS taking their own life (or being assisted in doing so) range from just over 6% to nearly 15%. These rates are high compared to the general population, and may result from a high rate of undiagnosed and undertreated depression in MS. Depression, which is significantly more common in MS than in the general population or other chronic illnesses, is treatable. People who think they may be depressed should contact their healthcare providers as soon as possible.

In the Canadian study I mentioned, of the remaining 63 deaths where cause could be determined, 28.6% (18) were death by suicide, and two other studied deaths ". . . which may have been suicides." According to that report, between 1972 and 1988 "The proportion of suicides among MS deaths was 7.5 times that for the age-matched general population."

We must, obviously, take into consideration that there were no MS drug treatments during this study and that it looked at patients of only two MS clinics.

Fear is what drove me to research and then write on this topic. Fear of the unknown, fear of the possible and a fear that not doing so would be a disservice to the MS community. I feel more at ease knowing just what my enemy might look like and, somehow less fearful. I hope the same for you.

Now, I'm going to go throw the ball for my dog because all this studying about MS, its complications, and death has reminded me that life with MS really is all about the living part.

In Memory of Those Lost to Multiple Sclerosis
05/31/2016 Kerry, Ireland

While I appreciate the sentiment, it always bothers me a bit when I am thanked for my service in the US Coast Guard on Memorial Day. Veteran's Day is the day we celebrate and appreciate all who have served their country in the military services. Memorial Day, on the other hand, is the day we remember with solemn thanks those who answered the call at times of war and crisis but did not return home. Armed Forces Day is the day we thank active-duty military personnel.

There are no veterans of MS, as there is no cure. We are all on active duty as we live the life, fight battles large and small, and combat a disease that has waged war on our immune system. There are no veterans, but there are those we memorialize.

Death by direct cause of MS is rare but we know of those who succumb to the not as rare as we'd wish "Complications of multiple sclerosis." I know two people whose death can be attributed to clinical trials of very aggressive MS treatment.

On the occasion of Memorial Day, I remembered family members I'd never met who perished on ships and beaches and jungles on behalf of generations living and yet to come. I also think of the men and women who succumbed to disorders of traumatic stress after their wartime service was completed.

Today, the memories of the MS friends and acquaintances no longer with us, are heavy on my mind. Names and faces are turning over in my head as I look out on a sunny May day in Ireland. One of these names, one of the stories I think hardest about today is that of 43-year-old Sherri Muzher.

When I lay awake some nights—the nights when MS sleep will let me neither sleep nor rise, it is a story like Ms. Muzher's that is whispered from my dark places. Not only does this story bring up my worst-case scenario with MS, she exhibits a bravery which I can only hope to mirror were things to get "That bad."

Sherri Muzher is asking for a way to end her life in time so that her organs can be of use so others may live.

Her lungs are already too damaged by MS to be donated to a person in need of lung transplant. The rest of her vital organs and tissues are, however, viable. She wants to be of ultimate use in her death in a way that MS stopped the brilliant law school graduate from being in life.

Only four states in America have laws allowing for physician-assisted end of life, also known as *Death with Dignity*. Her home of Michigan is one of them. Even states which do permit patient-directed end of life, donation of organs, by this point in their condition, is often impossible as only healthy organs can be used for life-altering and lifesaving transplantation.

Organs cannot be procured after the heart has stopped beating/ pumping oxygen to them, for more than a few minutes. Because of this, donation after brain death is generally preferred because the organs are still receiving blood from the donor's heart until minutes before being removed. The medical term is organ procurement.

Most illnesses which would grant terminally ill patients a death with dignity would likely ruin organs as they hasten death. Cases such as Ms. Muzher are quite rare, indeed. There are many, many ethical questions to debate about ending one's failing life in time to improve and/or extend another. A debate we'll see raging for decades beyond the end of Sherri Muzher's MS-shortened life.

I believe that this bright, young lawyer understands the required conversations will likely not happen in time to meet her wishes. Brave and bright woman that she is, however, she has chosen to bring the debate to us for such things to be decided, eventually. It is only through vigorous discourse and healthy debate that this complex and nuanced moral, ethical, medical topic can be sussed out. And it will not be in time for our MS sister, Sherri.

Sherri Muzher passed away on June 26th, 2018.

I remember Sherri, I remember my friends gone too soon at the hands of this disease, and I acknowledge those who have died with MS. I am reinforced in my determination that ours be the last generation to hear the words, "You have multiple sclerosis."

In memory of those who have gone before.

CHAPTER 8

It's a Marathon, Not a Sprint

THERE'S ONLY ONE THING WORSE THAN GROWING OLDER . . . NOT *having the opportunity to grow older. It is a privilege afforded far too few, to get to a point in life where we wonder if it's regular aging or MS causing one difficulty or another.*

As I'm now well beyond life's halftime show, I have come to realize that the long game is a far different undertaking than seeking quick fixes and/or speedy returns. Strategic planning has usurped tactical thinking for me as I realize that more than half of my adult life has been lived with the diagnosis of MS.

There are new curses to be endured, but there are also new joys to experience.

I live in the cool hues of gray that exist between the black ice of what might be and the white heat of what could have been. I have found beauty in those shades by assessing my needs, learning how to most efficiently fulfill those needs, and spending the time and energy I have left on people and endeavors that top-up my life tank rather than those that drain it.

What If . . .? Then I Will (x3)
09/12/2011 Seattle, USA

Multiple Sclerosis is a disease that causes us to ask, often, "What if . . .?"

I learned early on in my professional careers, first as a navigator in the US Coast Guard, a student and, finally, as a chef in many different capacities, that one can get easily lost down labyrinth-like rabbit holes chasing the hypothetical. Conversely, I also learned the unpleasantness of being caught with my preparedness trousers down around my ankles.

There must be a way to feel confident in our readiness while still living a life, rather than just preparing for it . . .

We all live our lives based on the experiences we've had, the knowledge we've earned from successes and failures and the wisdom we have gained by watching others' successes and failures. I once read "A smart man learns from his mistakes. A wise man learns from other's mistakes." I've come up with a solution that works for me, professionally, that seems to tick all the boxes for the new(er) challenges of living my life with MS.

The automatic answer to any "What if . . .?" question is "Then I would . . ." which, of course, will be followed by yet another "But then, what if . . .?" You can see how this could be an all-consuming exercise in preparedness becoming paranoia and rational becoming ridiculous. On the other hand, if entered into with restraint and forethought, the practice has allowed the two parts of my brain—the primordial and the advanced—to coexist.

I am, like you, faced with everyday challenges as well as the dark thoughts that can creep up in the quiet, sleepless hours of the night. "What ifs" can loom around every corner of a life with MS. Some are helpful, as in the case of a person planning for a strenuous activity. Many, however, are nothing more than futile attempts to control what cannon be tamed . . . those cascading "What ifs" have exponential gravitational pull the further down the string you go.

I limit my "Then I woulds" to three.

At three levels of scenario, I feel that I have answered enough of the possibilities that I can walk (or not) out the door feeling like my mental path has been cleared enough to get on with my day. Any less than that and I'm not sure I've plowed enough of a path. Any more than three and I may never even make it out of my bed for the excursion down the paths of the mind.

With very few exceptions, I find that my third preparation tier is always, "Well, then I'll call _____."

So, you might say that I only really need two answers, but that third is a nice realization that things aren't/won't be so bad that the two "Then I would . . ." solutions aren't enough to get through most situations.

While my "What ifs?" were big and hairy, nasty questions at the beginning, I realize now that they are a tactical issue to be dealt with by using the equally tactical weapon of "Then I would . . ." I leave those Big and Scaries for other times when they can be discussed with loved ones or my therapist. No need to take on a monster by myself!

"What if my eyesight makes it hard for me to write today?" Then I will take a cool shower, eat something and see if it gets better.

"What if it doesn't get better?" I'll take a kip and rest for a while.

"What if you still can't write after your nap?" Then I'll call a friend and ask them for help.

A Second Wind
1/25/2013 Seattle, USA

The last time I wrote an article that included a musical reference I was on some pretty serious pain killers after my hip replacement, and I got some serious (and quite deserved) flak from my sister for its sappiness. Well, we finally found the box with our music CDs in it today and it was nice to listen to a few tunes as we got on with our day's work.

Billy Joel was on the playlist and his song "You're Only Human (Second Wind)" caught my attention.

I started thinking about a "second wind" in relation to living with MS. In fact, an answer from a recent interview with Mike Jensen, a photographer living with multiple sclerosis, came to mind.

When I asked Mike about what he might have learned from living with MS his answer was spot on, "This is a marathon, not a sprint." he said, "There are no touchdowns, and the game is never over. Don't sweat the small stuff. Life in general, and MS in particular, is about learning to accommodate loss, hopefully with some grace and your dignity intact."

Just like running a marathon, there are going to be times that we come up against 'The Wall', there are going to be times we feel like we can't go on, there will be times that we just want to chuck it all in and sit on the side-line . . . then there is the second wind.

I don't think an MS second wind is going to happen every day or every time I feel fatigued. In fact, I suspect that they only come on every few years and maybe only once or twice in an entire lifetime with MS.

Maybe it's at the point where we get our heads around multiple sclerosis and begin to try and wrap our hearts around our new life that we feel that burst of energy (though we still might be very, very tired). I think this renewal may be more of spirit than of body and, let's face it, our spirit can be dealt MS blows just as can our body.

So, I hope I haven't been too sappy with this analogy (I'm sure Angie will let me know if I did—what else are sisters for??) but I thought I could go into the weekend thinking of the concept.

A Middle-Aged Look at the Concept of Cure
08/18/2014 Dublin, USA

There was a time in my life when birthdays were a good time to look back and mark accomplishments. There was a time when they were a good time to look forward to what might lie ahead. In general, I now look at birthdays as simply a good time to have a good time.

When a family member only a brace of years behind me mentioned that I was now middle-aged, I woke to this topic. What if they don't find a cure before my life comes to an end?

When pressed in an interview a few years ago in 2009, I admitted that I didn't think there would be a cure for MS in the next 25 years I answered the question in this way "When I'm alone with myself and my thoughts, my answer is an absolute. However, when, I'm in the company of the brilliant minds doing research, I come away with a less certain, and more positive thinking on the question. Without sounding too wishy-washy, I'd have to hedge with the answer, "I don't think so." Five years in and I can't honestly say that my answer wouldn't change much.

Even if the Eureka Moment were to happen today in some lonely scientist's lab, it would be nearly a decade before The Cure could be thoroughly tested and on the market (okay, we could see it fast-tracked in maybe 7 years). That's another good chunk of time for my disease to progress.

This isn't a "Poor us, we're never going to be cured" thought. Quite to the contrary. The title of my writing has always been *Life with MS*, the life part comes first. I am living with this disease. I don't "suffer from," I'm not a "victim of," I haven't "succumbed to" . . . I have come to a cold-war Multiple Sclerosis détente and I LIVE with MS.

I have learned to do things differently than I had before and will have to do things differently than I had expected to do them. I will keep fighting for a dignified life for people with MS and to raise funds for researchers to find better treatments and that eventual cure.

I'm just coming to understand, accept and figure out a way to embrace the possibility that I may live the remainder of my life with MS and that this disease may (or may not) have a hand in the end of my life.

There comes a time in life when you look back with the understanding that there is, in all likelihood, more of it behind than there is left in front. When that happens, it's time to focus on the things that are important, to figure out the happiest path and to give up living by someone else's rules. That happened for me last week.

I live with graying hair, a widening arse, receding gums, worsening eyesight, and a shortening fuse. I live with an amazing wife, a loving pack of Wheaten Terriers, in a place I've dreamt of since childhood and with friends better than money could ever buy. I also live with multiple sclerosis.

Not a bad hand, even if I can't discard that one bad card . . .

A Cup of Coffee and a Nap
10/17/2014 Kerry, Ireland

Many people—MS and otherwise—find themselves in need of a rest during the day. My energy usually wanes around 2:00 in the afternoon. Sometimes it's just a dull ache of tiredness and others it's lay-down-or-fall-down, mind-crushing MS fatigue.

Sometimes these kips turn into full-on MS sleeps, and I wake hours later in the same position I started. In the midst of an exacerbation of my multiple sclerosis, this kind of sleep might be required. For the everyday fatigue, however, sleeping for that long can muck up that night's sleep and send me into an awkward sleep deprivation spiral.

I have mined a few helpful hints from medical professionals and fellow patients in order to avoid sleeping too long while still getting enough rest to make it through the day.

It's important for me to treat a mid-day rest as just that, rest. I don't treat it like going to bed. I hope a few of these tips might help you as well.

1. Find a quiet place to relax but don't look for silence (soft music is sometimes helpful for me)

2. The room should be darkened, but not black.

3. Beds are great, but reclining chairs, sofas and even soft grass in the shade of a tree can work well.

4. Get comfortable but not too comfortable. Lose the shoes and coat, loosen your tie and belt but don't get into your pjs and dive beneath the sheets.

5. Have a cup of coffee (or tea or cocoa) before you nap. Counterintuitive as it might sound, the warmth can help you relax, and the caffeine will kick in just about the time you want to wake.

6. Plan your rest period. I'm told that 20-40 minutes should be the maximum we nap. Beyond that we risk deep sleep which can be difficult to wake from and leave us both groggy and crabby for hours after.

7. Try to wake gently. Setting an alarm with music or having someone wake you with a soft voice will bring you back gently.

8. Re-enter the world gently. A few stretches and deep breaths can ready you for the rest of your day.

9. Freshen up. A toothbrush and facecloth tucked into your desk will help revive you after your nap

10. Don't have caffeine after the nap. That afternoon pick-me-up could leave residual stimulant in your system causing a poor night's sleep ahead.

These tips work for me and allow me to enjoy the remainder of my day without the half-awake groggy feeling.

My Shoes Can Tell My Story
01/23/2015 Kerry, Ireland

Who needs timed walking assessments or Hollywood-inspired motion-sensor tests? If I want to know how my gait is being affected by MS all I have to do is look at my shoes.

I bought a pair of shoes nearly three years ago and I love them, perhaps too much! I wear them most days, for most of the day.

These shoes fit me perfectly. They are sturdy enough to fit the orthotic inserts I require yet comfortable enough to wear all day. I used to wear slippers in the house but those arch-supports require shoes and these dearies are just the thing. They shine up if I need them to look decent in a casual situation and can just hang around the house on the Bad Days.

Though I've taken them to a number of cobblers, they have been deemed terminal—there is no saving their soles.

On one trip to a larger town about forty-five minutes bus ride from home, I looked at the shoes off my feet. I *really* looked at them. "MS" was written all over them. Well, at least the left shoe.

While the right shoe showed wear consistent with near-daily use for the past 1000-odd days, the other shoe is an abomination.

The leather at the toe is deeply scuffed and the front of the sole ground back to the stitching. The firm heal is unevenly worn-down on the outside and the leather of the outer upper is bulged like an over-filled wine skin.

I have drop foot on that side and, while the shoes can accommodate my bespoke Ankle Foot Orthoses (AFO), but I don't wear it as much as I might (see how I didn't "should" myself there. I'm learning!). That accounts for the toe damage. Because of that symptom, I often find myself lifting my whole leg from the hip and I must put my foot down oddly, thus the extended outer and wear on the heel.

I'll be sad to see this old favorite pair of shoes go. I am days away from having holes in the bottom of both and there is nothing the shoe doctors can do to save the poor souls (see how I did that there?). I just thought it was interesting to have a look at something as odd as shoes in diagnosing some of my MS symptoms and the severity of them. I hope I can find another pair which I can grow to love as much as these old friends.

Take a look in your shoe closet. Do you see signs of your multiple sclerosis?

Driving Directions
06/09/2015 Vermont, USA

As a consultant in the food world, I always adhered to the adage, "Free advice is taken at face value." That is to say that people respect and respond to an opinion much more when they're paying top dollar (or Euro) for the advice. For those of us living with a chronic illness we need to consider the source of well-intended advice as well.

In recent days I've been traveling around New England in support of my book, *Chef Interrupted*. Though I traveled the area extensively when I lived here, it's been <cough> over 20 years . . . some things have changed.

On a recent leg of my travels that took me to Montreal, Quebec, I was asking for driving directions to get out of the city.

Several helpful opinions were offered as to streets, underpasses, expressways and shortcuts to take. Then I realized that everyone giving me directions were auto-free, cycle-commuting, city dwellers. They were giving great directions for a bicycle, but I was driving a hired car.

While I eventually made it to my destination without event, the experience reminded me of the multitude of 'directions' someone living with this disease is proffered.

"You know what, you should . . .," "I think . . .," "I heard that _____ helps." We've all heard them, we all appreciate the good-natured thoughts and feelings behind the advice, but they often do not fit into our real life with MS.

Even other people with the same disease may not know exactly what we're going through when they give us advice as to how they overcame one obstacle or another. Particularly early on after diagnosis or when we're having a difficult time, 'directions' can be as free-flowing as maple sap in spring. We must filter and refine that advice to see how, or if, it might fit into our lives.

Right for us or wrong, most (but not all) advice is coming from a helpful place. We'll say, "Thank you" and then have to decide what's best for ourselves and our families and go down our own road with purpose and intent.

From Somewhere on the Road of Life
06/30/2015 Kerry, Ireland

Living with multiple sclerosis and looking ahead in life can sometimes feel like we're staring at an unfamiliar, winding road mostly obscured by the foul mist of dragon's breath. Often, therefore, we have all had our turn looking into the rear-view mirror of life to gauge our MS.

From diagnosis we try to discern the onset of our symptoms. When we visit our doctors for annual exams, we try to recollect the previous year's events.

Driving along our pre-diagnosed road we may have felt a bump or heard a scrape and wondered "What was that?" The occasional puncture or rattling wheel may have had us pulled over from time-to-time, but the cause of our delay was often short and explainable and we were shortly along again on our way.

After we heard the words, "You have multiple sclerosis," much changed, and we realized they were speedbumps we'd been hitting at full speed for all those years. We began wondering when the next one might be hidden and if it this was the one which would break an axel.

Now, as I tire of straining to see 'round the next foggy bend, I look back and see that the MS speedbumps have mostly gone from my journey. In their stead, MS has placed a centrifugal governor on my engine that limits my speed, my power, my range.

I could (and there was likely a time that I did) stomp on the accelerator pedal and curse my engine for not taking me to the places I intended at the speed I chose. I've ground some gear boxes and burnt through a few clutch plates as I tried to get my chassis to move at its former speed . . . and caused more damage to the driver's spirit than to the vehicle's body.

Of late—and quite recently to be honest—I've come to realize the presence of that governor on my life. My movements have slowed, my reactions are dulled, and the general pace of my life has laggard behind the pace of my former personal and professional cohort.

Rather than curse my engine, pressing an unresponsive pedal to the floor and succumbing (again) to MS road rage, I've decided to embrace the pace.

I won't go as far, I can't go as fast, I'll have to stop for rest and fuel more often than I'd like. If I can't keep up with the prevailing speed limit, I'll move over and let others pass. As in the theme song from Friends, my life may seem like it's stuck in second gear. No matter, I'm still moving.

Who knows, maybe I'll even fit a blade on the front if the road becomes blocked and plow the way for a few others on my journey.

The Irish Goodbye
03/31/2016 Kerry, Ireland

"Céad mile failte" is the saying in Irish, "A hundred thousand welcomes" and boy, isn't it true! When you arrive at someone's house and are greeted with a firm, two-handed handshake and a look directly in the eyes, you get a heart-felt, "Ye are very welcomed!"

The welcoming rituals of tea (milk? sugar?), biscuits, sandwiches, cakes are legendary.

The Irish are also renowned for their goodbyes.

The funerary wake is an Irish invention. These days-long events could have been mistaken for a céilí were it not for the presence of a corpse. So too were the American Wakes—which saw generations of young emigrants departing the Irish shores for the new world—famous for their celebration in the face of sadness.

The Irish say goodbye almost as well as they say hello.

Except when they don't.

The "Irish Goodbye" as it is known, is actually a survival mechanism developed by necessity by eventgoers who don't want to attract attention (and the prolonged excuses of *why* they are leaving so early and without a cuppa, cake and something to take with them).

The quick glance toward the door after meeting the partner's eye or some pre-arranged signal to indicate the stealthy procedure's beginning. Slowly you make your way to the door in hopes of not being recognized for making the Irish exit.

It's not out of disrespect to hosts or guests. In the case of the Irish Exit, one just doesn't want to spend the next three-quarters of an hour leaving. We just need to be gone.

It has been interesting to see others perform what I now know as the Irish Goodbye when I've always thought of it as "The MS Exit." For years I've situated myself near the door at parties. Caryn and I have an unobtrusive signal that can be seen across a room to note required egress from an event. Who would have thought that 15 years of living with multiple sclerosis would have been training for our move to a foreign country?

Sometimes it's a chronic condition behind the reason someone skates out of an event early and without much of a goodbye to attract attention. Sometimes, it's just a cultural thing.

Lowering Expectations on a Soft Day
06/01/2017 Kerry, Ireland

The mist that settled in on our little town overnight was that thick, hanging kind of damp. The sort that made me think of the film *The Matrix* as if the atmosphere around me had stopped in time and I was left to dodge droplets of wet, suspended in the still air.

The previous few days had been clear, bright, and cold; the kind of winter days that make you feel like you should get out and get something, *anything*, done. Which, as we know, can be difficult with MS in the picture.

Whether or not I rose to that allure or not isn't the point. Today was a day that seemed to be a handwritten note from the universe excusing me from the days required activities.

When you couldn't walk from front door to front gate without even your socks feeling wet, outside activities were off the table today. The extra layers between my windows and our warm, burning star kept much of its light from brightening my house as well.

So, I took advantage of a day that wouldn't let me do much easily and I did even less than that. I was kind to myself today in a way that required no excuses because of my disease. Nobody wanted to be out in this soft day if they didn't have to be.

"Sure, it's good for the complexion" might be the answer if someone were to mention the state of the damp. By not going out into it, I didn't have to try to see the brighter side of the day, I didn't have to fake it until I made it, I didn't even have to embrace a positive attitude to feel good.

I watched the outside from the inside. The Pack and I were content to potter. The house was clean (enough), it was a fasting day so I didn't have to concentrate on feeding myself, even the temperatures had risen so I didn't need to build a fire. Today was a day to let my body and mind recover.

Recover from the holidays, recover from the year that was, recover from the burdens MS puts on it. Today was a soft day in my little town . . . and I was soft on myself.

Why is it, I wonder, that I feel that I must wait until the weather gives me permission to struggle a little bit less. Sure, I always want to push my personal envelope, but some days I'm pretty sure where those edges are and I don't need to break a sweat in order to confirm.

My body seems grateful for the break. My mind is calmer and my spirit is at peace. I just hope I can remember this feeling when the sun taunts me into believing that hay must be made.

Six days into the New Year and I may have found my resolution.

The Beauty in a Difficult Point
08/22/2016 Kerry, Ireland

We don't get to see "The Beautiful Game" of hurling much in West Kerry, this is Gaelic Football country. The two games are not dissimilar in their rules, finesse and skill required. They can also be equally confusing and brutal to the first-time observer.

Each team's supporters are staunch in their conviction to club and county. We are in the final throes of the All-Ireland Championships with the second semi-final due to be played next weekend. Kerry meet Dublin on Sunday and the Green & Gold will be waving in nearly every garden and from all the streets and buildings in our little town.

When we gather at the pitch or in our local pub to watch the matches, I always admire fans of the sport for their love of the game as well as for their team.

Whenever a difficult point is scored, from a tough angle or from heavily defended territory, even fans of the opposing team will give credit for a fine play. In fact, a ball that makes it over the bar and between the posts that should, by all rights, make it over, is simply acknowledged. It's the point that is attained through struggle and against adversity which is celebrated.

"Ara, sure. Wasn't that a fine point?." "Fair play to your man. That was a beautiful score." is bantered from bar stools and crowded tables filled with ancestral footballing rivals.

It makes me think of how difficult it is for many of us to get some task or another 'over the bar' relative to our non-MS counterparts. It makes me admire my MS brothers and sisters every time they score from an angle that MS has given or into the stiff headwind of our disease.

I've no need to pat someone on the back for scoring a mundane accomplishment if they are not fighting our opponent. That same accomplishment for a person with multiple sclerosis may be worthy of knowing praise from those of us who understand the adversity of the game we play.

I've said before that a trip from bed to bath could be a marathon for some of us and a flight of stairs might as well be Everest. Some people with MS do conquer the great obstacles but the rest of us didn't have those scores in us even before we MS kneecapped us. For us, the ordinary has become the extraordinary, the mundane for others is monumental for us.

So, fair play to you who were able to make it through a full day of work. Well done if you were able to feed the family this week. A rousing round of applause if you were able to do that thing again that you weren't for a while. A standing ovation in recognition for a beautiful point . . . even though it may once have been a gimme. We know that these things aren't as straight forward as they once were.

Frustration
02/21/2017 Kerry, Ireland

Likely the best gift I was ever given was the Oxford English Dictionaries (OED). While this was before the days of the online version, it was the CD version I was given, not the 20-volume book set.

I love words. Their sound, their definitions, their etymology .... Talk about the gift that keeps on giving!

So, there's this sense I've been feeling of late, and I haven't been able to put a word to it. It's not fear. It's not dread. Nor is it anger, loathing or annoyance (though that is getting pretty close).

I do not believe that it's just me, who is experiencing this sense. I don't want to call it an emotion because I'm not sure that's what it is.

It's not a past, present, or future sensation but rather an all-encompassing one. An impression that some things are beyond my ability to change them; that they must be experienced as they are or were or will be.

This is not fatalism, as in, simply giving over to the situation. In fact, quite the opposite. When it comes to MS I don't give over much without a fight. But sometimes the fight becomes tilting at windmills and all there is to show for it is an exhausted jouster.

No, it's almost as if I'm an observer of my body's match against MS—maybe the manager of the side or its #1 Fan. No matter how well I've prepared or supported my lads, all I can do is watch as their weaknesses are exploited and the disease scores another goal.

This isn't an all-day, everyday thing. More like a squall or passing shower that brings with it a quality of hostile takeover or silent scream. It's raging against a wall . . . it's frustrating.

Yup. That's it. MS is frustrating.

OED told me that the noun *frustration* is, "The feeling of being upset or annoyed as a result of being unable to change or achieve something." And that's exactly what I am sometimes, frustrated.

I'm not overwhelmed by frustration; I'm annoyed by it. I'm not stopped by it; I'm upset that there are things I want to change about life with MS but cannot.

I hear it from the people in the MS Community around me.

I read of the things we long to do, couched as well as possible, with words like "anymore" or in sharp responses to topics that aren't what everyone wants to read.

We all feel it to some extent. No matter how Pollyanna we are (or act) we sometimes just experience MS as the verb *frustrating*, "to prevent (a plan or attempted action) from progressing, succeeding, or being fulfilled. To cause (someone) to feel upset or annoyed as a result of being unable to change or achieve something."

I do as much as I can when I can, and I employ whatever assistance I need to get those things done. Sometimes, like the storm cloud that comes out of nowhere, I also get frustrated by the things that I cannot do or do well (well enough?).

I suppose we all do . . . and I suppose that's just going to have to be all right. It's just frustrating.

A Relegation Game
04/04/2017 Cork, Ireland

I've often said that living with multiple sclerosis isn't a death sentence, it's a life sentence.

What I mean by that is we quite literally don't die *from* multiple sclerosis, we die *with* MS. We are sentenced to a life of living with this disease and that means trying to find a way over/under/ around or through the mountains that are dropped in our path.

Maybe it's because of two sporting events that converged this weekend, but I'm beginning to think of this living with MS thing another way as well. The NCAA basketball tournament just ended with my local team making it all the way to the finals. Also, my local Gaelic Athletic Association (GAA) football team fell through some unexpected cracks and has made it to the finals as well.

The tournament style of play that I've been used to in America for my whole life was a win-or-go-home game. No second chances. You are judged on your performance of the day and it doesn't matter by how much you win or lose a game. You either win or you lose.

In the play of many other sporting contests, aggregate scores, bonus points for goals scored away from home, spread of a victory or loss can all add up to a winning side losing in the long run. And then there is relegation.

My Kerry GAA football team is in Division 1, but we were dangerously close to relegation to Division 2 on Sunday as we hadn't performed at all well in the league this year. If The Kingdom (as we're known) had lost and two other teams won their games, we would have been sent down to the lower tier for next year. I'm happy to say that we won—and won by a large margin—and those other teams lost big, so we somehow went from fear that we might slip a division, to being catapulted to the championship match.

First, living with MS is like relegation sports because it can be so damned difficult to explain to someone. They think you either win or lose. We know that there are many factors that determine the outcome of a season, not just how many games in which we were victorious.

As well, we may be on a good or bad track of it with our lives but something out of our control can quash our hopes and change our outlook. I'm thinking of those teams who thought they might have a chance to make the finals but lost . . . and so did someone else, and another team won by a large margin, and they are suddenly the team headed down a division.

And finally, the whole world seems to focus on Division 1, don't they?

I feel like I have been relegated due to my overall aggregate scoring history with MS, but that doesn't mean that I'm not still in the game. Simply because my body and mind don't let me play at championship level, I haven't given up nor do I no longer find joy in the game. I have been relegated to Division 2 (or maybe even Division 3) but I still strap on my boots and give the ball whatever kicks I can. That's still taking part in the sport. Taking part in life.

I have had to get used to this new system of measuring my successes and my failings but once I got over the shock and sadness of my relegation, I realized one win. I'm still in the game of life.

The Anniversary I Don't Celebrate
04/16/2018 Kerry, Ireland

Anniversaries are funny things.

There are nuptial anniversaries, anniversaries of births, deaths, and significant cultural happenings, and then there are annual acknowledgments of personal anniversaries. Most of these are times for celebrations of some sort (even in the case of deaths, to an extent).

I'm acknowledging an anniversary this month, but I don't think I'll be celebrating it.

As you might expect, it's the anniversary of my diagnosis with multiple sclerosis of which I write.

That is not to say that I don't celebrate every one of the 6,205 days in the seventeen years since diagnosis. I simply do not celebrate the day my MS was discovered.

In fact, as I type "discovered" it makes total sense.

My MS was, indeed, diagnosed on the 25th of April 2001. But like the "discovery" of the New World—which was inhabited and not new at all—celestial bodies, or new species, my multiple sclerosis was around before it was diagnosed. Not for as long as undiscovered stars have been in the skies but at least 15 years before the doctors planted the MS flag on my life.

That was the day I began living with the life-sentence that this disease has become for me. For the first several of those years I didn't really live in tandem with MS. I sort of lived under the heavy, smothering fire blanket of the disease as it quashed so many joyous aspects of my life.

Those early years were a time of finding (or failing to find) balance in my life.

Tinkering with meds and doses. Figuring out when to push-on and when to rest. Determining when to hold the line and when to tactically retreat. Perhaps most importantly, what to hold on to and what to cut free from a life cluttered with nonsense and ego.

Like a boxer who remembers each bout but not every landed blow, I know my brain and body are different for the prolonged beatings MS has given me. I'd like to think that I'm a wiser fighter now than I was then, but multiple sclerosis is a cagey opponent. It can still land a solid punch that staggers my body and spirit.

Like that fighter, I've been laid flat by more than one of those jabs. I look to my corner—my support network of family, dear friends, and my medical team—when down, but I've also learned to use life's 10-count to the fullest in order to regain my senses. I then, once again, toe the line in this life-long, bare-knuckle brawl.

At this point in my fight with MS, I do not expect to win. Neither do I expect to lose. A bruised and battered draw is the only realistic goal of the pragmatic pugilist I have become.

I don't celebrate the fight as some people with diseases might. I do not put too much weight on the date—though so much of my life changed on that day—because the day I was told I had MS wasn't the first day of my disease. I do, however, acknowledge the anniversary.

For, if nothing else, it was the day that I entered a corridor and the door closed behind me. It took me years, but I came to realize that that hallway was filled with new doors for me to open.

And, while many of those doorways lead to unexpected opportunities, some of them open into a boxing ring.

There is No Longer a Back Burner
07/23/2018 Kerry, Ireland

A good few years ago, on Christmas holidays at a rural dairy farm in western New York, I put pristine ingredients onto the hob to simmer for what I expected would be the best New Year's dinner I'd ever cooked.

On New Year's Eve, bones and trimmings of goose, duck, venison, chicken, and a turkey went into the pot and were brought to a simmer before traditional aromatics of onion, carrot, and celery were added with a few peppercorns and herbs. Then the stockpot was moved over low heat on a back burner to simmer through the afternoon and overnight.

An unexpected—but far from uncommon for the farm—power surge in the night spiked the electricity to the stove and I woke to the unmistakable smell of burnt food from the kitchen.

My stock was ruined, plans for our cassoulet were quickly revised and a passable dinner was presented, but it was nothing like the feast we'd planned.

Another pot that I've tried to place on a back burner overflowed, this time it was my MS pot, I may have finally learned my lesson. My MS will no longer just simmer away quietly.

What I could once attend to on an as-needed basis, now requires more attention. Its sporadic nature, its penchant for splashing into other 'pots', its wont to make an awful mess of any other 'dish' on the cooker, have led me to change my life planning.

It feels like what were once stop-and-go diversions or temporary roadblocks in my neuro network are now cul-de-sacs, dead-ends or even gaping chasms in the road.

"Just what is he on about this time?" you may be asking.

Well, I was once able to span a few days of fatigue by dosing with prescription meds I first called my "Tradeshow Drug" then latter deemed "The Loan Shark" for the interest it demanded I repay. Now, that med might (or might not) help me make it through a moderately difficult day.

A cane (or sometimes crutch) was once needed to simply stabilize my walking. Now I find they often hold me up (and sometimes don't) just to stand for a few minutes on end.

My ability to focus on any task that requires my full attention, has lapsed from laser to strobe and now is often a dim and dingy bulb that flickers as the storm of MS rages outside my room.

As I try to put my stamp on the world around me, as I strive to make a small difference in my community, while I make every attempt to make our life normal for Caryn and our Pack, I now have to do so knowing my MS pot can no longer be trusted to simmer away while I attend to the rest of my life.

It's ironic, of course, that warm and comforting smells of a roasted duck stock are making their way from the kitchen to my writing desk as I convey these thoughts. I suppose that's proof that the back-burner metaphor for my MS is no longer appropriate.

It's not the stove that is the issue. It's multiple sclerosis, and it will no longer be ignored.

The Chronic Triangle
04/30/2019 Kerry, Ireland

At a recent book festival event I attended, a publishing consultant spoke of the three-pointed balance of schedule, budget, and quality in the book printing world. One must be aware of the importance (weight) of each point of the triangle and their influence on the remaining two.

You can have whatever you want for one point of the three, but the other two will be directly affected. Anyone with a chronic illness knows this balancing act, even though our points of the triangle are differently named.

The three corners of the chronic triangle are Time, Energy, and Recovery.

If the area of the triangle was great enough, it would be much easier to balance the thing. The tighter the corners are together—the less of each we have—the more difficult to find balance in life.

TIME:

I begin with the thing of which all people have a finite quantity. There are only so many hours in the day, only so many of those hours we can allot to any particular task, and also it's only so fast that anyone can do some things.

The more time something takes, or the faster we try to do it, the more influence the task will have on the other corners, thus the balance of our life.

ENERGY:

This is a biggie for people with chronic illness. I often refer to the "energy bank account." Others make use of the spoon theory. Call it what you will, people with MS have issues with profound fatigue and often find that simple tasks take more of their energy than their 'healthy' counterparts.

The amount of energy it takes to do something faster or even that it takes us longer will diminish that energy reserve and make the other two corners wobble.

RECOVERY:

This is the piper holding out his hand for payment after the dance is over.

The amount of time spent recovering from a task which required time and energy to perform, is often in direct proportion to the amount the other two corner commodities expended. Sometimes, increased time of recovery can add to the amount of time and energy we can expend on a task.

Often, however, the recovery time can be unknown until after the fact, so we can only guess and assume the weight on this third corner as we attempt to balance.

As I said, if we have nearly an unlimited supply of each of our three weighted corners, it is much easier to fudge the balancing act. When the area of our triangle is shrunk by multiple sclerosis or by any other chronic illness, finding how to balance the triangle becomes much more difficult.

Too much energy expended, and the recovery side upends the balance. Having to focus too much on time (speed) can expend too much energy and the triangle slides off on the recovery corner. Too much (or too little) concentration on the recovery angle and we waste both time and energy. Too little attention to it and we spend days before we can even consider balancing any other tasks for lack of energy and time.

It is not an easy task, this triangle balancing. It's made more difficult by the fact that the size of the triangle grows and shrinks, especially soon after diagnosis.

I'm not saying that I've figured out the balancing of the chronic triangle. In fact, it is my extended recovery from that book festival at the weekend that led me to better understand that it even existed.

I believe that evaluating potential tasks or events while keeping this chronic triangle in mind will help me in deciding if doing them will be worth the effort, or even possible.

Time, Energy, Recovery on three corners around me . . . here I am, stuck in the middle with MS.

When One Step Back is Really Two Steps Forward
10/28/2019 Clare, Ireland

Of late, I've been feeling a drain on my energy checkbook. Not only have I been making some larger than usual withdrawals with a recent book release and a spate of houseguests, it feels like my deposits have been getting smaller as well.

These deposits don't always (or even usually) come from rest. I find that personal interactions and soul-fulfilling pursuits can fill my account far better and far faster than succumbing to a required nap or simply unplugging from the world around me.

The past few months have been particularly difficult as long-anticipated culminations converged and the simple joys were bypassed for 'greater good' stuff in my life. It wasn't that I didn't know it was coming. It wasn't that I didn't plan for required recovery. It simply hit at least as hard as I'd expected, and the downtime required may be more significant than foreseen.

So, I've begun to thin and prune some of the more energy-depleting aspects of my life to allow some of the smaller branches have their light.

When I say "begun," I am talking baby-steps . . .

I've given the Irish MS & Me Blog team a 1-year notice that I'll be stepping away from my duties as assignment editor at the end of 2020. Not an immediate return sort of thing, but it does afford time for transition and sometimes the long view; big picture strategies can be as comforting as the short-term, tactical changes.

I've also given my word to myself (and my wife, Caryn) that I'll not start another book project for at least a year. This last one, with a good bit of travel over six months last year, and the extra effort working with a committee can require, really wrung me out.

Finally, I have committed to defaulting to "No" when asked to take on new projects until I have fully weighed out the overall cost:benefit ratio rather than simply seeing an opportunity to do something for short-term enjoyment.

What I feel I achieve by cutting back and not taking on tasks, is a clearer head and the feeling that a burden has been lifted from my spirit.

You see, I know that I have been unable to give all of these (and so many other) projects the full attention they deserve. I am 100% aware that someone else is likely the better person, if not for the experience I can offer than at least in the time and full attention they can bring to the table.

By trimming away some of these obligations, I know that I am giving in a bit to MS. I'm thinking of it more as a strategic retreat rather than surrender. I am stepping away from some things so I can lean in on fewer; and I plan for those fewer things to be activities that deposit into my account rather than cause my slim balance to go into overdrawn.

The old saying is "One step forward, two steps back." I feel like these difficult but required cutbacks are me taking one step backward so I can make a giant leap forward.

Life in the Slow Lane
06/12/2017 Kerry, Ireland

It was a good few years ago that the tough decision was reached to sell my vehicle. It was a considered choice, and my wife, Caryn, and I tested several possibilities in advance of the decision.

To be sure, sitting in the passengers' seat for most of our journeys after that sale was an adjustment. Now that we're in the land of right-hand drive cars (with the passengers' seat on the left, where the steering wheel is in America) it almost feels like I'm in control again until I reach for the brake or try to swerve.

On the motorways it's not only me and the driver who have traded places. The slow lane and exits are on the left side while passing lanes are on the right.

In many ways, things are like before, even though it's more than obvious that things are far from the way they used to be.

I suppose it's something of a metaphor for my life. I might feel like many parts of my life are nearly the same. I may be able to fool myself into thinking not much has changed. Hell, I can even look to those who don't know our reality as though very little is different as my MS progresses.

We, however, *know* that things are different.

As we cruise along in the left lane of life, on the left side of the car, I see the life I once thought I controlled, whizzing along as though I still had the wheel. The world of other cars interacts with me and I with them. But it is an illusion.

I've fooled myself into thinking I still control what I no longer drive. I've conned myself into seeing my old world as it once was. Perhaps, to be more kind to myself, I've learned to be happy enough that I can still partake in life, still get out in it and make a difference even if I'm not able to steer the course as I once did.

It all comes into sharp focus when I realize that traffic is passing, and my slow lane turns into an exit ramp. That's when I realize that I'm only a passenger for some of life's journeys now. Not all of them. I still have the help of my bike and for occasional short trips, the car.

A recent interview of me in a national newspaper stated that I've ". . . been living with multiple sclerosis for most of his adult life." I have indeed lived more than half of my adult with a diagnosis of MS. Perhaps I've come to the realization that the enjoyment of life isn't always about being in the driving seat.

As long as I can still get from point A to point B, I have learned to question whether I really need to be steering in order to enjoy the journey.

The Golden Hour
10/09/2020 Kerry, Ireland

No one profession has a lock on the term *The Golden Hour*. Trauma surgeons and stroke professionals know it as the first hour after injury during which the patient has best chance of survival and optimal recovery. Photographers use it to mark the half hour before to a half an hour after both sunrise and sunset.

For myself, living with multiple sclerosis for the majority of my adult life, The Golden Hour could be called by many other names.

The Lucid Hour, The Hour of Possibility, The Exercise Hour, The Only Hour . . . .

Before diagnosis, but while definitely experiencing the disease, I remember feeling like my ability to make it through a working day was shrinking. I worked in a field where 12/14-hour days were not unusual. Both the early and the late of those working hours pressed in on me as my undiagnosed MS progressed. Caffeine intake steadily increased to little or no avail. Planes and trains became mobile nap carriages, and still, my days shrank.

The useable hours became bookended by a haze of cognitive fog, visual distortions, and dread. It was like viewing time through a tunnel with the edges falling in on themselves . . . and it kept shrinking.

I got out of bed later and groggier, faltered midway through, and stumbled into the end-of-day stupor earlier and earlier. With life's norms swimming in the confused waters of constantly turning tides, I found myself becalmed and bobbing, disorientated and depressed and my world folded in.

Nearly two decades beyond the diagnosis now, little has changed about the situation, but my coping skills have assuredly evolved. I have learned the telltale signs, found and created reliable detours. I plan with more flexibility and assess changing situations like a storm reporter anticipating a hurricane's landfall. The dwindling commodity of useable hours in my days has brought about a creativity with what I do have. I still covet what I no longer possess.

My Golden Hour (or when I'm lucky, Hours) are precious currency to be spent wisely or invested bearishly. A couple of days' Golden Hours are set aside for contemplation and writing, a few for the kitchen, and some for moving my body in ways I still can. These are moments I look forward to and for which I grieve as they pass or when they fail to present themselves for use.

Just as rain or wind can skew the atmospherics for a photographer's panacea, a well-designed Lucid Hour can be fouled by a myriad of singular or combined factors beyond the control of a person living with multiple sclerosis. The Hour of Possibility can be put asunder by the most benign-appearing circumstances. My Exercise Hour spirited away on the wings of fatigue or some other thief.

But we go on.

Often by using the less optimal hours of the day to stumble through our required tasks, by paying for assistance to perform the mundane which must be completed, we free up quality time for what we might begin. Because that's just what we have to do if we're going to continue to live our lives with this disease dragging at our ankles and tarnishing the Golden Hours we have left.

That, and all the while, we try to see all that sparkles in the rough and the rust.

Age or MS? The Answer is "Yes"
09/23/2021 Kerry, Ireland

I woke on the morning after my birthday last month and felt every day of every one of the 51 years I'd lived weigh down on my body with the accumulated gravity of the decades. I hadn't played it up (my birthday was on a Monday this year and I'm also a bit long in the tooth for a birthday bender), but my body felt like I'd spent the day windsurfing, horse riding, trampolining, and boxing . . . a much better opponent.

Most of the feelings subsided over the ensuing week or so, but others have lingered as they fade. Making me wonder if any of the bits that are hanging around are a result of MS or if they're just part of *normal* aging.

As I have passed the halftime show of life, it's one of the questions I find that I both ask myself and answer for others. As we all want to be 'normal' even in our abnormality, it feels like a natural question as we age along with our disease. The answers may seem as they should be easy to come up with, but they can be complex in nature.

The easy part is to ask yourself if you think it's an exacerbation or pseudo-exacerbation.

The definition of an exacerbation has to do with a new symptom (or worsening of an existing one beyond when it was at its peak) which lasts longer than 24 hours and is not related to fever, overheating, or other like factors. The pseudo version is the worsening of an old or existing symptom, within the parameters of how you've experienced it before, that may be brought on by the above factors and usually lasts less than a day.

The second part of answering the question of age or MS would be looking back at days or few weeks prior and noticing the symptom in question. If you could do it before and can't do it now (as in rather suddenly), then it may be MS related. If it's been a slow progression of something which might naturally wear out then it may be age.

But then we get into the secondary-progressive conundrum.

The gradual worsening of a symptom of the reduced ability to do something physical, mental, etc., can be how some people experience the secondary-progressive phase of MS. And that as many as 80% of people with relapsing-remitting MS later transfer to this progressive phase make SPMS a possible (if not even likely) suspect.

But we should never assume that it's just an MS thing.

There are aspects of MS which are annoying but only rarely are they directly life-threatening. Other aspects of aging—having to do with cardio-vascular health, in particular—should never be fobbed off as likely just being our MS being its normal, annoying self.

Never consider chest pain, shortness of breath, dizziness, sudden difficulty speaking, or other signs of stroke as just an MS symptom with which you'll have to learn to live. They might be, but they could also be warning signs of something more dire indeed.

It's never a bad idea, if you are asking yourself "Is it MS or is it age?" to ask the same question of your MS medical team. They may suggest a baseline evaluation from a neuropsychologist, physiotherapist, or simply review their notes to see if there are signs of the symptoms of concern in previous visits. You never know what they may have noticed and jotted in your chart that you were unaware of even experiencing.

Speaking of which, those closest to you are also a good resource. When I 'suddenly' realize that I'm doing something quite differently than I remember—be it stammering when I speak, catching myself walking past a mirror, lifting something oddly, or any of the scores of things I know I do strangely—I ask my wife if that's how I've been doing them for a while.

I am usually surprised (horrified!) to find that that's how I do things now, or that yes, I often look like I'm throwing down gang signs as I try to balance myself as I walk. That's a particular favorite to notice myself doing . . .

The short answer to the question, "Is it age or is it MS" is, yes. It's either one or the other, or both . . . yeah, it may just be both, but probably not. How's that for an answer befitting political debate?

The other part of the answer is "It doesn't matter." If it's a problem—if it it's bothering you—talk to someone about it. Be it MS or ageing or some other reason; if it's not right get it taken care of.

Life With MS Means *Living* With Multiple Sclerosis
03/21/2011 Seattle, USA

The past couple of days were one of those postcard Pacific Northwest weekends. Bright blue skies were streaked by only the highest and wispiest of stratus clouds, ornamental cherry trees shed their bud casings to show their furry pink selves and sweet grass covered with morning dew wet my tattered old denim. So begins the spring planting ritual.

Gardening, vegetable gardening, as I've never really had much of a knack for the flower stuff, has been a pastime and mild passion of mine for a good number of years. Maybe the urge to have my hands in the soil stems from months-long deployments at sea in my Coast Guard days. Maybe, being a chef, knowing where my foods come from is of great importance. Certainly, vegetables still warm from the sun and smelling of the plants are so close to perfection they are divine.

I know that one benefit to enjoying a hobby performed on one's knees is that gardening is *ideal* for a person with MS whose balance and stamina are profoundly diminished!

This spring weekend, I was cultivating soil, weeding beds, planting seeds, mounding potato hills, and enjoying the sound of the birds.

There is a certain place of calm observation that I have learned from living with MS. I attribute this newish awareness to yoga and to my daily need to assess how I'm doing.

Knees in the rich earth or arse-soaking dew from the still-wet grass, I had a front row seat to nature's symphony this weekend.

I couldn't tell you the names of all the winged musicians serenading me throughout my chores. There were likely finches, hummingbirds, robins, tits and thrushes, to name a few. Large Flickers pecked at a nearby telephone pole to add a percussive backbone to the ensemble.

Though our home is fairly close to the sea, no gulls floated overhead as it was far too beautiful for them to be anywhere but on the rippling waves of the sound.

When the changes of the Spring Tides occurred, however, a light salty breeze would carry the sound of our local sea lions along with the scent of seaweed and barnacle spit.

I have Multiple Sclerosis, and some days—perhaps to the distain of those super humans who climb mountains, run marathons, and do other feats that would be Herculean to me—Multiple Sclerosis *has me* too.

Even on those days, I know that I *live* with MS. We have all found a way to live our lives, enjoy our being and even create beauty and joy for others with this disease.

Life with MS means *living* with Multiple Sclerosis.

I am thankful for all who have helped me to learn this lesson and to those who have been patient with me while I was schooled in the ways of a chronic condition.

This weekend, I also took lesson from birds and worms and grubs and sea lions. I guess I should send them a thank you note.

CHAPTER 9

The Living Part

THE INNOVATIVE AMERICAN POET *and social activist, Langston Hughes, wrote,*

> *"Life is for the living.*
> *Death is for the dead.*
> *Let life be like music.*
> *And death a note unsaid."*

I have always said that living with multiple sclerosis is all about the living part. We could think of no better way to end this project than focus on that, The Living Part.

These are the pieces that I search out and go back to read when I need to listen to my own advice. Advice well-intended and often delivered fresh from yet another fall or after crawling out of one more dark hole down my road with MS. It's important for me to remember that, while it's not always bright and sunny, there can be beauty in the dimness, too.

I am far from a Pollyanna. That persona works for some, and I'm happy that they've found something which works for them. For me, however, I find that a hard look at reality, tempered with pragmatism, and a healthy dose of l'humour noir works best.

When even my flippant and macabre wit fails, however, I try to look around and see the inspiration of others and of nature itself. These are the times I've come to what appears at first to be a dead-end only to realize that it's merely a cul-du-sac, and by looking about me I can find the inspiration, the will, and the capacity to turn myself around, retrace my (often staggered) steps, and find the path which works for me.

"We haven't died a winter yet" is a favorite idiom in my little corner of West Kerry. We certainly have not. Even in the coldest months of my life with this damnable disease, I really do find warmth in focusing on the living part.

Profound Fatigue
06/23/2006 Seattle, USA

We've all done it; had to get up early one morning and then not reset the alarm the next. This morning my alarm was WAY too early for my needs. We usually take advantage of an extra bit of sleep in these cases. Today, I took advantage of the extra sweeps of the hour hand in a different way.

The sun shone so beautifully in the azure-blue sky this Pacific Northwest morning that I rousted myself and my Irish soft-coated Wheaten Terrier, Sadie, and headed out for a low-tide adventure. After a requisite stop at the local coffee drive-thru, we were off to the local strand.

Now, I'll admit right here and now that we broke no less than a dozen municipal codes, ordinances and laws this morning. Call the SPD on us, today I really don't mind.

We walked to a secluded bit of the beach and off the lead she went. For better than an hour, we played in the sand and the tide pools, she chased the crows and the gulls and even a couple of great blue herons (yeah, the wildlife folks would've liked that, I'm sure). She ran and ran and ran. I smiled and laughed and cried a little. We had not been off-lead at the sea since Ireland. Herself is older now, and bigger too, but she's still the Kildare puppy with whom I fell in love all those months ago.

We often tell others (and ourselves) about enjoying the little things in life. Sometimes we even try to convince ourselves, (*especially* ourselves) that MS has helped us in that endeavor. I'm not dealing with that part right now. I'm just sitting at my desk, with Newkdara Sadie Peg O'My Heart out cold on the floor next to me and writing it all down with a silly smile (I think Sadie has one too).

I look at the way she's splayed out on the floor. Upon getting into the house, after a drink of water, she walked about fifteen paces and collapsed on the hardwood. I've had those lay-down-or-fall-down episodes due to MS; the health books call it "profound fatigue." It is joyous to see such an episode due to total, sated (and yes, profound), puppy exhaustion.

What has any of this got to do with living with MS? Not much at all, and everything, at the same time. Today, instead of writing about the MS, I choose Life.

Just a big rock in the bottom of the pool
12/26/2006 Seattle, USA

As I write this blog, it is already Boxing Day for our Aussie readers, nearly the Wren's Day for my Irish friends, and the kids on the left coast of America are just now breaking their first Christmas toys.

The moments (and days) after the gifts are opened, the goose (or turkey or ham or, or, or . . .) is served, the in-laws have left, the tree is down, the weight is gained, we sit and think, "All that work!"

It is not uncommon for the weeks after Christmas to be busy ones for the cells that ravage our myelin. Add the stress of worrying about a possible exacerbation to the trying to keep up with

Martha Stewart and even if we don't have an attack, we're likely to be pretty worn down.

I say to hell with it!

What I mean is best summed up by a saying my sister, Angie, has, something I'm going to try to keep in my head (and likely should have brought to the fore *before* the holiday) this week.

"It's just a big rock, in the bottom of the pool."

Angie was out visiting over my 40th birthday with her husband, Frank, in August. During that time, she was poking around the Pike Place Market for a memento of their trip. She found something she really liked, but it wasn't quite right.

Adorning the table of a local artisan, she found river rocks, large and small, laser engraved with words and short phrases. Angie has, for years, (over) used the phrase, "It's all good" and was hoping to find those words on one of the rocks. Her intent was to place the rock at the bottom of her swimming pool.

None of the rocks, however, produced.

She considered having the artisan create one especially for her, but the price for such custom work was beyond reason. I then asked her how many of her poolside visitors might actually take the plunge to see her rock. "Well then, I'll just tell them it's just a big rock in the bottom of the pool."

The light went on.

She didn't need some fancy, laser-manipulated bit of geology. In fact, were she to simply to find a rock—on one of our many day trips that week—it would lend personal significance to the silliness.

It was, however, the phrase, "It's just a big rock, in the bottom of the pool" which struck us both. What a great way of saying that in the greater scheme of things, even the blaring can be merely an apparition; it's just a part of a *whole* life.

Long story, long . . . she found the rock, it is in the bottom of her swimming pool. I've seen it and she does get to use her new catchphrase often.

She may never know how many times I think of that rock (and the fun we had finding it) but I surely need to remember that MS is likely to change the way people see me, but not who I am. MS has changed my life, but not its living. MS may steal my body, but it will not vandalize my spirit.

Yes, Multiple Sclerosis was not supposed to be in our life—we didn't plan for it and we don't like it. It takes and it takes, and it takes, but there is one thing it can only have if we give it: ourselves.

I guess this pontification is more a reminder to myself, even if just for today. Trevis, remember . . . It's just a big rock, in the bottom of the pool.

MS Didn't Give Us Nuttin'!
04/20/2011 Seattle, USA

The funeral mass for the first person I ever knew to have Multiple Sclerosis took place today. She lived a good life, a happy life, a full life. She's remembered today for her love of family of friends and of travel.

Goldine's life with MS taught me much, likely far more than she would have ever known. Her love for travel in particular (oft with one of her daughters to help), made me look at my life with MS differently from the start.

And today, in her honor, I state plainly that MS didn't *give* us anything. If there is goodness in our life after MS that wasn't there before; we *took it!*

MS is a sly and evil thief. I'll never give it the power of saying, "MS gave me . . ." and I think that if we do say something like that, we give too much credit to the disease and not enough to ourselves.

My doctor helped me with that one too. "Well," I once said to him, "At least I'll have time to write a book."

His response firmed my understanding of the difference between MS gave me . . . and I took _____ from MS.

"As long as you actually write the book, Trevis" was his retort (and I'm happy to say that it's almost done!).

MS didn't give you more time to enjoy the little things in life. You took the opportunity to love the minutia. This disease didn't make you more understanding of anything. You've made yourself a better person *in spite* (and there are fewer ways that "in spite" works so well) of what multiple sclerosis has taken from you, done to you and how it has affected those around you.

We are stronger now than we were before MS. Not because MS made us strong, but because we stood up (or stayed seated) and said that for everything taken we would take back and make ourselves better than MS.

I'm not trying to say that we win every battle or that multiple sclerosis can be overcome with unicorn piss and butterfly farts. MS can wring us out, beat us down, chew us up and spit us to the floor. It will only keep us down, however, if we don't take every opportunity to take something back from it.

I have learned so very much from the Life With MS Blog community. I learned that little bit from knowing a woman who took back everything she could from MS. I felt it my privilege to share it with you.

How Do You Get Your Juice?
07/18/2011 Seattle, USA

A long, long time ago in a land far, far, FAR away . . . I was the Drum Major of my competitive high school marching band. Yes, your beloved writer was indeed, the geekiest of band geeks! This time of year takes me back, in the Cuisinart of my mind, to the blend of heatstroke and joy that was our preseason Band Camp, the place where we put music and marching together with a well-choreographed field drill with color guard accents.

During those long, heat-filled summer days on a dusty back

field with chalk lines, faint, sometimes, as the Nazca lines, we would march and play and march some more and then put the playing together with the marching.

Mind you, the act of marching while putting hard metal mouth-pieces to lips could be far more than difficult. As those adolescent lips often counseled thousands of dollars' worth of orthodonture, marching anything but the smoothest path from set to set could make for a mangled, bloody mess.

In order to instill the habit of gliding across the competition field (or rugged, football-team-wrecked halftime canvas) our band had a method I've used when managing people. It's all about The Juice.

We were, of course, hydrated with enough water to keep us healthy during those long, hot days. We were, however, longing for more than just sustenance during those teen-aged days.

Each member of our group would be given a paper cup of orange juice (or some powdered drink, most likely) which was filled to the absolute tipping point. We would then form ranks and march across, around, up and down the field, holding our cups as if they were our instruments. The object, from the perspective of the students, was to keep as much juice in the cup as possible. The real training here was to get us all marching smoothly.

The concept of The Juice, as I managed with it, is in the knowing that we all have desires above and beyond our basic needs. People need a salary for their work but we work for so much more than a paycheck. I always tried to make sure that my employees were getting their Juice.

Now that many of us no longer work (or work full time, or in a position that gives us that extra *something*) due to Multiple Sclerosis, I thought I'd bring up the concept.

How do we get our Juice?

I know that it took me years (and, I'll admit it to you, YEARS) to find a way that I could engage that part of my person with drive and desire after my diagnosis with MS. Caryn and I check in with one another often to make sure we are getting our Juice.

As one of my co-leaders in Poker Night says, "We have gone from thrive to survive" with MS. Juice is the thrive part . . . we need to do so much more than simply survive (though some days, just surviving seems to take more energy than we have).

So, I begin my week thinking about the juice that I use to get, how I used to get it and where I now find that sweet, tangy joy which is above and beyond need.

We Took It Back
08/24/2012 Seattle, USA

Sitting in the back garden this week reading—something I haven't given myself the time to do of late—I hear the songs of a number of birds I'd not, knowingly, heard before. I sat the book down and just listened. The arborvitae hedge at the back of the yard is too thick and my chair wasn't well positioned, so I couldn't see all the birds that were chirping; I just listened.

Now, it appears, I have that time.

But this is a conscious decision to take back from what MS stole from me.

MS only took from us. It took careers, it took mobility, it took vision, you know what it took from you. I know what it took from me. Multiple Sclerosis did not give us time to enjoy the other parts of life. It *took* the other things with which we filled our lives (in some cases; I'm generalizing). If I decided to stop and listen to the birds yesterday, it isn't because MS gave me that time.

All MS did was leave me a big, huge, festering hole in my life.

How I chose, how *you* have chosen, to fill that time, that's the thing. Each of you has, like me, rolled up your sleeve and reached into that stinking dark place where MS ripped away our past and we grabbed hold of something deep within us and pulled it out.

I am a firm believer that we must give ourselves credit for what we have done with our lives after MS. I know (I mean I REALLY know) that I am a better person than I was before my diagnosis. I'll not, however, give this stupid disease the credit for *making me* a better person. I, along with dear friends and family, am the one who made me better.

We all know how to cope with difficulty better now than we used to. Did MS *give you* that ability? NO. MS just threw more difficulty on top of the heap. It's YOU who did that. YOU learned how to cope, not because of but in spite of.

MS didn't make us stronger. We made ourselves stronger. We, together as a group, have made ourselves stronger. I am better for knowing all of you and you are for knowing one another. MS didn't put us together. We reached out into the world, online, in our communities, and we found other hands reaching into the darkness and we latched on. And we have continued to grab those who reach into the abyss that this disease dropped into their lives.

MS didn't give us the ability to stop and smell the roses. MS knocked us down, kicked us into the gutter and tried to sweep us down the drain. It was we who crawled up, dragged ourselves along and found the damned rose bush to smell.

For all the self-esteem, self-confidence and self-worth that multiple sclerosis has robbed from us, I want all of us to stop giving this disease credit for anything good in our lives. If any good came from it, you earned it!

Give yourself permission to feel good about what you took back from this thief. You deserve it.

Now, back to my lovely birds.

Talking My Cane for A Walk
12/26/2012 Kerry, Ireland

There is one part of living with MS that has bothered me and that is a sense of reliance. I feel like I rely on others more than I'd like, I rely on assistive devices, and I rely on medications. MS can really take away a sense of control.

One of those assistive devices which I rely on is a sturdy cane. The part that bugs me is that I don't always *need* my stick (as they call them here in Ireland), but I don't leave the house without it for the knowledge that I will likely require its support at some point in my venture. That is where the reliance starts to bug me . . .

If I was headed out for a walk, for example, I'd take the cane and walk with it every step of the way even if the first few blocks (or steps!) were stable even without me firmly planting that wooden *vade mecum* beside me. I know this may sound like a petty complaint to someone who requires such assistance (or even more) on a constant basis and I hope you don't feel me being disrespectful to that need. I too have needed to rely on a wheelchair and walker to overcome my mobility challenges.

Taking and using my cane everywhere seems to almost make me *more* reliant on the damned thing; I use it when I might not really need to therefore, I feel like I need it more. And then there are the impressions from people who might see me using it one day but not the next and so on. But I've come to notice a cultural anomaly here in West Kerry that has helped me get over myself.

It is not uncommon (at all) to see someone walking along the footpath or road (or sheep path for that matter) carrying a stick in their hand. It may not be a full-on supportive cane, but some form of walking aid for those times when the ground changes or a brambly brush is encountered in the walker's pathway.

I'm sure, if you put your mind's eye to work, you can imagine an old farmer in their boots and cloth cap walking along a road with a sheepdog at heel and carrying a knobby walking stick in their hand. *That's* what I'm talking about.

This little trick is what I've come to do at the beginnings (and often after a short rest, etc.) of my walks. The trusty old cane is with me for support when I need it, I feel a bit less reliant on it and, as I've always enjoyed a cloth cap and tweed jacket, I even blend-in very well into my new countryside.

I have decided to use this new method of support whenever I leave the house. Even when I'm back in America, I'll not plant my stick and lean upon it on those strides that don't require it. Now, I know there will be times when my arrogance leaves me face down but I think I'm willing to take the risk for a bit.

Maybe it's my way of taking back a bit of control, maybe I'm trying to fit in, maybe it's just a mental game I play in order to think I've got a better handle on MS than it has a hold on me.

Now, I think I'll take my cane for a walk.

Committed to Failure
07/23/2014 Dublin, Ireland

The times when the humidity has me sweating through two, or even three, shirts in a day, relative temperatures (yes, I realize I live in Ireland but I've acclimatized to the cooler norms here) push my limits. I'm committed to "Do what I can while I can," but I feel like I'm failing more than I succeed. And it's got me thinking . . .

Though I'm purposefully living my life in a state of Multiple Sclerosis détente, I still find it important to set the bar high for myself. Only, that the bar is now relatively high because my new normal is nothing like my old normal one. Still, if I don't try I am destined not to fail but rather to forfeit. There is no shame in losing; there is no excuse to forfeit.

I simply refuse to take the option of trying off the plate of my life. That is the way to make sure that we do not fail. Walking to the end of the laneway is difficult, particularly on days like today. I could simply not try and there would be no chance of failing in my attempt. Forfeit to multiple sclerosis? Not this guy.

I could set the goals closer, perhaps to the next house or the one beyond. Sometimes, that's exactly what I am forced to do as getting there is only half the battle on 'one of those days'. Living life with easy goals, however, is my version of continual surrender and while I understand I don't have as much control as before, I will never surrender.

Don't get me wrong, sometimes stretching my goals means trying to make it through dinner without falling asleep in the mashed potatoes. I'm not talking about mountain climbing or running marathons here. I just try to do a little bit more than I think I'm able.

So, that leaves me with one final choice (in my book, it may not be so in yours). I choose to fail.

I choose to set the bar high and, on many occasions, I choose to fail. I intend to shoot for the moon not because, as Norman Vincent Peale said, "Even if you miss, you'll land among the stars." Rather, it is important for me to feel like I'm giving it my all, even if I fail. It makes those occasional successes, even if it's making it through an entire film with Caryn and the Pack on the sofa and needing help to bed after, sweet in spite of their simplicity.

We can choose to stay on the sofa.

We can choose to go to the front door.

We can choose to go past the front gate, only to find that we stumble along the way and must return.

It is our choice. If trying means the possibility, if not probability, that I'll miss the mark, then I choose to fail.

I guess it's all in how one defines success.

The Kindness We Do for Ourselves
01/14/2015 Kerry, Ireland

We've just finished the "It's better to give than receive" season and many of us have made New Year's resolutions that have us living some part of life with long teeth. We're only weeks away from the liturgical season when many will give up something dear to them for six weeks of penance and self-denial. I'm going to turn the table and talk about giving something to ourselves.

I've said before that MS is a thief. It takes more from me than I am willing to give, it doesn't matter whether I'm willing or not. For that reason, I've decided (well, Caryn and I have decided), that we need to be a little bit kinder to ourselves.

After three weeks of holidays and illnesses, our housekeeper is back, and I am joyfully writing with the sound of the vacuum cleaner whirring and the dogs running from room to room to avoid the same.

It's an expense we have budgeted and for which we have made sacrifices. We live a pretty frugal life here in Ireland. We live simply here so that we can simply live here. This little kindness to ourselves allows us to spend more quality time together.

The same goes for my love of gardening. Hands in the soil is a wonderful way for me to spend several hours even if I'm not feeling all that well. And, let's face it, I haven't as far to fall if I'm on my hands and knees.

The pretty annuals can seem a waste of money, a one-and-done splash of color. Rather, I spend money on inexpensive vegetable seeds and start them in old egg cartons in the spare room in March. Even now, amid a January storm, I can look out on a forest of Kales, Brussels sprouts and parsley in our front raised beds. That six Euros worth of seeds not only gave me hours of quiet joy in the garden and pounds of vegetables to eat, now the shades of green bring joy to my eyes and heart.

Pedicures for those with MS who find it difficult to attend to their feet are a requirement for many but they are also a source of great joy and well worth the expense as well. A subscription to a video streaming/music service can afford hours of entertainment when moving from one room to the next is a chore.

We spend one Euro per week on a bag of carrots so that I can feed the neighbor donkeys and I share a bit of the oats I use for porridge with the heifers who are wintering in the field behind the house. If you've never seen a donkey foal skipping across a field to come collect her carrot or felt the strong, rough tongue of a Holstein Friesian licking your hand, you may not think of it as a kindness to yourself but trust me, it is.

Sometimes MS and the big issues of life can make it seem like there is no way we can spend time, energy or money on something for ourselves. I say that it needn't be a lot of money, it needn't take much energy and we all have the same 24 hours in a day. How we choose to spend them is what makes all the difference.

I look at these little expenses, what I do for myself often makes me a better person for others in my life. It is worthwhile investment in myself when it nourishes me and I am a better person, better able to share the best of me with those around me.

Hope Without A Plan Is Just A Dream . . .
But Dreams Do Come True
02/02/2015 Kerry, Ireland

Ten years ago, I stood beneath a pub sign squeaking in the cold wind with my brother as we sang to my sister's B&B room three stories above and across the street. We were in a town in west Kerry. I don't expect that we sang well but as we stood there, I began to hatch an idea about living in that town the coming winter.

I had always hoped that one day I might live in an Irish town into my advanced years. As we all know, however, MS can make the view into our retirement planning hazy at best and completely obscured on most days. So, I decided that it would be that winter that I would live out that dream.

It takes a lot of planning (and a bit of luck) for such a dream to become a reality. Treatment with the heaviest guns my doc could offer had opened a window of opportunity and I didn't know how long before it slammed shut again. So it was then or never in my mind.

That winter of 2005-2006 in Ireland is the setting for my book, *Chef Interrupted; Discovering Life's Second Course in Ireland with Multiple Sclerosis*. And I thought going into the trip that it would be the culmination of a lifetime hope. What I realized while there is that it wasn't the fulfilment, but rather the beginning of a new dream altogether.

Ever since returning from our honeymoon in Ireland, Caryn and I had been dreaming of actually shifting to Ireland for a semi-permanent stay. The idea was daunting and fraught with figurative tripwires. Not the least of them being the expense of the idea.

We rented out the main part of our house. We really enjoyed the light and space and layout of our home, but we wanted to make Ireland happen as fast as practicable. We moved into the house's 500 square foot mother-in-law apartment in the basement. With three dogs (at the time) and my MS, we shifted our life into what we called "The Boat" for its compact size.

With a few modifications like a Murphy bed, brightly painted window wells and the entry stairs, we made the best of our small space.

We scrimped and saved and shared space more closely than many college dorm-mates. It hasn't been easy, but The Boat has been home for better than two thirds of our married life. We've had to say goodbye to two of our beloved pack over there under that window. We cried together over MS symptoms on that chaise. We celebrated an Oaxaca-inspired Thanksgiving right where I'm typing this blog and cooked *that* dinner on that little stove. I can see (and nearly reach) all of those places from where I sit.

Not everyone has a dream to move halfway across the globe. Not all of us can make the biggest of our hopes come true. The fact is that hope without a plan is just a dream. If we're going to live any part of our lives with purpose and joy, we must take the wheel away from MS and do our best to drive our lives in the direction of our desires.

Hope without a plan, hope without an amazing partner, hope without love and care and support . . . it's all just notions.

We are now nearing the fruition of a dream and we did it by planning and working and forgiving (a lot!) all along the way.

Thank you, Petal. It couldn't have been done without you.

Gorse Fire Season, Making Way for Something New
02/09/2015 Kerry, Ireland

Yesterday was a stunning day here in west Kerry.

Not that it was particularly warm but the bright, blue sky stretched all the way down to the mountains. There is the smallest hint of Spring in the hazel trees and when the sun came out from behind the fluffy, bleached clouds, the February chill cracked . . . and a sliver of heat seeped out.

Thick sea fog was pulled to wisps of candy floss by the time it reached the shore. Meanwhile, the mountainsides belched thick, amber-tinted smoke. It's the season of Gorse (Ulex) burning here in the county.

The Western Gorse that grows on our hillsides is an extremely thorny evergreen shrub. While it's not the invasive version of North America, it crowds out the wild grasses that many sheep farmers rely on to put their animals to on the meadows. It's a legal, seasonal burning.

Perhaps we should all declare a season for burning away the stuff in our lives that is stopping the tender grasses to grow.

Away with the friends who block the sunlight from our fertile ground. Be done with family members who suck the nutrients from us. Say goodbye to those who abrade us with thorny comments and cover us in the stinking sap of unkind actions.

When I looked across the valley to the stone-walled fields on the hillsides across, I could see large fields where gorse had been allowed to take over. From dry-stacked fence to dry-stacked fence the evergreens had taken over and made the fields unusable. Just a few feet away, however, the adjoining field which had been properly burned from time to time was lush and teeming with ewes birthing bouncy young lambs into the world.

There are true friends out there waiting to fill our field with the buzzing of new life, colleagues who would love to have a good ol' chinwag and kinder relations waiting. When we clear the detritus of the soul-sucking shrubbery to grow untended and make room in our field wholesome, nourishing company.

I get e-mails and messages almost weekly from people living with multiple sclerosis and another chronic condition—toxic relationships. These relationships can cause as much emotional damage as MS does physically. It is up to us to assess our own situations and carry out the prescription that we all know will solve the issue.

There will be smoke, there may be flames but, in the end, there is a new beginning. There is potential for a newly revealed stronger self, ready for healthy, loving relationships to grow. The field of our life can still be a place of great joy and many can benefit from clearing what a dear friend calls The Deadwood from around us.

Spring is here. What better time than now to prune back, dig up and burn away relationships which have become invasive?

Maybe a little bit harsh, but I have seen the beauty of the well-tended fields.

The Shawshank Redemption and Chronic Freedom
04/28/2016 Kerry, Ireland

I think we all know my feeling about giving multiple sclerosis credit for anything positive in our lives. Chronic illness doesn't give, it takes.

When I asked an audience of online health advocates why they do what they do, one person pushed my 'gave me' button and, though I wanted to pass it up, I couldn't. Julie Cerrone, a health advocate and psoriatic arthritis blogger, said that while she hadn't chosen to be sick but that because of it, "It's given me my purpose."

And I couldn't stop myself.

I began with my usual caveats about each of us coping how we need to and that what I was about to say was my personal bailiwick. As I said this, an analogy came to mind that I'd never thought of before . . . but wish I had.

In the film *The Shawshank Redemption*, protagonist Andy Dufresne is locked in a prison cell for a crime he didn't commit, by forces beyond his control, you might say.

Andy's intellect and intelligence can only get him so far in coping with his double life-sentence but within himself he finds something deep down, something that was already there. It's a quote that we can all reflect upon each day to make our lives and those around us better, "I guess it comes down to a simple choice, really. Get busy living or get busy dying."

With a tiny rock-hammer of hope and a plan for a better life, Dufresne chips away at the seemingly impregnable walls of his cell, finds his way through the maze of his prison and finally uses a sewage pipe to escape into the cold but cleansing rain of his new life.

Like the fictional character from this Stephen King short story, we too have been locked-up but by our disease. Our attitude, education and faith can only get us so far. We have each figured out our rock-hammer, something that might seem insignificant relative to our disease, and we began to scratch and scrape and chip our way through our cell walls.

Then it was on to the bigger task of negotiating our way through the inner workings of the disease. How do we make our way around, through the guts of living with a chronic condition?

Some of us are still in the cell. Some of us are looking for that hammer. Some of us are still finding our way around the complexities of what the disease is doing to us.

To be the most successful in living with a chronic illness, something that each of the advocates I asked can list as an accomplishment, we have to slog our way through our own shit in order to finally live the life we dream of in the fearful darkness of our disease.

The reward may only be a cold rain with flashes of bright lightning to lead our way, like in the case of the film. But soon a new dawn breaks and, while we'll never escape the sentence handed down upon us, we can live a new life. We can still have hopes and dreams and most importantly to me, we can be models that there is a way out.

Julie Cerrone and the 90-odd other bloggers and advocates who attended Health-E-Voices 2016 have dug their way out, they have crawled through the muck, and most importantly they have mapped the way for others to find a sense of freedom . . . even if it is a chronic freedom.

Gather Ye Blackberries While Ye May
08/18/2016 Kerry, Ireland

There is a field at the end of our lane, just a few dozen meters beyond our cottage. I should say there was a field.

This rough patch of ground has been owned by a builder friend of ours for a number of years. While the economy was in the tank, there wasn't even a thought of building anything on this T-shaped plot of about fifteen acres.

In the years we've been living next to this field there have been horses and sheep illegally quartered there by people looking for a bit of grass for their animals, a family of donkeys put there every winter (with the owner's permission) and seasonal raids during which we've foraged for everything from nettles and wild garlic to wild primroses and sloe fruit for gin. We've also picked buckets and buckets of wild blackberries at the end of each summer.

Our puppies played with the donkeys. We met one foal just moments after she was born; the mare pushed her to me so that she might get to know us. We called her "Baby" and she was still wet from birth as she sucked on my earlobe thinking it might give her a bit of a meal.

We also took the dogs over to chase after the scores of bunnies and hares that bounced around in the long summer evenings. The call of the occasional cock-pheasant or the bark of a vixen fox could be heard now and then.

We tried to pick the wild sour cherries ahead of the birds but seldom got more than a handful of nearly ripe fruit.

With planning permission running out and a housing crunch in the whole of the country, the diggers and stone masons have been at work these last few weeks turning the old field into a teeming construction site and an eventual home for nine families. So, the blackberry bushes are gone.

There are other stands of brambles ready to burst into ripeness as the waning summer days give way to Celtic autumn, but now my legs have a hard time carrying me to them.

I may have to settle for the few thorny canes that bare less than optimal fruit on our little laneway this year. The berry-lined roads in the hills behind our house are out of reach for me this year and the nearby bushes have now gone.

"Gather the rosebuds while ye may," entreated Robert Hendricks in his poem *To The Virgins to Make Much of Time*. I think he might have been talking about my blackberries too.

We don't know what may change in us or for us as we live with multiple sclerosis. Some things that change were going to change, MS or not. Some things change because of MS. The one thing that won't change is the memory of those warm, juicy berries, oft broken in my clumsy fingers, as we plucked them from their thorny branches.

Half of them made it home; alright, a fraction of them made it to be put into cobblers and jams, to be frozen, stewed or baked.

This year, it will be the memory, which is sweet in my mind but, like the sour pucker of the odd wild berry that hadn't quite ripened, these memories will make me wince to know that the picking, for this year at least, will live only in those memories.

The Controlled Fall of the Songbirds
06/27/2017 Kerry, Ireland

I don't have a problem falling with my MS. I fall, I get back up, no problem except, of course when the fall is the problem. But I try to focus on the time in-between the literal and figurative MS falls in my life.

A slow stretch of the legs down the laneway with my pack today reminded me of that time between the falls.

Yesterday was one of those soft, damp days that you hear about in Ireland. Thick, gray mist hung in the air all day and the long light of near midsummer made for a constant shade from 5:00 am until after 10:00 pm. Days like that can make it difficult to tell what time it is.

The girls still needed exercise but going out for long in that soup wasn't high on my list, so I just threw the ball a bit for them. Our old girl, Sadie, came up a bit lame during our catch, thus (along with some MS sleep related stuff for me) the short, slow walk this morning.

As Sadie and I hobbled (and Maggie darted about like a bunny on speed) down the bóithrín, a brace of songbirds shot past, overhead in a flight pattern which reminded me of how I get on between those falls.

Their pattern of flight wasn't graceful. The two did not glide effortlessly as they passed. These birds wouldn't be listed as players in any avian ballet. The flapped their wings once or twice to gain loft of a few meters and trajectory and then folded their wings and *fell*.

They fell downward. They fell forward. They fell near, sometimes below, sometimes above, where they had first flapped. These birds weren't flying, they were falling just like I do . . . just like we do.

We flap when we can, as hard as we can and try to gain a relatively stable place in our lives. We move forward in not always the most graceful of manners, and we move up and down in our world physically, emotionally, financially, spiritually, factually, and metaphorically. But we move.

To the other birds, more graceful, more majestic, more suited for floating on currents of air, this couple of cousins may have looked odd at best, silly at least. And I must admit that I noted them for the oddity of their aerial maneuvering as well. But they were flying!

So, the next time I feel myself falling, in one form or another, due to this stupid disease, I'm going to try to remember those birds.

They made their way in the world as best they could. Sadie and I were doing the same this morning. And you know what? Even though Maggie might have altered the way she would have liked to have played on the lane, she was happy just being with us . . . no matter how poorly we flew.

A Game of Small Ball
03/13/2018 Kerry, Ireland

With baseball spring training in full swing, my mind turns to the game I played as a child and love as an adult. I've likened explaining the game to explaining multiple sclerosis. I have built my MS medical team the way a good manager builds their baseball team. But I think I can draw yet another analogy between how I now live my life with multiple sclerosis with how some players and managers approach a baseball game.

I'm known to say that you can divide the world into two kinds of people—those who divide the world into two kinds of people, and those who don't. The overall play of the game of baseball, however, can indeed be divided in two: Big Innings and Small Ball.

I used to live as a Big Inning player.

I swung for the fences, looked for extra-base hits, and stretched singles into doubles. I relied on power in the batters' box of life before MS. Even if it resulted in a fair number of fly-outs and strikeouts, it was a way of living that suited me because as it created a good number of runs scored. Now, however, I don't have that kind of power. If I'm going to score in this new life with multiple sclerosis pitching, I must play a different game. I've had to learn MS small ball.

Rather than relying on extra bases, towering home runs and the occasional grand slam, I take the "get 'em on, get 'em over, and get 'em in" approach to life.

If MS affords me a base on balls, I'll take the walk. If I can bunt to advance my cause rather than expending the energy of a full swing, I'll bunt. I'll occasionally even play for the sacrifice to move things along, knowing that it's the game that is important, not the at bat.

Perhaps the most satisfying of my Small Ball tactics when playing against MS is the occasional base I'm able to steal when its back is turned. I don't have the speed I once had to run on a good arm, but if I see an opening, I might just chance the thrill . . . even though I'm often caught short and pay for the attempt.

Still, it's worth the effort for the times I can swipe one from multiple sclerosis.

I haven't played serious baseball since I saw my first curveball at age 12. I knew then that I didn't have the stuff for the pro game. I love everything about the game, from the queue to get into the stadium, the way the crowd holds its breath when a manager puts on the hit-and-run play to saying, "Goodnight" to the ushers on the way home.

For me, the hit-and-run play has always been the most exciting play to watch. And living a life playing against multiple sclerosis, it's my best play to move things along and keep the score close. I put the runner in motion, and trust that I can still put the bat on the ball, even if it's just a sacrifice or a single. My team still advances.

The Textures of Happy
01/31/2019 Kerry, Ireland

I was rereading an old interview with rock & roll legend, David Byrne. The piece was written by Joseph O'Connor, the Irish novelist with a very famous pop-star sister.

Mr. Byrne was asked about his most recent album which O'Connor thought had an "Emphasis on sadness." Byrne replied that, ". . . sadness or melancholy is so rich compared to happiness, which always seems so light and fluffy and shallow to me. It's like a greeting card world full of fluffy animals and smiley faces."

He goes on with some pretty well-thought-out bits about the importance of embracing our times of sadness. Good stuff, but his dismissal of one-dimensional happiness is what I thought worth an intellectual rambling.

Pink and puffy, candy floss flavored unicorn piss is one kind of happiness, there's no getting around that. It's the stuff used for printing money with for as long as they've been pressing wax into records. There are, however, many textures of happiness which people who live with the constant burden of chronic illness know well.

We know "happy in-spite of," and "happy, but" perhaps more than we know the stuff of greeting cards and smiley faces. In fact, like the richness Byrne finds on the other side of the emotional number line, I think that the texture of on the bright side of life to be worth note and appreciation.

I don't find myself giddy at situations and prospects anymore. Rather, I know the bruised satisfaction of watching my team's victory from the sidelines. Mine is not the joy of holding a loving cup trophy high for perfect roses, but the pleasure of eating vegetables from my garden (or giggling as I'm attacked by dog kisses after falling over while weeding the beds!). Mine is a knowing delight of doing more today than I could yesterday not the overwhelming gayety of accomplishing what I never had before.

Our happiness has bumps and places where pink becomes red and bright becomes dark . . . but a happy dark.

There are enough reasons why people living with MS don't always feel happy. I like to think, however, that we maybe experience our *joie de vivre* more thoroughly than most, simply because of the horrors we know so well. Our turbulent buoyancy is more pleasurable not because we have escaped the anchor of our disease, but rather because we have risen above it to the extent which we have.

We don't soar with the eagles; we flutter with the songbirds.

Our laughter isn't the giggle of a toddler, attacked by a litter of puppies. It's more like my late, chain-smoking grandmother's guffaw at watching that youthful canine charge would have sounded. Ours is a chuckle at the poker table of life as we're about to reveal four of a kind to beat MS's Full House . . . just this once.

No, a life with multiple sclerosis isn't a giddy one, but it's still a joyous life. And sometimes, just sometimes, when I take that tumble in the garden and our wheaten terriers come in for the kill, I might even sound like that toddler overcome by puppies and for a moment my world *is* full of fluffy animals and smiley faces.

It's the Little Things
04/30/2020 Kerry, Ireland

People living with multiple sclerosis have become accustomed to variabilities in their condition. We have learned to adapt to new symptoms, new medications, new normal. If there is one thing that we get good at as we progress through a life with multiple sclerosis, it's getting on with the getting on.

One of the ways we've learned to cope is by focusing on those things that are both most important and most attainable. If something is high on importance list but low on the attainable, we seldom abandon the thing all together, we work on a work-around.

I have found myself dissecting many of my life's most joyful aspects which take more resources to achieve than I am able to expend.

In separating the thing into pieces, I have been able to sort and cull the bits that are either less enjoyable than others, take the most effort, and/or those which the ultimate bill (physical or financial) would leave me reeling.

As I've gone through this exercise it has become clear that the little things, as the song goes, really do mean a lot.

Tending large gardens might be out, but a window box, a pot or two, even a small, raised bed still bring great joy, and a few herbs and veg for the table. Long walks on the beach might have to be replaced with a seat in the sand as Caryn and the dogs make their seaside lap. A hike in the mountains has been replaced by a simple view of the hills behind the house.

I can no longer serve-up (nor afford) vast dinner parties, but I can make a dish or two for my wife and me. I can write menus and recipes for others to enjoy. I can read about what the great chefs and good cooks of the world are cooking and eating.

Extravagant bouquets from the florist mightn't be in the budget these days but a bunch of wildflowers collected down the laneway can adorn the table if the legs will allow the trip.

When I recently asked people in my MS community to look out their windows and report on something lovely, the answers were all about the little things.

There were birds at feeders, on branches, and bathing themselves in rainwater puddles. Flowers, budding leaves, and freshly mowed grass figured frequently as well. Accounts of children in swings, tending flower beds, and playing with dogs abounded. Lots of pets, in fact, brought people joy as they looked from their homes out into the world.

Little bits of joy were even found in the less than ideal.

"Raindrops on roses . . . literally" read one reply.

Rather than mentioning the clouds, the wet weather, or that it may have been difficult to see anything joyful at all out the window, this person with MS saw joy in the very thing which would cause some people to see nothing but the gloom of it all.

Yes, we work our way around as we live with the difficulties, the trepidations, the trials and the terrors of life with MS. But when we find joy in the small things, we find a way to enjoy aspects of what used to bring us pleasure, and we use those little things to help us past the obstacles we know will greet us every day.

It's not how we would have chosen to live our lives. And it surely doesn't make all the difficulties go away. It's just the only way we know how to make it worth the living.

And that's what makes the little things so big.

Living Down a Country Lane
11/03/2020 Kerry, Ireland

The word in the Irish language is bóithrín, anglicized to boreen or bohereen. It's generally translated into "small road," but the bóith part means cow. I think of it more as a field-to-field cattle track that has become a road as the houses down our laneway were constructed.

Our cottage is the last but one, tucked in off this little laneway.

As I've made my way up or down the lane over the years, I've learned to expect the unexpected. Be it small potholes that can become crater-sized after overnight rain, or a lost and bewildered tourist who made the three wrong turns to reach our end of the lane. You just learn to get-on down a bóithrín.

You have to plan things when you live down the end of a cow track. You never go anywhere emptyhanded as you never go out for just one thing. You always ask your neighbors if they need anything while you're out. You always have tea bags, milk, and biscuits on the shopping list for those who wander down, intended or not.

Cars are rare enough on the bóithrín that I can let the dogs off the lead to run a bit if it's the kind of MS day when up and back is all my weakened legs can manage. Our youngest, Maggie, will let us know that we should expect a delivery within a couple of minutes when she hears the postman's van splashing through those potholes.

We've had other visitors down our bóithrín as well.

There have been the cattle from the field behind who squeezed through their gate to come and eat grasses from the side of the lane. The rescued jack donkey from the other end of the road who must have heard the two females in the field past our end and spent half-an-hour at the gate with me and our oldest dog, Sadie. Or the neighbor's ducks and chickens who like to hunt along the lane and know that I'll throw a handful of oats if I see them coming.

It's not easy, living down a bóithrín like this while coping with symptoms of multiple sclerosis. Then again, it's not particularly easy living anywhere when the beast is awakened.

We've learned to navigate the real and figurative potholes; we've come to rely on the kindness of neighbors and to repay good deeds in kind. I've come to understand loneliness, and I've learned to ask when I need help or a bit of company.

I've also come to understand that there is an expertise which comes from living at the end of an old cow track. Others who wander down this way might need directions on more than how to get back to the main road. We've learned to recognize when someone requires more assistance than they may be comfortable letting on.

Life down this old country road is a lot like the life I've learned to live with MS. Potholes and unexpected joys alike.

Good Days and Bad Days Writ Large
11/30/2021 Kerry, Ireland

It has been a year since this experience and I'm just now able to write about it. You know these things are coming from the day a fluffy bundle of joy arrives home with you. You know it, but you tuck it away like the knowledge that you've a progressive, debilitating disease that will probably get worse. You tuck it away because on the good days—and the day in question, 30th November, was one of the best in my life—can help you though the bad.

That was the day I kept a promise to my Wheaten Terrier (and myself) made 6 years earlier.

On the top of a hill, with my back against an ancient stone wall and looking out on to where the brown-green Irish hills slumped into the gray sea, I promised young Sadie that I would bring her back one day. That I would bring her "home," as it was the land of her birth and the 3 months I'd spent here over the winter of 2005-2006 with her had made it my heart's home as well.

We took off from the Ireland of pony traps, turf fires and cups of tea with neighbors. We landed in Seattle, America three days before the Seahawks first ever Super Bowl game. Not only did Sadie and I not know what time or day it was, I had the feeling I'd left one world and arrived in another world decades later.

The anniversary of the day we landed in back Dublin, and I kept my promise to her will forever be one of those you tuck in your heart for the darker days we all know will come.

The ensuing eight years that Sadie and I spent discovering the beaches and lanes, streams and hills of our peninsula were the best of my life and of hers as well. 30th November was a day worth celebrating. Was, and still is, but . . .

As Sadie passed her 16th birthday in July of 2020, even before that if I were to be honest with myself, it was apparent that it would be her last. She'd gone completely deaf by that point and a degenerative neurological condition was making her daily (and nightly) routine more difficult.

She still loved to get out on the strand, to sniff the rabbit holes in the field behind the house, and to lay at my feet as I wrote my books. But, like her Da taking advantage of a good MS day and paying the price in those following, her recovery time was getting longer while her stamina during the good times got shorter.

We lost sleep together as she tried to get comfortable and doze for an hour or so at a time before wanting to go out—usually just to sniff the night air—before settling back in for another nap. We shortened our morning walks to the point that they were really just a short wander a few houses up the lane and back. And we had to wait for a cloudy spell or when the sun was behind the trees, as the bright light disorientated her and she would stumble.

And, one day, she just decided that she'd had enough.

Sadie was the kind of dog you only get to partner with once in your life and that's only if you are very fortunate. She told me when she'd had enough, and it was my duty to respect her assessment of her quality of life. It is the most difficult right decision to make. Those who know, know.

I suppose she knew, somehow, how difficult the anniversary of her passing would weigh on me until the day of my own. I look through thick saline as I try to even type the story of it all.

Fitting then, that she left us, as quietly and ladylike as you'd expect from the extraordinary life that she was, on the very date we celebrate our return to her native and my adopted home.

There are good days and bad days in any life. Those of us with chronic illness know keenly the difference between them and the imperative to enjoy the good for the good they can be, for mind, body, and heart when the days are not so good. Sometimes we have both on the same day, but seldom are they at the far end of the number line in one go.

The 30th of November will, forever, be the best of days. So, too, will it be the worst. But I'll remember the 2,920 days in between the two because that's how Sadie and I learned to do it.

RIP Newkdera Sadie Peg O'My Heart

The Headwinds of a COVID Winter
12/11/2020 Kerry, Ireland

There are things that people with MS and other chronic conditions have learned to compromise in order to get done what must get done. We collapse on Friday evenings and rest all weekend just to make it through another working week. We save our energy for hours or days on end, just to complete a task of importance. There are children to raise, relationships to which we must attend, and appointments that can't be missed.

We count, recount, and save our spoons throughout our days in hopes that what must be done will be done and that there might be something left to give us a stir at the weekend.

As we've learned to live with our conditions, we've got pretty good at this technique most but not all of the time. We've also learned that a team effort can be of great help. Even if it's only moral support, a friend or community can boost us more than we knew we required.

I've come to equate much of my life with MS to my regular cycling into our town to collect the messages (Irish slang for picking up a few groceries), particularly as the seasons progress.

Ours is a windy, westerly orientated, peninsula, which juts out into the North Atlantic. The lanes and roads I bike to get to and from the shops radiate to and from every direction of the compass rose. Still, like those saved-for reprieves of a life with MS, I typically find respite from the forces of nature on one or more of my journey's legs.

As actual winter collides with the figurative cold, dark season of another COVID-19 surge and associated lockdowns, I realize that my cycling metaphor has become more on-point than I'd prefer to admit, even to myself.

During the winter months, it's not uncommon for cyclonic storms (or even just cells) to sweep across our little prow into the sea. The wind on these days will back or veer over the course of hours or even minutes. What was a headwind on my trip in for a liter of milk can just as easily turn around to meet me again on my journey home.

Like the challenges of staying connected to those who give us strength to make it through/past/over or around our MS obstacles and as restrictions keep us further and further apart, my wintertime headwinds make it difficult to even consider completing the trek.

We all have our coping skills, life-hacks, and tips we've collected along the way. We've become fair hands at out-witting the disease which would rather keep us on the sofa than allow us into the world we love. We learn how and when to employ them and even become proficient in anticipating when the next MS wind might blow.

But when even those tools are foiled by the swirling zephyr and blocked by public health precautions, we must all find ways to accomplish the tasks we've no choice but to do. That we will have to dig deep, we may have to ask for help, and it might even mean grabbing a proffered line and simply holding on until the winds abate.

Many of us have missed contact with friends, with family, and with our accustomed MS support networks over the period of the COVID-19 pandemic. Somehow it seemed different as spring and summer daylight and weather gave us both real and figurative brightness and warmth. This winter will be different. We'll all need to rethink our path from time to time, or every time our cupboards need to be filled.

Know there is help. Know there are people who understand. Don't be afraid to seek those who can assist. It's going to be a long winter, and the headwinds that are MS will not abate simply because we've now other concerns to cope with.

The Power of Hope
02/26/2021 Kerry, Ireland

Hope is one of those words you read and hear a lot in the world of chronic disease. We hope for the good days, we hope to be able to afford the best care, we hope for our families, and we hope for an eventual cure. Hope is an ethereal concept. Nearly an emotion, partly a state of being. Hope is marking time in the parade of life.

Surely it is about as wishy-washy a verb as there can be in our language. Hope can seem the treading water of life with MS.

I have serious issue with hope.

When pressed into service to help announce the new Fast Forward initiative a number of years ago, I turned a phrase I still contend is one of my best, "Hope without a plan is just a dream."

We can hope for something all we want. Without a plan and subsequent action on said stratagem, hope is not only expecting to hit the lottery, it's writing cheques on your winnings without purchasing a ticket.

But there is a power in hope.

Hope is the spark, the idea, the germ of the proverbial mustard seed which can grow into a great bush of possibility. It must be fanned, it must be thought through, it must be planted and tended. With that work hope is the unseen wind which drives the waves. The invisible force of gravity that raises and lowers tides.

The best place to witness hope is at the bottom of the curve.

In the late 1990s, under the Clinton Administration, I was named as a goodwill ambassador for the US Agency for International Development (USAID) to Ukraine. On my way there, I laid-over a couple of days in Budapest, Hungary.

The Hungarian economy had been through decades of blood-letting with only the sparsest of attention to the wounds such syphoning leaves. The people had been through decades of harsh rule after centuries of on-again-off-again splendor. Things were bad for the Budapesti, but they had been worse, and that made all the difference.

Things were difficult, the past had been a string of bleak years, and they had reason to be down about their lot. But they were not.

When asked about the dichotomy I was witnessing between the reality of their situation and the upbeat mannerism of the locals, my translator gave me the best interpretation of hope I've yet to hear.

"We are at the bottom." he explained to me, "We have been through the falling and we have survived. Now we look up and though it is a long way to climb, we know that we are no longer falling, and even if we do, we know that we can survive the fall. It isn't getting better yet but it has stopped getting worse."

Hope is the end of an exacerbation when the symptoms stop getting worse and we wait to see if they get better. Hope is getting approval for a new disease modifying therapy and anticipating the first dose. Hope is the moment we stop seeing assistive devices as detrimental to our persona and beneficial to our wellbeing. Hope is the moment intangible takes form when flint meets iron.

Hope is a most personal of coping strategy for each of us to tend in our own way. On its own, hope is nothing. With the perspective of history and experience, however, hope is the knowledge that we can survive the fall. Sometimes that's all we need to get us through the long climb from the bottom.

Flight of the Gannet
04/15/2021 Kerry, Ireland

On a recent good day, that's weather *and* MS good day, my Wheaten Terrier, Maggie and I found ourselves taking advantage of both.

The outskirts of our town afford stunning views from the cliffs at the harbor's mouth. There is a short (and safe) walk from small carparks on either side of the now-automated lighthouse (which guides fishing boats in and tourists out). With weather and health on our side, we laced-up, wrapped-up, and packed-up for some sea air and a quiet stroll.

As we passed the old folly in the pasture, on a bluff on the town side of the lighthouse, pies of 'evidence' of the field's residents were obstacles for me to avoid and waypoints for Maggie's stop-sniff-pee process of hiking. As we crested the hill and looked down into a small hollow where the silage bale sat, we found the cattle hovering behind a stand of gorse in full bloom.

Maggie and I continued toward the lighthouse. The reason for their sheltering in the hollow would become evident to us later.

Once we arrived at the harbor mouth and destination, we carefully descended (Maggie bounded with great enthusiasm) the stairs cut into the rock. It leads to several places to sit and observe the beauty of it all. The stairs go well down to the breaking surf but I decided if we only went part way down meant only having to go part way back up again!

I settled into a comfortable spot while Maggie took to exploring the scents of sea and shore. From tufts of rock samphire to crags and joints of the fossilized sediment. If not for the cheese sandwich I eventually unwrapped, I'm not sure she would have remembered I was there!

Paintings and poems have been conceived from vistas like Maggie and I shared that day. All much better than I could convey. But the ariel dance of gannets drew my attention.

The first time I saw a gannet fly from here, I thought that it was one of the numerous types of gulls who inhabit this part of the island. Perhaps bigger than most, but from a distance, the specifics were difficult to discern. Until the bird fell from the sky.

As if struck by a huntsman's shot, the bird's wings folded back and it plummeted into the waves below. I drew immediate analogy with my diagnosing MS attack as I watched the bird splash into the sea. Then it popped above the surface, gobbling a small fish as it did.

The bird hadn't fallen, but rather dived.

Watching the small group of gannets, I expected and even anticipated their dives and saw them for the grace and purpose they exhibited and so much more so than on that first sighting.

Their dives from beautiful flight appear to be the end of it all, but they resurface and once again take flight. Sometimes they bob on the rolling sea a bit longer than others. I suppose the fall from flight can affect them just as the more difficult times can leave me a bit stunned after a rapid descent from new normal into depths of difficulty.

The gannets were still flying, diving, bobbing, and taking off again as Maggie and I left our sheltered perch to make our way home. Refreshed for seeing the birds and the reminder that I'll always bob to the surface after my disease sends me crashing beneath the waves, I was also reminded that the good days don't always stay good.

The cattle had been sheltering behind their knoll because they sensed the coming squall. Maggie and I had not noted its approach as she joyfully sniffed, and I relearned lessons from the Northern Gannet. We paid a cold, damp price for the lack of vigilance when a horizontal hail shower struck us in the open between spots of shelter.

It seems that the birds weren't the only element of nature from which I would relearn a lesson on that good day which turned bad with little warning but great effect.

We Are Not Their Heroes
04/26/2021 Kerry, Ireland

I suppose it's important that I start with the fact that I rarely take much in the way of umbrage when it comes to disability speak. By that I mean to say that you can call my multiple sclerosis a disability, a handicap, a disease, an impairment, a condition, or any of the other labels from the lexicon. As to me as a person with MS, I don't mind much what I'm called either.

I refer to myself as a person with MS. To take offense at what others might use for themselves or what tag someone might put on me is just more energy than I'm willing to expend. A spate of responses to my writing has me realizing that some of these titles can be weighty burdens, indeed.

As the Facebook page I'm involved with is not a private page (family and friends benefit from access to our community nearly as much as those living with the disease), this also means that people's comments on the page can often be viewed by their other Facebook friends. Those friends will sometimes comment back, perhaps assuming that they are making a private comment to their friend.

It must be said that I was uncomfortable with the level of admiration and adoration I've read in these replies. I came late to the term Inspiration Porn as coined by Stella Young but what I was reading was Ms. Young's societal objectification writ large.

We needn't be called (or seen) as "heroes" for living our best lives with this disease. I'm not an inspiration because I make it out of the house most days. And you are not to be seen as the object in, "Sure I've got my troubles, but at least I don't have MS!" rationale.

Society has somehow made some of us their well-mannered, trick-performing pets to be admired for putting on our big-boy/girl pants and holding down a job. They seem comfortable making us the poster children for *their* own use and at *their* own discretion. Nobody gave them permission, well at least we didn't, but they took the right anyway.

We are not heroes. Not for them, at least.

We do find inspiration in one another. We learn from each other's mistakes and successes. We offer up our workarounds and life hacks. We discover, we acquire, we share, we teach, we coach, we inspire our fellow travelers on the MS path. But that inspiration is with intent and with consent. To be objectified as an inspiration is right out.

To be considered as someone's hero simply because we are trying to live as normal a life as MS (and society) will allow is hardly heroic. We'll not be objectified simply so they can feel that, "At least my life isn't *that* bad."

Our disabilities do not make us exceptional people. If we are exceptional, we are that all on our own.

We are people, not perspective. We are humans, flawed and disabled but trying to get on with it. We are not their heroes.

MS Has Changed My Vision
08/23/2017 Kerry, Ireland

Multiple Sclerosis, the insidious thief of a disease that it is, can and has taken much from me. It has taken functions, it has robbed me of strength, and it has stolen stamina. MS has replaced feeling with numbness, abilities with disability, and self-reliance with dependence.

Multiple sclerosis has also changed my vision.

More than just the nystagmus, which can have my eyes shaking in their sockets, or the double-vision when I'm overtired or overheated, MS has changed the way I see things.

I no longer see a lot of the big picture issues of the world as one image, rather as a mosaic of individual lives and stories. The tapestry of compromise politics I now see as individual threads woven for the good of one person or group over another. I see the underdog not as superhero but rather as the humble shoeshine boy simply trying to get on with life the best he can.

Sometimes I see the journey from bedroom to bathroom as my marathon. Other times I see the simple task of writing a cheque as complex calculus. And always, just outside of my ability to focus, I see the possibility of my next MS attack.

This change in my vision, brought on by living with MS, has also keenly focused my gaze on the positive things that happen in our world.

I now see how one person can, indeed, make a difference in the lives of another or even in the lives of many. I see the value in the simplest acts of kindness and the worth of every person no matter their relative ability. I see the importance of living with purpose and intent. I can see the results of small groups of committed people trying to change their world.

I also see things differently in the mirror.

Surely the body and face of the man looking back at me is changed by both MS over the years and those years themselves. The body is changed by infusion after infusion of corticosteroids and limited activity. The hair is course and gray (and thinner) after years of chemotherapy to fight this disease. But the smile is a wry, knowing smile of someone who has won the battle of another day and has a plan for the next.

I am not the man I was over a decade ago when I was diagnosed. My body is not the same, my life is not the same and my vision is not the same.

I see shades of gray where white once met black. I see possibility where I used to take success as a foregone conclusion. I see kindness in the smallest places and self-servers in the highest offices. I also see the importance of those who create and hold our megaphone to help us get our words to the world.

I have lost sight of some old goals and aspirations after the mist of multiple sclerosis made them all but impossible to find once again. Now I focus on new milestones, on a future for the next generations and on success in arenas I never thought I'd play.

Multiple sclerosis has changed my vision. It changes the way I see, what I see and the things I look for. The view isn't always what I'd like to see in my life. But it sure is better than closing my eyes altogether.

We've Got This
11/11/2021 Kerry, Ireland

There are a lot of things I've learned, unlearned, forgotten, relearned, and changed my thinking about since my diagnosis with multiple sclerosis in 2001. There were times of full-throttle charges and times of digging-in for a long siege. I've been on the verge of making medical decisions only to put on the brakes or change course. I would change some of my answers to questions on the topic of living life with MS and other answers have become more nuanced over those decades.

One of those answers to a question asked me by Seattle news anchor, Dennis Bounds—has stayed the same, but in my head I've waivered.

"What is one thing do you think people with MS want those of us living around you, those who do not have it but either live with, are close to, or want to help people with multiple sclerosis, to know about living with the disease?

We were on stage at a fundraising luncheon, and this was the 'Closer' question. The one with which my answer was supposed to not only encourage people to write a bigger check, but also the one they were supposed to tuck into the back of their mind and take home with them.

I didn't know what Dennis' questions were going to be, and it had been a fun, funny, and informative interview to that point. For the most part, I'd been speaking of my experiences with the disease, with the medical profession, and with patient advocacy organizations like the National MS Society, whose event it was that November afternoon.

This question caught me up short. We weren't broadcasting, so I didn't have to worry about dead-air time, but I didn't want the pregnant pause to go full-term, nor did I want our audience to think I was being overtly dramatic. My hesitation before responding, however, was because I understood the importance of my answer. He wasn't asking me to answer for myself, but rather for the whole community. The weight of the impossibility of that wasn't lost on me as I composed what I call a soundbite-plus.

"We've got this," I said succinctly.

But then added, "But we might need some help."

I then went on to explain that there is no way for us to find the edge of our abilities unless we push ourselves in that direction. To be let try things on our own, to be allowed to fail, and to remount the horse and try something different is how I explained it.

We don't know when or where along the path of our life living with this incurable disease we will need a boost back up on that horse, and we surely will, but that's what we'll need. Not for the journey to be cut short by those protective of us. Not to be led by a tether so we don't go off a path someone else decides should be ours. And surely, not to be told that we've fallen off our saddle too many times and that we can no longer ride.

We, therefore, have a responsibility to be aware when we may have fallen a few too many times (likely more than we needed to learn the lesson) and to know when to say "when" to one thing or another. We are rightful in our assertions that it is our life and we get to set a course down the path we think best. With that right, however, comes the personal responsibility to know when (as well as *how* and *who*) to ask for help.

"No man is an island, entire of itself;" said John Donne, and no truer is it than when I think back to my answer to Dennis' question more years ago than I can now remember. Be it in matters physical, emotional, financial, or any of a myriad of life's endeavors we pursue, "We've got this . . . but we might need some help."

We end with the same words I have used to sign-off from blogs and webcasts from the very beginning of our Life With MS journey.

Wishing you and your family the best of health,

Cheers!

Trevis

Afterword

ONCE UPON A TIME, I WAS SET ONTO AN UNFAMILIAR PATH of complex medical terms, hospitals and tests where every step I took seemed to be another step towards uncertainty. If you've been diagnosed with MS or other chronic illness or have been impacted by the life-changing diagnosis of a family member or friend, you want to find out more. To know, to learn, to support, to move from a place of uncertainty to somewhere more bearable.

When I was told the catastrophic news that I had scars in my brain, along my spinal cord, I stumbled and staggered back into the everyday world with pieces of myself scattered to the wind. All of a sudden, my ambitions disappeared, I was left staring at a blank wall unsure what to do next. I thought my dreams of being a broadcaster or a writer or whatever, that living a good life, were shattered. Unable to know how to even begin to mentally process the diagnosis, I did what I knew best. I went to my local library and stuck my head into books. This quest for information at least made sense to me. There were a few books, some medical texts and supportive contact information and leaflets from the MS Society. Eventually I hit on a formula that worked for me and 15 years on I'm still on my quest. I live BEYOND the dreams and ambitions I once had, no longer underestimating my ability to get through

one more day. I have endured. In my professional life, I have connected with thousands of people with MS from every country in
Europe and from places across the globe. We have worked together,
people from all walks of life, cultures and languages, learning and
strengthening one another. Encouraging, empowering and fortify-
ing one another's resilience one conversation at a time.

Using my experiences as an organizer and a community-
builder in Ireland and Europe, recognizing the intersectionality in
all our lives, I worked to bring out the fortitude and power of this
collection. I've been fortunate to meet and work with thousands
of people from across the world, LGBTI+ people, straight people,
humans from every continent and every culture living with MS.
I know the struggles people with MS and their families have—
whether it is accessing basic healthcare, trying to stay at work to
put food on the table or staying well while living socially excluded.
I also know the brutal sting of stigma, of having a condition that
somehow, makes you, rather than the haters, *less than*.

In the months before the world first heard the term COVID-
19, Trevis and I talked about crafting 'The Perfect' collection from
thousands of his articles. We didn't get it perfect, but it's pretty
damned good. At a time when the world was dealing with a pandemic, we focused on bringing the best of Trevis to you. As the
months passed, in conversations that were often filled with laughter, sadness and ruthlessly honest, we built. I got to know a younger
Trevis, in the early years of his diagnosis; figuratively, I moved with
him from the big city life of Seattle in the United States of America
to the small town of Dingle in the rural west of Ireland. Reading
his words of love, of fear, the words strained with absolute desperation and desolation, his story revealed echoes of my own.

We have compiled something that we hope will work for you,
Dear Reader. We could not be all things to all people but we have
brought together something that those like us, affected by so-called
'activity-limiting illnesses', could enjoy and use as a resource. We
have learned to connect to our past and recognize how the rhythm

of our new sounds from this collection would draw in others in the present times. Perhaps you have had dalliances with Trevis' work before and are familiar with this Chef Interrupted or you have been with him on his own Life with MS journey over the years?

People tell stories to connect, to have fun, to celebrate, to grieve, to learn and understand the world from another person's perspective. If we are lucky, in our listening, we get a bit of what we need to nourish our spirit. At times we hear little nuggets of wisdom that we put into our pockets and take them out to help us when we're having a challenging day. My wish is that you enjoy what we have crafted, in this version of Life with MS, and it will encourage you in your own life. Never ever underestimate your ability to get through one more day.

Emma Rogan
Dublin, Ireland

APPENDIX I

Symptom Thesaurus

*I*N APRIL OF 2013, I POSTED *my '12 Lessons Learned from a Dozen years of MS.' One of those lessons was that someone should write an MS Symptom Thesaurus. The idea was well received and over the ensuing years, we gathered a great number of chronic symptoms and language we can all use to describe them to others who might need to know what, exactly, we're experiencing. It was time to describe our symptoms in ways that have worked for us, in ways that others might understand and in language which will empower us to tell our story (or our ills) to our doctors.*

Like the great dictionaries, no one person could do that alone. Some of the descriptors are mine, but the Life with MS Blog community stepped up (as they always have) to our Call to Readers and offered up their ideas as well. While they are symptoms of multiple sclerosis and the way people with MS would express them, they are also chronic illness-wide experiences.

THE SYMPTOMS:

Fatigue:

Debilitating, lay-down-or-fall-down, out-of-body, profound, mind-numbing, a mental weight belt, a bungee tethered, oppressive, weakening, sapping, wearying, encroaching, all-enveloping, catatonic, paralytic, Dementors, thick, muddy, suffocating, dulling. An ocean wave out of nowhere that just knocks you down. Overwhelming sleepiness. Almost too tired to breathe. Mentally and physically thru mud or waist-deep water . . . attached to a weight. A tired that sleep won't fix. Like the plug was just pulled or the switch flipped turning off our power. Like viewing life through a very thick glass. Caffeine-proof tired. So exhausted that it's sickening.

Pain:

Ranging from discomfort to suffering. Sizzling. Like someone has just waxed a long nerve. Cold, diamond-crusted sandpaper on sunburn. A sharp, pointed stick under the sole of my shoe. Sharp, dull, or rotten. Prickly, insular, jolting. Constant, occasional, underlying or overbearing. A thin, hot piano wire or a thumb pressed into my eye. Buckling, stunning and immobilizing. Burning hot or freezing cold—walking barefoot on hot coals or a frozen lake. Like you're a Hollywood film Voodoo doll being stuck with pins. Muscles being squeezed in a mop wringer. Hot nails driven into muscles.

Cognitive Fog – Cog Fog:

Sometimes called "cognitive dysfunction" "cognitive difficulty" "cognitive impairment" "cognitive problems," Cog-Fog can be annoying, frightening, frustrating, and isolating.

Mental fuzziness and total mental disassociation with the world around us. Lost in my own neighborhood. Words stacked-up in my cognitive funnel. Like one foot is nailed to the floor as I spin trying to figure out what to do. Using the wrong words, not knowing what to say, how to speak, or why the people in the room were looking at me. Holes in the brain. Living in a quick clip edited montage scene in a foreign language film. Easily overwhelmed to the point of frustration and mental paralysis. Can be triggered by bright light, large crowds, loud music, lots of things moving at once, and/or objects moving quickly.

Numbness / Pins & Needles:

Two separate things, but often associated. Numbness is the lack of sensation while pins & needles is called paresthesia. We'll begin with the latter.

- **Paresthesia** – Tingling, sizzling, fizzy, burning, itching, crawling skink, prickling, sparkling, effervescence of the skin. Buzzing of bumblebees under your skin. Ultrasensitivity to touch or pressure.
- **Numbness** – A heaviness. Thick, dumb, dead, unresponsive. Nothingness. Fat and fuzzy. Slow to respond if at all. Like part of your body has been to see the dentist.

Muscle Weakness:

Signal interruptions. Loss of strength. Like a limb is heavier than it really is. A hollow feeling in the muscles. Having to move a part of my body with another part—like using my hip to raise my foot off the ground. As if my shadow is trying to move something. Like being in a dream trying to move something that just won't budge. Walking through water or mud. Causing a weightlifter's expression just to raise a cup of coffee.

The "MS Hug":

Tightness between the ribs. Banding or girdling around the torso. Squeezing the breath out of you. Boa Constrictor around the body. A huge rubber band. The worst muscle spasm. Panic-inducing. Iron maiden, gasping for air. Strapped to a backboard or bound in a strait jacket. All of your ribs bruised at once. Like being picked up by a professional wrestler around the middle.

Lhermitte's Sign:

A brief, stab of electricity down the spine when the head and neck are bent forward. "WOW! What was that?" Odd, but not unpleasant buzzing. Like muscles in the neck and back (all the way down to the tops of the legs) being very tight and having not been stretched in a long time. Pulling on a cold, electric rubber band. Almost good, like rubbing a bruise or stretching cramp can be painful but feel good. Eye-blinking shock. Mouth-watering pain. Like moving my head one centimeter further forward and I'll break something.

Spasticity:

Muscle stiffness or contraction to the point of rigidity and pain. Curling of my fingers and/or wrist, unintendedly throwing gang signs. A sense of muscle atrophy. Change in a limbs natural resting position. Like my limbs are starting from a place further back than normal when I want to move them. A tightening of one muscle group which pulls on things further down the body. A crippled looking limb.

Bladder Issues:

Urgency, frequency, hesitation. The pee-then-pee-then-pee trifecta. Thinking you're done, but not. Feeling like I've "broken the seal" and have to return to the loo every 20 minutes. "I have to go now, NOW . . . too late." Waking tired because I've been up to pee more than a pregnant woman at a watermelon eating contest. Doing 'the pee-pee dance'. Leakage. Like a dominant dog at a fire hydrant museum. Having an emergency bottle in the glove box of the car because, you never know . . .. Casing a place for all the bathrooms like a 1920s gangster looking for exits. That knowing twinge when you've a UTI.

Fine Motor Skills:

Varying in severity from intriguing, to nearly comical, to painful, frustrating, and even depressing. Like wearing thick gloves and working in slow-motion. As if you're using someone else's fingers. Typing is like I've ham-handed, dodgy fingers at a child's toy piano. Like an astronaut in my thick spacesuit trying to arrange flowers in zero gravity. Getting toes into socks is at best my take on a Charlie Chaplin bit . . . at worst, more Buster Keaton.

Balance Issues:

Like walking in the wrong shoes. The wall is the only thing keeping me from the floor. One-sided. Feeling I've had one too many when I've had none. Standing on a badly listing ship. As if one leg of my trousers is soaking wet and dragging me down. As if I'm trying to make my way through the hallway of a funhouse where the floorboards move from side to side . . . in the dark. The wobble before the fall. Turn, step, crumple, repeat.

Vertigo:

The ugly stepbrother of Balance Issues. Can vacillate from light headedness and simple dizziness to an out-of-body experience. World-spinning, eyes-closed as I crawl to the toilet to vomit. As if you're in an earthquake with the earth rolling like a wave or standing on an under-inflated air mattress. A passing waft of sickening unease like you've walked through a cloud of cheap perfume. Woozy and faint. Like swimming through a thermocline—the point where cold water meets warmer or fresh water meets salt—a change in buoyancy and gravity like you're moving from one world to another.

Swallowing Issues:

One that quite literally grabs me by the neck. Acute onset throat constriction. Inability to or swallow. I'm sure I look like some long-necked bird on a National Geographic documentary trying to swallow something too large. An invisible "punch in da t'roat." Like a painful lump suddenly appears in my airway. Adrenalin rush, fight-or-flight instinct reaction. Panic. Fear.

Speech Problems:

Like the natural rhythm and tune of my voice is breaking away like the ground around me. I sound like an equal cross between Siri and my 10th grade chemistry teacher. Or that I sound like Robin Williams doing an impression of someone on drugs. I speak too slow, I speak in slurred syllables, I speak as if I accidently took quaaludes for laryngitis. Like I breathed in at the end of a phrase and then started talking in Bill Clinton's voice. No matter how hard I try, how hard I push the air out of my lungs, my volume doesn't change. Rapid-fire, explosive volume, staggered tempo, lost control like a 4-year-old who just learned something new about dinosaurs and tries to tell you with as few breaths possible.

Foot Drop:

Peroneal nerve damage—a particular (and insidious) type of muscle weakness. For me the most dangerous. Lift from the hip (or all the way up to my shoulder) when walking. Step-drag-step. Like I've got a sticky clutch. Running with one dress shoe, one runner. Lopsided. Floppy. Slapping foot when I'm without shoes. Scuffed toes. EVERYTHING is a tripping hazard! Obvious. Embarrassing. 'Disabled' looking. A foot-stutter. Ministry of Silly Walks . . . with a long swim fin on one foot. An accident waiting to happen. Manageable!

Isolation:

The Invisible Man. Society has pulled a scrim between them and me. The thought of going sledding with friends on the morning of a hangover. Like living in a crappy studio apartment above a really great party (that was a Mike Myers line about growing up in Canada and I LOVED it!). As if I'm a boxer being asked to answer yet another bell for yet another round for yet another beating. "I'd love to, but . . ." Like life is window shopping with no money. Tethered.

It can even feel as though I'm living in one of Rod Serling's old *Twilight Zone* sketches in which everything in the world is different, but the protagonist is the only one who recognizes it. The subject of speculation. I heard them call-off the search party . . . but I'm still alive.

Trigeminal Neuralgia:

The Worst Pain Ever! Nuclear toothache. Electrical rot. Blinding pain, shooting pain, stabbing pain, stripping pain . . . suicidal pain. A hot wire being pulled from the ear through the jaw, face, nose, and mouth. Like your face is giving birth and passing a kidney stone at the same time.

MS Sleep:

Here is one of the most difficult to describe, because MS Sleep in an intensification of every other type of sleep issue. There is the "I'm absolutely shattered, but my brain won't shut off" sleep which is like trying to sleep on the verge of the neurological superhighway at rush hour. The Anesthesia Sleep where you wake in the same position in which you fell away and don't know if it was a 20-minute nap or a 20-hour coma. Waking as (or more) tired than when you crashed into bed the night before.

There is "Sleep now, Here, NOW!" sleep when a pile of rocks would do as well as a soft bed. The sleep of the dead. The sleep of the cursed. The sleep deprivation torture.

One thing MS Sleep isn't, is middle-ground sleep.

APPENDIX II

LWMS³

The Life With Multiple Sclerosis Self-Evaluation Scale (LWMS³):

For over a decade I had been asking our Life with MS community "How's your MS today?" on the third Wednesday of the month. It was a chance to check-in with both the group, as well as with ourselves. It was also a good tool for people to look back upon and show their progress (or progression) over a previous period when going in for medical appointments.

The problem with the question and therefore the answer is that we all see things in the moment differently than we do in retrospect. Not only were the observations subjective (you can't really help that when you're answering a question about yourself) but mayn't have been as helpful as I'd hoped.

We decided to create a scale which, while being subjective, was a way to not only record how we were feeling but also help us to realize that we may have been through worse before. We took into consideration a number of clinical observations which our medical professionals use.

The Functional System Score (FSS) which takes into consideration:

- Weakness or trouble moving limbs
- Tremor or loss of coordination
- Problems with speech, swallowing, or involuntary eye movements
- Numbness or loss of sensation
- Bowel and bladder function/dysfunction
- Visual function
- Mental functions

The Expanded Disability Status Scale (EDSS) uses the FSS to establish a score based on:

- 0 = Normal
- 1 – 1.5 = No disability but some abnormal neurological signs
- 2 – 2.5 = Minimal disability
- 3 – 4.5 = Moderate disability, affecting daily activities but you can still walk
- 5 – 8 = More severe disability, impairing your daily activities and requiring assistance with walking
- 8.5 – 9 = Very severe disability, restricting you to bed
- 10 + Death

Multiple Sclerosis Functional Composite (MSFC) which uses:

- Walking speed, using a timed 25-foot walk
- Arm and hand dexterity, using the 9-hole peg test
- Cognitive functions, such as how well you can do math calculations using the Placed Auditory Serial Additions Test (PASAT)—Also known to many as the Tool of the Devil!!!

Those tests and evaluations work well for doctors in a clinical setting and researchers segregating subjects into like groups. We went for a more holistic scale that helps to mark our place on the MS continuum from day to day, month to month, and along our whole-life journey with the disease.

The LWMS3 is a simple scale where:

- 1 = The best I've felt (symptom wise) since my diagnosis with multiple sclerosis
- 10 = The worst I've felt (symptom wise) since my diagnosis with multiple sclerosis

Still an, obviously, subjective scale but you are the subject. You are the only one living inside of your head, your body, your spirit. You are the only one who can answer this question.

By comparing how we feel on any day (and I try to do this on the same day every month in order to be consistent in my later report to my doctors) to the best and worst we have experienced during our life with the disease, I have found that I 1) really examine my symptoms and how they make me feel relative to the whole rather than just feeling their weight on the day, 2) bring realism to the table, and 3) though I am not a 'silver lining' guy, it helps me to remember that whatever symptom I'm contending with has probably been worse for me at some point and I got through it before and it either got better or I figured out a way to live with the symptom in its heightened state.

LWMS3 allows me to both grade my overall feeling as well as specific symptoms relative to the best I've felt and the worst I've felt since 20th April 2001. An anniversary I do not celebrate.

Acknowledgements

Thanking those intrinsic to this book reads like the begats of Genesis Chapter 5.

In 2003, my dear friend, Bethany Spinler introduced me to David Levy. David, a colorful raconteur who seemed to know everyone (and even more people seemed to know David), introduced me to publishing consultant Jennifer McCord. Jennifer helped to understand that my first book wasn't the one I should have been writing and set me down the path that would eventually become my memoir, Chef Interrupted.

During that process, Jennifer brought editor, Sheryl Stebbins into my world and we've had many joyous collaborations since. Sadly, in the time between the editing and publication of this book, our dear Sheryl died. Her keen eye, light touch, and fierce commitment are greatly missed by us all.

Jennifer also made introduction to Marilyn Allen who became my literary agent. Marilyn is that rarity in agents—the one who became a true (first transcontinental and now transatlantic) friend. I wouldn't want to do this without Marilyn at my side.

Another line of genealogy for this text must begin with Patti Shepherd-Barnes, President Emeritus of the Greater Northwest Chapter of the National MS Society. Patti introduced me to Erin

Poznanski at the Chapter, and we all worked on a number of projects together. For one of which, Erin introduced me to Carolynn Delaney, with whom I later began working on MS webcast programs for HealthTalk.

Carolynn introduced me to Rose Pike who, now rather infamously, asked if I would like to write a blog for HealthTalk. That was April of 2006. HealthTalk begat a relationship with Everyday Health and introductions and collaboration with more editors than I can remember. Natalie Cagle was the first. Almost two decades on, Ingrid Strauch is my current editor at Everyday Health. They've all made me read far better than I write.

Through my involvement with both the National MS Society and Everyday Health, introductions were made to Ava Battles, Chief Executive of the MS Society of Ireland. MS Ireland was starting *MS and ME*, an MS blog of their own. Ava enlisted me to lend a hand. In doing so, she introduced me to the woman I would come to call my 'MS Sister' and who helped me to build what is now the book you have in your hands. That's my dear Emma, who labored with me for over two years on this project.

A special thank you to Dr Tim Coetzee PhD for agreeing to write the foreword for us. Tim also introduced us to a stack of leaders in the MS world who have supported the book from its early days.

Only those closest to us know how much living a life with multiple sclerosis takes out of a person. When you decide to write a book about that life, it's a whole other level of drain. My wife, Caryn and Emma's children, Thalia and Kai kept us both afloat and gave us the support needed to get this project over the line. Go raibh míle maith agaibh, agus grá ár gcroíthe chugaibh.

TREVIS L GLEASON, AUTHOR

Chef by training, Food Scientist by education, Writer by passion, and Advocate for people with disabilities . . . by necessity. A former US Coast Guard navigator, USAID ambassador, and culinary instructor, Gleason serves on the Editorial Board for MS Ireland, and as Cathaoirleach of Corca Dhuibhne Food Network. Along with his previously published books, he has written pieces for most major newspapers in Ireland as well as a number of food magazines, professional journals (including New England Journal of Medicine and Lancet Neurology), and academic papers. His blogs, Trevis L Gleason's Life with Multiple Sclerosis, are the longest-running posted MS works on the web. He lives between Seattle, Washington USA and West Kerry Ireland with his wife, Caryn and their Wheaten Terriers, Maggie and Mona.

EMMA ROGAN, EDITOR

Writer and Advocate, dedicated to diversity and inclusion in international policymaking for multiple sclerosis and other neurological conditions. She has worked with value-based European rights and service organizations for over two decades and was the 2012 winner of the Vodafone World of Difference Award.

Emma is the loving mother of two wonderful children and lives in Dublin, Ireland.

Printed in the USA
CPSIA information can be obtained
at www.ICGtesting.com
CBHW011035131223
2613CB00008B/176